D1327407

STATISTICAL REASONING
and
PROCEDURES

Robert B. Clarke
San Jose State College

Arthur P. Coladarci
Stanford University

John Caffrey
System Development Corporation

CHARLES E. MERRILL BOOKS, INC., COLUMBUS, OHIO

Library of Congress Catalog Card Number: 65—21170

Printed in the United States of America

Preface

The overall purpose of this book is to introduce the basic concepts, strategies, and procedures of statistical description and inference. Within this broad purpose, we are most concerned with helping the reader develop an intuitive understanding of statistical reasoning. Such an understanding, of course, can only be developed with reference to applications of specific statistical procedures. However, in order to help the reader grasp the underlying logic, we have limited ourselves to the most widely used and basic procedures.

Written primarily for those with little algebraic sophistication, basic concepts and general principles are developed and rationalized with reference to simple numerical examples and intuitive explanations rather than algebraic derivations and proofs. However, those who prefer to lean more heavily on algebraic processes will find that a more mathematical approach can easily be integrated with the material. Where symbols are used, we have, in general, attempted to follow current practice, with one notable exception. For reasons discussed in Chapter 10, we have used the symbol CR (*critical ratio*), although it is not commonly seen in other current books or recent psychological literature.

The illustrations and exercises in the various chapters are drawn largely from the behavioral sciences and more specifically the fields of education and psychology, since these latter are the fields represented by the authors. The exposition, however, is applicable to other areas as well. The processes and strategies are generic in their application.

The usefulness of this book has been increased greatly by the kind

cooperation of a number of people who assisted in its preparation. We
are particularly grateful to those colleagues who read and criticized earlier
versions of the manuscript and to the students at San Jose State College
and Stanford University who, in their classes, used and reacted to much
of the preliminary material. We also wish to acknowledge the services of
Doris Fevrier and Tre Ford who handled, with patient competence, the
myriad details of final manuscript preparation.

We are indebted to the Literary Executor of the late Sir Ronald A.
Fisher, F.R.S., Cambridge, to Dr. Frank Yates, F.R.S., Rothamsted, and
to Messrs. Oliver & Boyd Ltd., Edinburgh, for permission to reprint Tables
Nos. III and IV from their book, *Statistical Tables for Biological, Agricultural, and Medical Research*. We are also indebted to Professor Quinn
McNemar and John Wiley and Sons for permission to reprint Tables B
and G from their book, *Psychological Statistics*.

R. B. C.
A. P. C.
J. G. C.

May, 1965

Table of Contents

Chapter 9

Statistical Inference and Probability   158

Chapter 10

Sampling Distributions of a Statistic   171

Chapter 11

Hypothesis Testing   194

Chapter 12

Student's T Distribution   217

Chapter 1

Introduction

Once upon a time, Joe Tourist returned from a visit to Japan, having "learned" many things on his thirty-day guided excursion to the mysterious Orient. When one learns something new, he may feel a strong obligation to enlighten his friends; it was in this unselfish spirit that Joe Tourist spoke to all who would listen. "One thing I found," he said, "is that Japanese children almost never cry in public."

To the uninitiated reader, this anecdote may appear to be a rather inappropriate introduction to a textbook dealing with techniques and concepts of statistics; however, it may well serve to suggest the relevance of statistical competence to the everyday affairs of men. The fact is that Joe's "discovery" about Japanese children exemplifies the two major functions of statistical analysis. Suppose we were so unneighborly as to ask Joe how he arrived at the conclusion that Japanese children almost never cry in public. How would he respond? The odds are that Joe would remind us, with pardonable pride, that his is an eyewitness account—not merely hearsay or questionable folklore. "I personally saw several thousand children during my visit to Japan," he informs us, "and only one was crying!" The reader will observe that Joe at this point has provided a *description* of directly observed events—frequency of public crying among "several thousand" Japanese children. More specifically, he has reduced the several thousand separate instances to a *summary* (one out of several thousand). Since it is reasonable to interpret "one out of several thousand" as "almost never," can we let Joe off the hook? Not yet. The attentive reader will have noted that Joe's conclusion was about *all* Japanese children, not merely the several thousand directly observed.

1

That is, he generalized about an entire population of children on the basis of what he knew about a portion of that population.

Our hypothetical friend, then, summarized a number of observations or facts and made generalizations on the basis of these. As the content of this textbook will demonstrate, these two processes (summarizing and generalizing) represent two broad foci of statistics. One who understands statistical concepts and techniques is likely to summarize and generalize more intelligently and carefully. What is particularly important to realize at this point is that competence in these areas is useful to all of us. That is, summarizing and generalizing pervade human experience, for weal or woe. If the reader is not already persuaded on this point, he should engage in a little reflection on his behavior in the past few hours. It is probable that he will easily recall at least one instance in which he has summarized a number of observations or facts and made a generalization on the basis of these. It may be as explicit as, "The 1965 Zeus is certainly not a good car—almost everyone I know who has bought one has had a good deal of trouble." On the other hand, it may be more difficult to recognize: "From what I've heard, I'm not going to like statistics."

Summarizing many facts and making generalizations are processes of great importance in education and psychology. Suppose, for instance, we wish to compare the effectiveness of two methods of teaching reading. One group of children is taught using method A, and another group is taught using method B. Then, a standard reading-achievement test is given to each child in both groups. It will be necessary to summarize the test scores in some way if a meaningful comparison is to be made. Furthermore, it is important that any generalizations from the results for these specific children to those for children in general be made in a systematic and careful fashion. Or, consider a second example: A psychologist may be interested in the child-rearing practices among a certain social class. He may interview a sample of parents from this class to find out how they raised their children. He would then be faced with the tasks of summarizing the interview data for his specific sample of parents and generalizing his results to the entire social class.

The first eight chapters of this textbook are devoted to an area referred to as *descriptive statistics*, which includes the techniques and concepts involved in describing and summarizing observed facts, or *data*, as they are often called. Some of these techniques and concepts are already familiar to the beginning student (e.g., the *average*). Others, such as measures of relationship and variability, will probably be encountered here for the first time. The remainder of the text deals with problems involved in generalizing. This aspect of statistics is usually referred to as *statistical inference*, since it deals with how inferences of a *general* nature can be made and interpreted on the basis of a *specific* set of observed data. This is, to many, the most interesting aspect of statistics; however, competence in statistical inference depends upon a sufficient grasp of descriptive techniques and concepts. Hence, the latter should not be minimized—for this reason as well as for their practical utility in descriptive tasks.

GOALS OF THIS TEXT

In order to clarify the degree of statistical sophistication we hope the reader will acquire by working through this text, three levels of skill in this area should be described:

The first level is that at which one can perform the specific clerical and computational operations involved in organizing, summarizing, and analyzing various types of data. Someone has to substitute the right numbers in the appropriate formulas, perform all the necessary arithmetic, construct the appropriate tables, charts, graphs, and so on. Although these are essential operations in a statistical analysis, they do not, by themselves, require any understanding of the basic concepts involved in statistical reasoning. In most situations, if adequate instructions are given, these operations can be performed by any reasonably intelligent individual who can follow directions; understands the basic arithmetic operations of adding, subtracting, dividing, and multiplying; and can perform these operations either manually or with the use of automatic equipment. Such an individual need have no real understanding of the "why" behind the operations he is performing or of the meaning of the final results he will obtain.

The second level of skill is that at which one has sufficient understanding of the nature of statistical reasoning to (1) interpret and evaluate the results of much of the research reported in educational and psychological literature, (2) discuss research matters intelligently with professional colleagues, and (3) design and conduct research with the help of a specialist in statistical methods. At this level of understanding one *knows what he doesn't know* and can determine what type of help he needs from a specialist. Furthermore, he knows how to communicate effectively with such a specialist.

At the third level of skill we find individuals with some degree of specialization in statistics. Many of these individuals are concerned primarily with applications in such areas as education, psychology, business, and economics; whereas others have a mathematical and logical background sufficient for developing and modifying statistical theory and techniques. Such a skill level obviously requires some advanced training as well as experience.

The major concern of this text is with the second level of skill and understanding. Our purpose is not to develop statistical clerks nor to develop specialists in statistical methods but rather to develop individuals with some general insight into statistical reasoning and its application in education and psychology. It is this second, or "middle" level of understanding that is crucially and increasingly needed among the particular groups of readers we have in mind—those preparing to enter the ranks of the major professions in modern society. The general practitioner in such professions as education, social work, psychology, or medicine has neither the need nor the time for statistical specialization. The complexity of his tasks and the profound consequences of his conclusions, however, place upon him a greater than ordinary obligation to be informed and critical. It is necessary, for example, that he be able to read research literature that would be quite incomprehensible to the layman. Furthermore, he should be able to cooperate and communicate with the specialists who are producing the research relevant to his problems. Finally, as the story of Joe Tourist reminds us, we all summarize and generalize—but, unlike Joe, the professional worker must do it with particular care and skill.

SOME PRELIMINARY CONCEPTS

Variables

A statistical investigation always involves a group of observable units, whether the units be people, laboratory rats, automobiles, or anything else. Each unit is observed for one or more characteristics of interest. For instance, in studying methods of teaching reading, each child may be scored on the characteristic of reading achievement. Such a characteristic is known as a *variable*, because the observations vary from individual to individual. That is, not all the children obtain the same score; some obtain higher scores and some, lower scores. Other examples of variables are math-test score, age, sex, number of brothers and sisters, height, weight, and color of eyes. Each of these characteristics will vary from child to child. Thus, *the data of a statistical investigation consist of observations on one or more variables.*

Ordered Variables and Qualitative Variables

The possible values or scores of some variables can be meaningfully ordered according to magnitude. These will be known as *ordered* or *quantitative* variables. For instance, consider the variables of course grade, height, or family income. An *A* grade is higher than a *B*, which is higher than a *C*, etc.; 61 in. tall is taller than 60 1/2 in., which is taller than 59 in., etc.; and an income of $7,500 is greater than an income of $7,350, which is greater than an income of $7,000, etc. Ordered variables can be contrasted with such variables as hair color, political party affiliation, or sex, of which the various scores or categories differ on a qualitative rather than a quantitative basis. The differences between the hair colors of blonde, brown, red, gray, and black are differences in kind rather than magnitude. The same could be said for the various political parties or the two sexes. Such variables will be referred to as *qualitative* or *nominal* variables.

Ordered variables can be divided into those which are *numerically scaled* and those which are not. For instance, the possible scores or values for variables such as height in inches or income in dollars per year are on a numerical scale. Suppose, however, we used as the possible scores for height the general categories of very short, short, medium, tall, and very tall. Scored in this way, height would still be considered an ordered variable, but the possible scores or values would no longer be on a numerical scale. A letter grade in a course would be another example. The letter grades *A*, *B*, *C*, *D*, and *F* are ordered but are not on a numerical scale.

Discrete and Continuous Variables

Numerically scaled variables may be of two types, *discrete* or *continuous*. A discrete variable is one for which the possible scores or values increase in "discrete" steps. An example would be the score on a five-problem test in which no partial credit is given. That is, one could obtain a score of 0, 1, 2, 3, 4, or 5, but no score in between. The number of children in a family is another example of a discrete variable. The possible scores for a group of families are 0 children, 1 child, 2, 3, or other whole numbers of children with no scores in between these values. A continuous variable, on the other hand, is a variable that can take on any value over an entire range. Persons' body weights, for instance, are considered continuous, because the possible values include not only whole numbers of pounds but any fractional values as well. That is, an individual can weigh not only 150 or 151 lb. but also 150.2 or 150.236845 lb. Height is also considered continuous. A person could be assigned a height "score" of 67.38526 in. if a sufficiently accurate measuring stick were available.

The above distinction, however, is only a theoretical one. All numerically scaled variables, *as actually measured*, are discrete because of limitations on the accuracy of the measuring instruments used. Consider height, for instance. If we use a measuring stick accurate to the nearest 1/16 of an inch, individuals can have scores (i.e., measured heights) of 60 in., 60 1/16 in., 60 2/16 in., 60 3/16 in., etc., but no scores in between these values. Even if our measuring stick were accurate to the nearest 1/10,000 of an inch, the obtained measurements would still be discrete; individuals can have scores of 60.0000 in., 60.0001 in., 60.0002 in., etc., but nothing in between.

For our purposes, a more useful distinction between continuous and discrete variables is one based on the number of possible scores or values for the variable. Compare, for instance, the scores that might be obtained on a two-item test (no partial credit) with the scores that might be obtained on a 100-item test (no partial credit). For the two-item test there are three possible score values, 0 (for those who failed both items), 1, and 2. To go from the lowest possible score to the highest possible score would require only two discrete "jumps," 0 to 1 and 1 to 2; however, for the 100-item test, there would be many possible scores, 101 to be exact. The range from the lowest possible score of 0 to the highest possible score of 100 would be divided into 100 jumps instead of just two. In this sense, scores from the 100-item test show greater continuity than the scores from the two-item test.

The practical implication of the foregoing is that numerically scaled variables, although discrete, are often analyzed by using statistical techniques that, in theory, are applicable to continuous variables only. Accurate results will be obtained from such analyses if, for the variables involved, the obtained scores range over a sufficient number of values. What constitutes a sufficient number of values depends on several factors, including the nature of the statistical analysis, the type of conclusions to be drawn, and, most important, the number of cases to be used in the analysis. For certain kinds of analyses, accurate results will be obtained by treating even *dichotomous* (two-valued) variables as continuous, if the number of cases is large enough.

ARITHMETIC OPERATIONS AND ALGEBRAIC CONVENTIONS

We have pointed out that the emphasis in this text is primarily on developing some understanding of statistical concepts and techniques that have proved useful in educational and psychological research; the development of computational skill is not a primary concern. Computation will be minimized in the chapters that follow; however, explanation of the concepts and techniques would be ineffective without reference to illustrations of their applications, and such applications necessarily involve computation. Consequently, the reader must have at least some grasp of certain arithmetic and algebraic conventions if he is to read our treatment with profit. A few of these conventions are mentioned below, but the reader who feels uneasy would be well advised to obtain a copy of any high-school general-mathematics text or of Helen Walker's very useful text,* which is written specifically for the beginning student of statistics.

Absolute Value

The absolute value of a number is its numerical value, independent of its sign. "Absolute value" is indicated by a vertical line on each side of the number.

$$|+9| = 9, \qquad |-9| = 9$$

Adding Signed Numbers

A positive number will be preceded by a plus sign or by no sign at all. A negative number will always be preceded by a minus sign. When adding two or more negative numbers, add the absolute values. The sign of the sum will also be negative.

$$(-6) + (-12) + (-7) = -(6 + 12 + 7) = -25$$

When adding a positive number and a negative number, subtract the smaller absolute value from the larger. The sum will have the sign of the larger absolute value.

$$6 + (-12) = -(12 - 6) = -6$$
$$\text{or} \quad 7 + (-3) = +(7 - 3) = +4$$

Subtracting Signed Numbers

When subtracting one signed number from another, change the sign of the number being subtracted and change the arithmetic operation to addition.

$$(+6) - (+8) = +6 + (-8) = -2$$
$$\text{or} \quad (+5) - (-7) = +5 + (+7) = +12$$

Adding and Subtracting Signed Numbers in the Same Expression

First, change the signs of all the numbers which are to be subtracted and change the arithmetic operation involving these numbers to addition. Then add the signed numbers.

---

* Helen M. Walker, *Mathematics Essential for Elementary Statistics* (New York: Holt, Rinehart & Winston, Inc., 1951).

$$(+3) - (-6) - (+4) + (-5) =$$
$$(+3) + (+6) + (-4) + (-5) = +9 + (-9) = 0$$

Conventions for Indicating Multiplication

In statistics it would be confusing to use the letter x to indicate multiplication since that letter is also used to symbolize a value. Instead, use is made of two algebraic conventions. The first, and most common, convention is to show the multiplication of two values by writing them in juxtaposition to each other. Hence, "2 times 5" is indicated by writing (2) (5); "6 times σ" is written 6σ. The other accepted but infrequent practice is to place a dot between the values to be multiplied: $2 \cdot 5$ and $6 \cdot \sigma$. When the latter practice is followed, the reader must be careful to distinguish between the multiplication sign and a decimal point.

Multiplication of Signed Numbers

Multiply the absolute values of the numbers; then count the number of negative numbers. If the number of negative numbers is even, the sign of the product is positive; if it is odd, the sign of the product is negative. (The product of two numbers with like signs is positive; in the case of unlike signs, the product is negative.)

$$(-6)(-2) = +12$$
$$\text{or} \quad (+2)(-2) = -4$$
$$\text{or} \quad (-2)(-3)(-5)(4) = -120$$

Division

When dividing two signed numbers, the quotient is positive if the two numbers have like signs; it is negative if the two numbers have unlike signs.

$$\frac{-6}{2} = -3$$
$$\text{or} \quad \frac{-6}{-2} = +3$$

Determining Squares and Square Roots

For all the problems in this text involving square roots, the table in Appx. 1 will provide sufficiently accurate results. The first column (N) lists numbers from 1.00 through 10.00. The square for any number in this column can be read directly from the second column (N^2), and the square root is found in the third column ($\sqrt{N}$). The fourth column ($\sqrt{10N}$) gives one the square roots of numbers from 10.0 thru 100.0. For instance, the square root of 2.53, which is between the numbers 1.00 and 10.00, would be found in the third column opposite the value $N = 2.53$ (i.e., $\sqrt{N} = \sqrt{2.53} = 1.59060$). On the other hand, the number 25.3 is between 10.0 and 100.0; therefore, the square root of 25.3 would be found in the fourth column opposite the value $N = 2.53$ (i.e., $\sqrt{10N} = \sqrt{(10)(2.53)} = \sqrt{25.3} = 5.02991$).

Appendix 1 can also be utilized to determine the square roots (accurate to three significant digits) of numbers other than those between 1.00 and 10.00 or between 10.0 and 100.0. For instance, to determine the square roots of the numbers .00296347 and 6,286,712, the following steps are performed.

1)   The number is rounded to three significant digits.

$$.00296347 \text{ rounded} = .00296$$
$$6,286,712 \text{ rounded} = 6,290,000$$

2)   The decimal point is moved an *even* number of places to obtain a number either between 1.00 and 10.00 or between 10.0 and 100.0.

Moving four places to the right in .00296 gives 29.6
(between 10.0 and 100.0), and
moving six places to the left in 6,290,000 gives 6.29
(between 1.00 and 10.00).

3)   The square root of the number obtained in Step 2 can be determined directly from the table.

$$\sqrt{29.6} = 5.44 \text{ (rounded to three significant digits)}$$
$$\sqrt{6.29} = 2.51 \text{ (rounded to three significant digits)}$$

4)   Move the decimal point of the square root obtained in Step 3 in a direction opposite to the direction moved in Step 2 and half as many places. This gives the square root of the original number accurate to three significant digits.

Moving two places ($4/2 = 2$) left in 05.44 gives .0544;
thus $\sqrt{.00296347} = .0544$ (accurate to three significant digits).
Moving three places ($6/2 = 3$) right in 2.510 gives 2,510;
thus $\sqrt{6,286,712} = 2,510$ (accurate to three significant digits).

The point that should be emphasized with regard to the above procedure is that in Step 2 the decimal point must be moved an *even* number of places only.

Use of the Summation Sign

A variable was earlier defined as a characteristic that takes on different score values for different individuals. In statistical work, a capital letter, such as X, is allowed to represent the individual's score. Consequently, arithmetic operations which are to be performed on the scores of all individuals can be represented in terms of X. For instance, suppose it were necessary to find the sum of the scores of 100 individuals. This operation could be represented in the following manner: X_1 (first individual) $+ X_2$ (second individual) $+ X_3$ (third individual), and so on through X_{100} (hundredth individual); however, such a means of representation would be quite awkward, for its complete statement would require several lines. Consequently, the operation of adding all the X scores to obtain the sum is stated in symbolic form, using the upper-case Greek sigma (Σ) to indicate "summation" or "add." To symbolize the operation, "add all the X scores," we can write ΣX.

In order to find the arithmetic average of a group of scores, it is necessary to add up all the scores and divide by the number of scores. These operations can be represented by the symbolic expression ($\Sigma X/N$), where N represents the number of scores. Suppose we wish to obtain the arithmetic average of the scores, 6, 3, 8, 6, and 4.

$$\Sigma X = 6 + 3 + 8 + 6 + 4 = 27$$

$$\text{average} = \frac{\Sigma X}{N} = \frac{27}{5} = 5.4$$

It is sometimes necessary to square each score and then find the sum of all of the squared scores. These operations would be represented by the expression ΣX^2. Using the above scores:

$$\Sigma X^2 = (6)^2 + (3)^2 + (8)^2 + (6)^2 + (4)^2$$
$$\Sigma X^2 = 36 + 9 + 64 + 36 + 16 = 161$$

The reader should note the difference between ΣX^2 and $(\Sigma X)^2$. Using the above scores:

$$(\Sigma X)^2 = (6 + 3 + 8 + 6 + 4)^2 = (27)^2 = 729$$

It can be seen that ΣX^2 does not equal $(\Sigma X)^2$.

Frequencies, Proportions, and Per Cents

Throughout the text, the reader will encounter frequencies, proportions, and per cents. It is important that he clearly understand what these are and that he be able to convert any one to either of the others.

The term *frequency* will be used to mean the number of cases in a sub-group of a larger group. Suppose, for instance, we flipped a coin 25 times and it came up heads 14 times and tails 11 times. The frequency of heads would be 14, and the frequency of tails would be 11. The symbol f will be used for the term *frequency*. That is:

$$f_{(\text{heads})} = 14, \qquad f_{(\text{tails})} = 11$$

The term *proportion* will be used to mean the ratio (either in fractional form or decimal form) of the frequency in a subgroup to the total number of cases in the larger group. That is:

$$\text{proportion} = \frac{f}{\text{total cases}}$$

For the coin-tossing example, the total number of cases (i.e., tosses) was 25; therefore:

$$\text{proportion of heads} = \frac{14}{25} = .56$$

$$\text{proportion of tails} \; = \frac{11}{25} = .44$$

A proportion is converted to a per cent by multiplying by 100. This multiplication can easily be performed by moving the decimal two places to the right.

$$\text{per cent of heads} = (100)(.56) = 56 \text{ per cent}$$
$$\text{per cent of tails} \; = (100)(.44) = 44 \text{ per cent}$$

Chapter 2

Frequency Distributions

Numerical data, in the form in which they first occur, are often not easily interpreted. It is usually necessary to arrange original data in some orderly fashion before conclusions can be drawn about them. Consider, for example, the following IQs for a sixth-grade class, taken from the alphabetized school record.

> 120, 86, 106, 107, 126, 102, 105, 99, 108, 131, 90, 101, 112, 97, 127, 106, 117, 107, 102, 102, 114, 123, 93, 113, 115, 95, 118, 109, 119, 103, 117, 105, 115, 104, 109, 112

What can be said about these thirty-six scores by inspecting them in the foregoing form? It can be seen that most scores are greater than 100; with some further searching one may also determine that the lowest IQ is 86 and the highest is 131. With some re-ordering of the thirty-six scores, however, these and other characteristics may be noted more quickly. More specifically, we may summarize the data by arranging the score values in order of size and indicating the frequency with which each score value occurs. Such a summary is called a *frequency distribution* and can appear in two forms: tabular and graphic.

TABULAR REPRESENTATION

The most detailed type of frequency distribution is that in which the number of cases (i.e., frequency) is counted and indicated for each separate score value. Such a frequency table for our 36 sixth-grade IQs is shown in Table 2-1. This simple distribution is far more useful than the

Table 2-1

Simple Frequency Distribution of Otis IQs for a Sixth-Grade Class (N = 36)

IQ	f	IQ	f	IQ	f	IQ	f
131	1	119	1	107	2	95	1
130	0	118	1	106	2	94	0
129	0	117	2	105	2	93	1
128	0	116	0	104	1	92	0
127	1	115	2	103	1	91	0
126	1	114	1	102	3	90	1
125	0	113	1	101	1	89	0
124	0	112	2	100	0	88	0
123	1	111	0	99	1	87	0
122	0	110	0	98	0	86	1
121	0	109	2	97	1		
120	1	108	1	96	0		

original listing of the scores. We can see immediately that the range is 86–131; we can identify the most frequently occurring score values efficiently; and, with simple counting, we can quickly make such statements as, "Half of the pupils have IQs greater than 107." When the range of scores is limited, the foregoing tabular representation may be appropriate; however, when the obtained scores range over many possible values, listing every score value becomes quite cumbersome and, furthermore, may obscure the pattern of the data. In such a case, it is usually more efficient and useful to group the scores into *class intervals*. To illustrate with our 36 IQs, all of the scores falling in the 5-point range 100 through 104 may be considered as a group (a class interval). In this instance, the frequency associated with the class interval 100–104 is 6. If we grouped all 36 scores into class intervals of 5 score units, the frequency distribution shown in Table 2-2 would result. Frequency distributions constructed according to class intervals rather than individual score values are more economical of space and time. They also reveal the pattern of scores more clearly. We can see from Table 2-2, for example, that the scores tend to cluster around 107 (the midpoint of interval 105–109) and fall off rather equally on both sides.

Score Limits and Real Limits

The class intervals in Table 2-2 are identified in terms of the lowest possible score and the highest possible score in each. These are known as the *score limits* of the intervals. For instance, the lower score limit of the interval 85–89 is 85, and the upper score limit is 89.

If, for purposes of analysis, the data are to be treated as though they were based on a continuous scale, a distinction should be made between

Table 2-2

Frequency Distribution of IQs for a Sixth-Grade Class (Constructed Using Class Intervals of Size 5; N = 36)

IQ	Midpoint	f
130–134	132	1
125–129	127	2
120–124	122	2
115–119	117	6
110–114	112	4
105–109	107	9
100–104	102	6
95–99	97	3
90–94	92	2
85–89	87	1
		$N = 36$

score limits and *real limits*. Consider for a moment an IQ score of 90. On a continuous scale such a score would be considered to include anything from 89.5 to 90.5. Similarly, an IQ of 89 would be considered to include anything from 88.5 to 89.5, and so forth. In other words, the obtained IQ scores may be thought of as intelligence values rounded to the nearest integer. Thus, the *real limits* of the interval 90–94 are 89.5 and 94.5. This may be represented as in Fig. 2-1(*a*). In general, when data are treated as continuous, each possible score value can be considered as including anything from a point half-way between it and the previous score value to a point half-way between it and the following score value. This is illustrated in Fig. 2-1(*b*) for several class intervals of heights, measured to the nearest tenth of an inch. The interval size is .5 in. A measured score of 60.0 in. is considered to include anything from 59.95 in. to 60.05 in., a measured score of 60.1 in. includes anything from 60.05 in. to 60.15 in., and so forth. The score limits for each interval are the highest and lowest possible measurements within that interval that can actually be obtained using our measuring stick. That is, the score limits for the lowest interval represented would be 60.0 in. and 60.4 in.; however, the real limits for that interval are 59.95 in. and 60.45 in.

There is at least one type of situation in which each score value is not considered to include everything from a half less to a half more than the expressed value. Consider the variable of age. An individual's age is ordinarily gauged by his last birthday rather than by his nearest birthday. That is, one would be considered 20 years old from the first moment of his twentieth birthday until the first moment of his twenty-first birthday. An age of 20 would include everything from exactly 20 to exactly 21, an age of 21 would include everything from exactly 21 to exactly 22, and so forth. Thus, for age as of the last birthday, the interval 20–24 will have

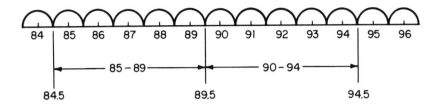

(a) Representation of IQ Intervals of Size 5

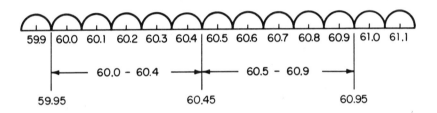

(b) Representation of Intervals of Height Measured to the Nearest 1/10 of an Inch. The interval size is .5 in.

Figure 2-1. Illustration of Class Intervals

real limits of 20 and 25. On the other hand, if, as some insurance companies do, one determines age by the nearest birthday, the interval 20–24 has real limits of 19.5 and 24.5. In each case, the interval width is 5 years. The foregoing distinction is illustrated in Fig. 2-2. The import of real limits will become clearer as we employ them in subsequent procedures and problems.

Midpoints

For purposes to be discussed later, it is often convenient to allow all of the cases within a class interval to be represented by a single score. Most commonly, this score is taken to be the midpoint of the interval. The determination of the midpoint is quite simple: merely add half the interval size to the lower *real limit* of the interval. Thus, for the distribution of IQ scores in Table 2-2, the midpoint of the interval 90–94 is 92 (i.e., 1/2 of 5 = 2.5; 89.5 + 2.5 = 92). For a distribution of ages based on the last birthday, the midpoint of the interval 20–24 would be 22.5 (i.e., 1/2

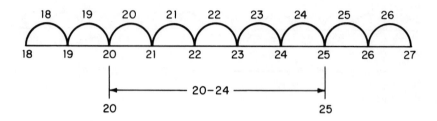

Age to the Last Birthday

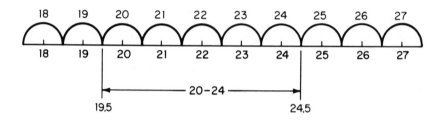

Age to the Nearest Birthday

**Figure 2-2. Illustration of Intervals of Age
(Size of Intervals Five Years)**

of $5 = 2.5; 20 + 2.5 = 22.5$). For a distribution of ages based on the nearest birthday, the midpoint of the interval 20–24 would be 22 (i.e., 1/2 of $5 = 2.5; 19.5 + 2.5 = 22$).

Error Due to Grouping

In succeeding chapters, various statistical measures used to describe a collection of scores will be introduced. These may be computed directly from ungrouped data; or, as will sometimes be more convenient, they may be computed from a frequency distribution in which scores have been grouped into class intervals. If grouped data are involved, certain assumptions concerning the placement of individuals within a class interval must be made, because the exact scores of individuals will be lost after grouping. One such assumption is that the scores within a class interval may be accurately represented by the midpoint of the interval. In practice this assumption is seldom, if ever, met completely. Consequently, results based upon data grouped into class intervals will usually differ somewhat from those which would have been obtained from the original scores.

The degree of error due to grouping will depend in great part upon the number and, thus, upon the size of the class intervals used: the greater the number of the intervals, the smaller the error is likely to be. When we use a sufficient number of intervals to narrow the interval size to a single score, there is no error, since we are back to the original individual scores. Consequently, if a relatively large number of intervals is utilized, errors due to grouping will be small enough that they can be ignored for most purposes. When relatively few intervals are used, a correction technique, to be discussed in Chap. 4, may be applied.

Choice of Class Intervals

If too few intervals are used, excessive errors due to grouping may result. Furthermore, the overall picture given by the resulting frequency distribution may be far too general to be of any use. The reader, in order to understand this last point, may imagine the data of Table 2-1 grouped into only two intervals of thirty units, 80–109 and 110–139. On the other hand, there is a disadvantage in using a very large number of intervals. If the sample is relatively small, many of the intervals may contain very few or no cases (as in Table 2-1), and a very uneven frequency distribution will result. This makes it difficult for one to obtain a picture of the general pattern of scores. The purposes of a frequency distribution are lost when more than the necessary number of intervals are used.

Considering these various factors, how many intervals should be used? Experience suggests that, in most cases, somewhere between 10 and 20 will be best. In constructing Table 2-2, we first decided to employ approximately ten class intervals. The size of each class interval was then determined by dividing the total range of scores ($131 - 86 = 45$) by 10. The quotient is 4.5, which is the approximate size of each class interval if 10 classes are desired. The interval size, therefore, can be either 4 or 5. We prefer the odd number (5) since it would result in a whole-number midpoint rather than a decimal one—a matter of convenience. Furthermore, it is simpler for most to think in terms of multiples of 5 rather than of 4. Now we determine the place to begin the lowest class interval. Since this interval must include the lowest score (86), its lower score limit can be as small as 82. We chose 85 as the beginning point because it is a multiple of 5. Hence, the bottom class interval in Table 2-2 is 85–89, inclusive, and all other class intervals follow from this.

GRAPHIC REPRESENTATION

It is common practice, in presenting data, to represent frequency distributions in graphic form for visual interpretation. There is a variety of possible graphic representations. We shall consider, in this section, two that are commonly employed: the *histogram* and the *frequency polygon*. In Chap. 6, we shall present another: the *cumulative percentage curve*.

The Histogram

The common practice in graphical presentation is to indicate the units of measurement on the horizontal axis (abscissa) and the frequency on the vertical axis (ordinate). In the case of the histogram, the frequency associated with a given class interval is shown by the height of a rectangle erected at the real limits of the class interval, the midpoint of the class interval being in the center of the rectangle. When Table 2-2 is treated in this manner, we have the histogram shown in Fig. 2-3.

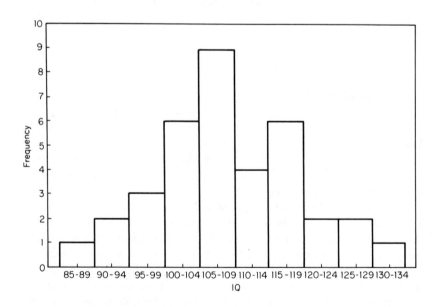

*Figure 2-3. Histogram for the Frequency Distribution
of Thirty-six IQ Scores of Table 2-2*

The Frequency Polygon

For a frequency polygon, the frequency associated with each class interval is plotted as a *point* above the midpoint of the interval, and the points are then connected with straight lines. The frequency polygon for Table 2-2 is shown in Fig. 2-4. If the frequency polygon is terminated

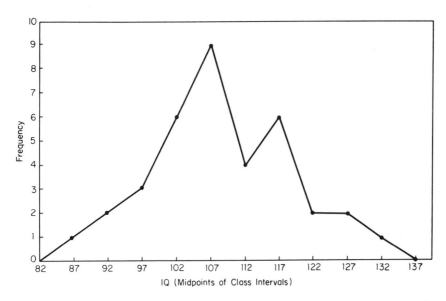

Figure 2-4. Frequency Polygon for the Frequency Distribution of Thirty-six IQ Scores of Table 2-2

above the midpoints of the highest and lowest intervals which contain any cases, it will remain "floating" above the horizontal axis. The usual procedure is to bring the frequency polygon down to a zero frequency at the midpoints of the intervals just beyond the highest and lowest intervals containing scores. This has been done in Fig. 2-4.

Smoothing the Frequency Polygon

The frequency polygon in Fig. 2-4 has "dips" and "peaks" in it. The line connecting the various frequencies is not "smooth." This is frequently the case when the number of scores is small. When the purpose of presenting a frequency polygon is to show the general nature of the distribution, one may modify the polygon by smoothing it. An instance of situations in which smoothing is appropriate is the reporting of sample scores. Uneven polygons can arise for a sample distribution through chance factors even when the total population is smoothly distributed. In such a case, smoothing the frequency polygon is more informative of the population.

A frequency distribution may be smoothed by drawing, freehand, a curve that generally "averages out" the dips and peaks. It is, however, customary to be more precise than this; and, accordingly, the method of "moving averages" is commonly utilized. Actually, there are many variations of the moving-average principle, of which we shall illustrate only one. The procedure is simple. We shall "smooth out" the irregularities in the Fig. 2-4 polygon by changing each plotted frequency to an average (mean) of the frequency below it, the frequency itself taken twice, and the frequency above it. When this is done, Fig. 2-5 results. For instance,

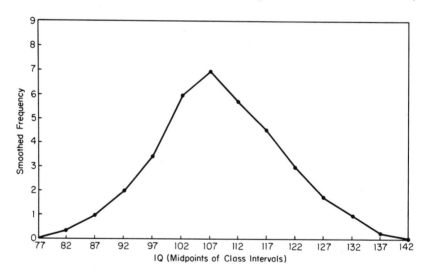

Figure 2-5. Smoothed Version of Frequency Polygon in Fig. 2-4
(The smoothed frequencies were obtained
using the method of moving averages.)

the original frequency for midpoint 112 was 4. The smoothed frequency for that midpoint is 5.75, which was found by computing the mean of $9 + \overbrace{4 + 4} + 6$ (i.e., 23/4 = 5.75). Each smoothed frequency for Fig. 2-5 was obtained by the same process.

Consider the smoothed frequency for the midpoint, 82, of the interval 80–84. The frequency for the interval 75–79 is 0, the frequency for the interval 80–84 is 0, and the frequency for the interval 85–89 is 1. Thus, although the interval 80–84 originally had no cases in it, its smoothed frequency is the mean of $0 + \overbrace{0 + 0} + 1$, or .25. A comparison of Figs. 2-4 and 2-5 will show that the method of moving averages does indeed result in a smoother frequency polygon. The particular moving average utilized in Fig. 2-5 assigned twice as much weight to the frequency in the interval itself as to the two adjacent frequencies. Other variations of the method of moving averages differ with respect to how the frequencies are weighted and how many adjacent frequencies are included in a single average.

RELATIVE-FREQUENCY DISTRIBUTIONS

Suppose we wished to compare the IQs of our class of thirty-six sixth-graders with the IQs of a group of seventy sixth-graders from another school. A direct comparison of the frequency distributions of IQ scores for the two groups would be difficult because the total numbers of cases differ. The solution to this problem is quite straightforward.

Before any comparisons are made, the frequency in each class interval is converted to a proportion by dividing by the total number of cases. Such proportions are known as *relative frequencies*, and distributions presented in terms of relative frequencies rather than actual frequencies are known as *relative-frequency distributions*. The relative-frequency distributions for the two groups are presented in Table 2-3. If the two frequency polygons are then constructed on the same set of axes, using the

Table 2-3

***Relative-Frequency Distributions of IQs for a Class
of Thirty-six Sixth-Graders (A) and a Group
of Seventy Sixth-Graders (B)***

IQ	Class A		Group B	
	f	Rel. f	f	Rel. f
130–134	1	.028	0	.000
125–129	2	.056	1	.014
120–124	2	.056	3	.043
115–119	6	.167	8	.114
110–114	4	.111	10	.143
105–109	9	.250	12	.171
100–104	6	.167	16	.229
95–99	3	.083	10	.143
90–94	2	.056	7	.100
85–89	1	.028	3	.043
	36	1.00	70	1.00

relative frequencies, a direct visual comparison can be made. This is done in Fig. 2-6.

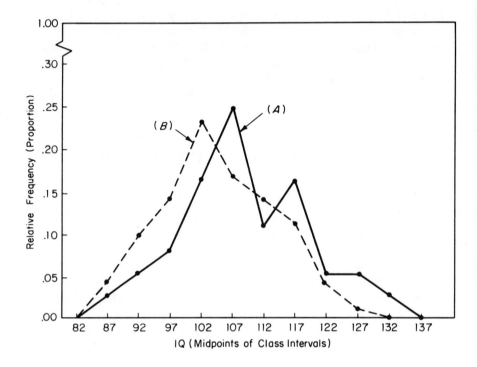

Figure 2-6. Polygons for the Relative-Frequency Distributions of IQ Scores of Table 2-3

The concept of a relative-frequency distribution is a very useful and important one, not only for comparisons such as that above but also for understanding some of the basic sampling theory underlying statistical inference. The latter application will be discussed at length in subsequent chapters.

The Relationship between Area and Relative Frequency

In constructing a histogram, or frequency polygon, the frequency (or relative frequency) for each interval is represented by the height of the curve above that interval; however, an equally important representation of frequency involves the area under the curve. Consider once again the histogram for the frequency distribution of Table 2-2. Suppose that the histogram were constructed on a very large piece of paper in such a manner that each interval were 3 in. wide and each unit of frequency on the vertical axis were equal to 2 in. This is represented (although to a reduced scale) in Fig. 2-7.

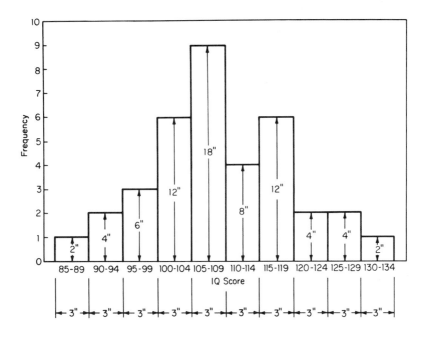

Figure 2-7. Histogram for the Frequency Distribution of the Thirty-six IQ Scores of Table 2-2, Constructed to the Scale Indicated

The area for each bar can be obtained by multiplying the width of the bar (3 in.) by the height. Furthermore, the proportional area for each bar can be determined by dividing the area for that bar by the total area under the entire histogram (all the bars combined). The actual areas and proportional areas are presented in Table 2-4. Notice that the proportional areas for the respective bars are equal to the relative frequencies presented in Table 2-3. Consequently, the proportion of cases, or the relative frequency included in one or more class intervals, equals the proportion of area under the histogram included in those intervals. For instance, the relative frequency with which individuals fall below a score of 99.5 is .167 (i.e., .028 + .056 + .083 = .167), which is the same as the proportion of area under the histogram below a score of 99.5. The reader

Table 2-4

Areas and Proportional Areas for the Bars of the Histogram in Fig. 2-7, Where Each Interval is 3 In. Wide and Each Unit of Frequency is 2 In. High

IQ	f	Area (sq. inches) $(W)(H)$ = Area	Proportional Area
130–134	1	(3)(2) = 6	.028
125–129	2	(3)(4) = 12	.056
120–124	2	(3)(4) = 12	.056
115–119	6	(3)(12) = 36	.167
110–114	4	(3)(8) = 24	.111
105–109	9	(3)(18) = 54	.250
100–104	6	(3)(12) = 36	.167
95–99	3	(3)(6) = 18	.083
90–94	2	(3)(4) = 12	.056
85–89	1	(3)(2) = 6	.028
		216 sq. in.	1.00

should assure himself that proportional area will always equal relative frequency regardless of the scale used.

The interpretation of area as relative frequency was developed above using a histogram, because the reader undoubtedly recalls the procedure for determining the area of a rectangle. However, the same interpretation can be given to area under a smooth frequency curve, since such a curve can be considered as a histogram with infinitely narrow bars. This is illustrated with very narrow bars in Fig. 2-8. Notice that the smooth curve

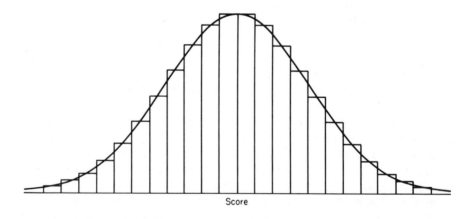

Score

Figure 2-8. A Smooth Frequency Curve with a Histogram Superimposed

is very closely approximated by the histogram which has been super-imposed.

Now, it should not be difficult for the reader to see that better and better approximations could be obtained by using narrower and narrower bars (and, of course, more of them). Thus, for a smooth curve as well, *the proportion of area below any score is equal to the proportion or relative frequency of cases falling below that score.* For example, consider the smooth distribution of scores in Fig. 2-9. Eighty-four per cent of the area

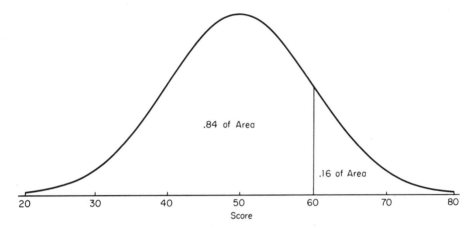

Figure 2-9. A Smooth Frequency Curve
with Proportional Areas Indicated

falls below a score of 60. Thus, we know that .84, or 84 per cent, of the cases have scores below 60.

This relationship between proportional area and relative frequency is extremely important, as will become apparent in later chapters on prob-ability and statistical inference.

FREQUENCY DISTRIBUTIONS FOR NOMINAL
(QUALITATIVE) VARIABLES

Thus far, the discussion of frequency distributions has been confined to data that can be treated as continuous. Although data of this type will be our major concern throughout much of the text, it should be mentioned that the notion of a frequency distribution can be applied to nominal variables as well. Consider, for instance, the variable of "college major." A frequency distribution summarizing the majors for 433 undergraduates

Table 2-5

*A Frequency Distribution of Academic Majors
for the Undergraduates of a Small College*

Academic Major	f
English	102
History	87
French	35
Spanish	43
Art	39
Music	56
Speech & Drama	71

$N = 433$

at a small college might resemble that in Table 2-5. This frequency distribution may be represented pictorially by a bar diagram such as that shown in Fig. 2-10. Notice that the bars have been drawn with slight spaces

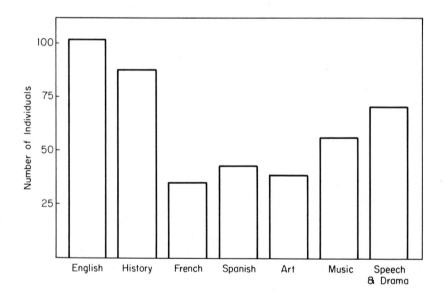

*Figure 2-10. Bar Diagram for the Frequency Distribution
of Academic Majors of Table 2-5*

between them. These spaces make it easier for one to distinguish between a bar chart for nominal data, or data to be treated as discrete, and a histogram constructed on a continuous numerical scale.

CHARACTERISTICS OF FREQUENCY DISTRIBUTIONS

Frequency distributions may vary with regard to a variety of characteristics; and these variations, if marked, are important in interpreting the data. Although we shall have much more to say about this in subsequent chapters, some general concepts and basic terminology will be introduced below.

Central Tendency and Variability

The most widely noted characteristics of frequency distributions, *central tendency* and *variability*, are illustrated in Fig. 2-11. Note that the two distributions of Fig. 2-11(*a*) center on two different points on the score scale. The scores from distribution *A* tend "on the average" to be somewhat higher than those from distribution *B*. Thus, it can be said that the two distributions of Fig. 2-11(*a*) differ with regard to central tendency. On the other hand, the two distributions of Fig. 2-11(*b*) are quite similar with regard to central tendency; they both center on approximately the same value. The distributions of Fig. 2-11(*b*) do differ, however, with regard to variability. That is, distribution *C* shows greater variability in that the scores for that distribution "spread out" more than the scores for distribution *D*. The two distributions of Fig. 2-11(*a*) show about the same degree of variability even though they differ with regard to central tendency.

Multimodality

Frequency distributions usually have only one peak, or point of highest frequency, as in the case of the thirty-six IQ scores described earlier. Such a distribution is said to have one mode, and is termed *unimodal*. Sometimes when two or more systematically differing groups are combined in a single group, the resulting frequency distribution may be *multimodal*. That is, it may have more than one peak or mode. For example, if we constructed a frequency distribution of the times in which the 100-yard dash was run by a combined group of boys and girls, the distribution probably would be *bimodal* (it would have two modes) because the girls, who are usually slower, would tend to cluster around a larger time value

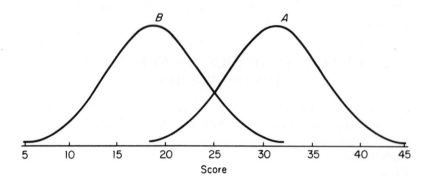

(a) *Distributions Which Differ with Regard to Central Tendency but Are About the Same with Regard to Variability*

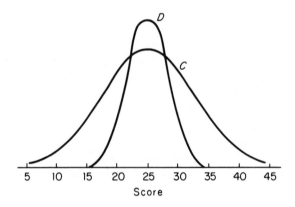

(b) *Distributions Which Differ with Regard to Variability but Are About the Same with Regard to Central Tendency*

Figure 2-11. Variations in Central Tendency and Variability

than would the boys. The result might be something like the frequency curve shown in Fig. 2-12(a).

Skewness

Distributions vary also in the extent to which they are bilaterally symmetrical. Symmetrical distributions (those in which left and right halves of the distribution are mirror images) are illustrated in Fig. 2-12(d, e, f).

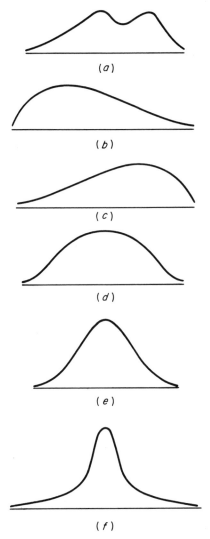

Figure 2-12. Variations in Distribution Shapes

When a distribution identifiably departs from symmetry, it is said to be *skewed*. If the skewness is like that shown in Fig. 2-12(*b*), we say that it shows *positive skewness*. The converse, *negative skewness*, is illustrated in Fig. 2-12(*c*). Skewed distributions are produced by many circumstances, some of them quite predictable. A positively skewed distribution, for instance, is often obtained in the case of the distribution of scores on a test that is too difficult for the group—few persons get high scores, and relatively more obtain low scores.

Kurtosis

A final dimension of distribution shape is the degree to which the distribution is either "flat-topped" or "sharp-peaked" relative to the "normal" shape of Fig. 2-12(e). When the tendency is toward flatness, as in Fig. 2-12(d), the distribution is called *platykurtic;* the sharply peaked distribution of Fig. 2-12(f) is termed *leptokurtic.* Little reference will be made to kurtosis in this text. The concept and terms are presented for the interest of readers who may encounter them in supplementary literature.

Exercises and Problems

The first four exercises and problems refer to the following situation. The staff of an elementary school is interested in the distance each pupil walks to school each day. A sample of thirty pupils is randomly selected from the school population, and for each pupil the distance between home and school grounds is determined from a large-scale map of the community. The unit of measurement is in yards, and the "score" for each pupil is rounded off to the nearest 100 yd. The raw data for the thirty pupils are as follows.

100, 100, 100, 300, 300, 300, 300, 400, 400, 400, 400, 400, 400, 400, 500, 500, 500, 500, 500, 500, 500, 600, 600, 600, 600, 600, 700, 700, 700, 700, 800, 800, 800, 800, 800, 800, 900, 900, 900, 1,000, 1,100, 1,200, 1,200, 1,300, 1,500, 1,800, 1,900, 1,900, 2,000, 2,100.

1. Should this variable be thought of as continuous or discrete? Explain.
2. For the purposes of constructing a frequency distribution based on grouped data, what is your decision regarding the size of the class interval? Why did you decide as you did?
3. Construct a frequency distribution, histogram, and frequency polygon for the foregoing situation.
4. From inspection of the frequency distribution, what can you say about the central tendency and skewness?
5. The following refer to the distributions of Table 2.6:
   a) Convert the frequencies for group C to relative frequencies.
   b) Convert the frequencies for group D to relative frequencies.
   c) Draw the relative frequency polygon for group C.
   d) Draw the relative frequency polygon for group D.

e)   Compare the relative frequency polygons for groups C and D with regard to central tendency, variability, and skewness.

Table 2-6

Frequency Distributions of Reading Speeds for Two Groups of Students (Reading Speed in Words Per Minute)

Words per minute	Group C frequency	Group D frequency
450–474	2	0
425–449	4	0
400–424	8	2
375–399	10	7
350–374	8	10
325–349	16	12
300–324	19	5
275–299	25	8
250–274	40	2
225–249	30	1
200–224	16	2
175–199	15	1
150–174	7	0
Total	200	50

6.   What are the smoothed frequencies for the following intervals, for the
group D distribution of Table 2.6: (*a*) 275–299; (*b*) 300–324; (*c*) 175–199;
(*d*) 150–174; (*e*) 125–149.

7.   For each of the following, give the interval size you would use, the number
of intervals, and the score limits of both the lowest and highest intervals:
a)   a group of 500 scores where the lowest score is 14 and the highest is 89.
b)   a group of 500 scores where the lowest score is 463 and the highest is
752.
c)   a group of 500 scores where the lowest score is 8 and the highest is 19.
d)   a group of 500 scores where the lowest score is 5.3 and the highest is 9.6.
e)   a group of 500 scores where the lowest score is 1.81 and the highest is
4.53.

8.   For the following test score intervals, indicate the interval size, the real
limits, and the midpoint: (*a*) 25–29; (*b*) 3-5; (*c*) 10–19; (*d*) 520–549; (*e*) 72–
79.

9.   For the following intervals (measurements in centimeters), indicate the interval size, the real limits, and the midpoint: (*a*) 1.2–1.5; (*b*) 1.25–1.29;
(*c*) 60–69; (*d*) .0021–.0024; (*e*) 5.621–5.622.

10.   Consider the following intervals for ages as of last birthday. For each interval, indicate the interval size, the real limits, and the midpoint: (*a*) 5–9;
(*b*) 21–24; (*c*) 8–9.

11. Consider the following two distributions: (*a*) scores of ninth-graders on a college-freshman algebra test, (*b*) scores of college-senior math majors on the same college-freshman algebra test. What kind of a distribution would you expect in the case of (*a*)? In the case of (*b*)? In the case of (*a*) and (*b*) combined? Explain.

12. Consider a class interval expressed in terms of the *score limits* 15–19, where the data are length in inches. What are the real limits and midpoint of this interval? Now consider the score limits 0–4 in the same situation? What is the lower real limit of this interval? How does one make sense of the latter case?

13. Under what conditions are the midpoints of the class intervals most likely to represent the raw scores adequately? Under what conditions are midpoints non-representative?

14. An investigator of juvenile delinquency in a western state determined the delinquency rates for the various counties and presented his results in the form of a frequency polygon (the baseline was counties listed in alphabetical order). Is the frequency polygon the most appropriate graphic representation in such a case? Explain.

Chapter 3

Central Tendency

As we have already seen, a collection of data may be described with regard to central tendency, variability, number of modes, skewness, and kurtosis. In this chapter, we shall be concerned with *central tendency*, or *average*. The reader is already familiar with some of the ways in which averages are used in summarizing and interpreting quantitative information. In this chapter we shall deal with three different kinds of averages or central-tendency measures which are frequently employed in statistical description: the *mode, median,* and *arithmetic mean.* There are other central-tendency measures, such as the *geometric mean* or the *harmonic mean;* but these have such specialized and infrequent use in education and the behavioral sciences that we omit their consideration here.

THE MODE

Among measures of central tendency, the mode is the simplest to determine. It can be roughly defined as *that score value which is obtained most often.* For example, consider the group of twelve scores, 11, 9, 9, 8, 7, 7, 7, 6, 5, 4, 4, 2. The mode would be 7, because more individuals obtained a 7 than obtained any other score. This example is merely to illustrate the above definition, for rarely in practice would the mode ever be determined for so few cases. Normally, the mode is computed only when the number of cases is fairly large and the scores have been grouped into class intervals. For grouped data, the mode is taken to be the midpoint of the interval which contains the most cases. This is often referred to as the *crude mode.* For instance, the crude mode of the distribution for

School *A* in Table 3-1 would be the midpoint of the interval 75–79, or 77.

As a measure of central tendency, the mode can be a useful statistic when a "quick" estimate is desired and there is no need to be very precise; however, it has a number of serious limitations. First, since the crude mode can fall only at the midpoint of an interval, its value will depend upon the particular set of intervals used in grouping the data. For instance, if for the School *A* data of Table 3-1, the intervals 52–56, 57–61, 62–66, etc. had been used instead, the crude mode would have differed by at least two points from the value obtained. Second, unless the number of cases is very large, the value of the mode may be unduly affected by chance factors. This is particularly true for relatively "flat" frequency distributions in which the frequencies for the intervals containing the most cases are nearly the same. For such distributions, a shift of just one or two cases may move the crude mode from the midpoint of one interval to that of another.

This last point becomes an extremely important consideration when the frequencies are equal for the two intervals containing the most cases. If the two intervals are adjacent, it would make sense to use as the mode the interval limit separating the two intervals. If the two intervals are not adjacent, the distribution would appear to be *bimodal;* however, the bimodality observed for a sample of scores from a relatively flat distribution might well reflect the operation of chance factors rather than any true bimodality for the variable in question.

THE MEDIAN

A more useful and informative central-tendency value is found in the *median*. It may be defined in two ways:

1) When a set of scores is arranged in order of magnitude, *the median is the value of the middle score if there is an odd number of scores, or the value midway between the two middle scores when there is an even number of scores.* This method of determination is illustrated below.

Scores	Median
1, 7, 10, 11, 15	10
4, 5, 6, 9	5.5 (half-way between 5 and 6)
1, 2, 3, 3, 3, 4	3 (half-way between 3 and 3)

2) When scores are arranged in a frequency distribution (the most common case), the median is defined as the *point below and above which 50 per cent of the scores occur.* The computation of the median for a distribution can be illustrated with the data in Table 3-1. The table compares two schools with reference to the mental ages of entering first-grade youngsters.

Table 3-1

Mental Ages of Entering First-Grade Children
in School A and School B
(50 Children at Each School)

Mental Age (in months)	Midpoint	School A f	School B f
100–104	102	1	0
95–99	97	0	0
90–94	92	1	1
85–89	87	2	2
80–84	82	7	6
75–79	77	14	9
70–74	72	12	10
65–69	67	6	15
60–64	62	5	5
55–59	57	1	1
50–54	52	0	0
45–49	47	1	1
		$N = 50$	$N = 50$

(School A: 25 cases below the 70–74 interval; School B: 22 cases and 32 cases bracketed around the 70–74 interval)

How can we determine the median for School A? Recall that we wish to find the value (mental age, in this case) below (and above) which half of the 50 cases may be found. Since we have a total of 50 cases, we wish to find the point on the scale that divides the top and bottom 25. Starting at the bottom we add the figures in the f column for School A and find that we reach exactly 25 cases when we have passed through the class interval 70–74. That is, half the cases are in and below this class interval and half are above it. What is the value that can separate the halves? It must be the point between the interval 70–74 and the next highest class interval, 75–79. This point is the upper *real limit* of the interval 70–74—and also the lower real limit of the interval 75–79. The median mental age for School A, therefore, is 74.5.

Finding the School A median was rather easy—too easy, in fact. We deliberately arranged the f column to permit a cumulation of exactly 25. The more common situation, however, is illustrated by the task of finding the School B median. We again need the point below which 25 cases fall, since the total number of cases is also 50. Now, when we add the figures in the f column, we find there are 22 cases through the interval 65–69; and if we add to this the 10 cases in the next class interval we shall have 32 cases—which is more than the 25 we seek. It seems, then, that the median for School B lies somewhere in the class interval 70–74—but exactly where? In order to answer this we must make an assumption about the way in which the cases in interval 70–74 are distributed within that interval. *The assumption is that these 10 cases are spread evenly between the real limits of the interval* (i.e., between 69.5 and 74.5). Once the assumption has been made, we can use a technique commonly referred to as *interpolation*.

Since there are 22 cases below the interval 70–74, we need 3 of the 10 cases from that interval in order to reach the required 25. It is assumed that the 10 scores are distributed uniformly throughout the interval; thus the proportion of cases (3/10 = .30) equals the proportional distance we must move along the interval to reach the median. The interval is 5 score units wide; hence 3/10 of 5 (i.e., 1.50) represents the distance from the lower limit of the interval (69.5) to the median. The median, then, is 71.00 (i.e., 69.50 + 1.50). This procedure, illustrated in Fig. 3-1, follows a sequence of five steps.

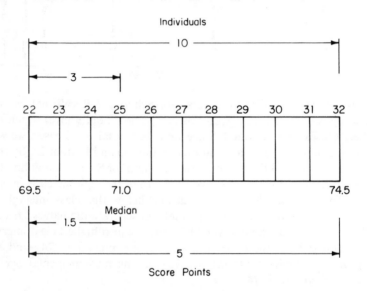

Figure 3-1. Representation of the Interval 70–74 for the Distribution of Scores for School B Presented in Table 3-1

1) Divide the number of cases (N) by 2.

$$\frac{N}{2} = \frac{50}{2} = 25$$

2) Cumulate the frequencies, beginning with the lowest class interval, up to (not including) the class interval containing the median.

The twenty-fifth case, and thus the median, falls in the interval 70–74. Twenty-two cases fall below that interval.

3) Determine how many additional cases from the interval are required to make $N/2$.

$$25 - 22 = 3 \text{ cases}$$

4) Divide the required number of additional cases by the frequency in the interval.

$$\frac{3}{10} = .30$$

5) Multiply the result by the size of the interval.

$$5 (.30) = 1.50 \text{ score points}$$

6) Add the product of Step 5 to the lower real limit of the interval. This gives the median value.

$$69.50 + 1.50 = 71.00$$

The five steps can be summarized in the following formula for computing the median of a frequency distribution.

$$\text{Mdn} = \text{L.L.} + i \left(\frac{\frac{N}{2} - f_c}{f} \right) \tag{3-1}$$

where L.L. is the lower limit of the interval containing the median, i is the interval size, f_c is cumulative frequency up to the lower limit of the interval, and f is the frequency within the interval

Using the data for School B:

$$\text{Mdn} = 69.50 + 5 \left(\frac{\frac{50}{2} - 22}{10} \right) = 69.50 + 5 \left(\frac{3}{10} \right) = 71.00$$

Even though he may prefer to use Form. (3-1), it will pay the reader to grasp the logic involved; once understood, the same interpolation process can be used to determine other information from and about distributions, as we shall see in subsequent chapters.

THE ARITHMETIC MEAN

The most basic and frequently used average is the *arithmetic mean*, which is defined as the sum of the scores divided by the number of scores. This definition can be expressed in terms of the formula:

$$\overline{X} = \frac{\Sigma X}{N} \tag{3-2}$$

where the symbol $\overline{X}$ (read "X bar") represents the mean of a set of scores on variable X; the summation sign, $\sum$, indicates the operation of addition; and N represents the total number of cases

To illustrate the application of Form. (3-2), we shall determine the mean of the following set of scores: 8, 8, 10, 11, 13.

$$\overline{X} = \frac{\sum X}{N} = \frac{8 + 8 + 10 + 11 + 13}{5} = \frac{50}{5} = 10$$

For grouped data, the exact values of the scores are unknown. Consequently, *for purposes of computing the mean, we allow each case within an interval to be represented by the midpoint of that interval.* Consider, for instance, the class interval 60–64 of the distribution of scores for School A in Table 3-2. The score or X value for each of the five cases in that interval will be considered to be the midpoint, 62; therefore, the sum of the scores in that interval may be obtained using the formula fX, where f is the frequency for the interval and X is now the midpoint value. For the interval 60–64:

$$fX = (5)\,(62) = 310$$

The sum of the scores in each of the other intervals (allowing the midpoint to represent every case) could be obtained in the same manner. These interval sums for the School A data are listed in the fX column of Table 3-2. If we add the interval sums in the fX column, we obtain the sum

Table 3-2

Partial Computations for Determining the Mean from Grouped Data Utilizing "School A" Data from Table 3-1

Mental Age	X (midpoints)	f	fX
100–104	102	1	102
95–99	97	0	0
90–94	92	1	92
85–89	87	2	174
80–84	82	7	574
75–79	77	14	1078
70–74	72	12	864
65–69	67	6	402
60–64	62	5	310
55–59	57	1	57
50–54	52	0	0
45–49	47	1	47
		$N = 50$	$\sum fX = 3700$

of the scores of all fifty cases in the distribution. This total sum is symbolized as $\sum fX$. The mean of the distribution can now be determined using the following variation of Form. (3-2).

$$\overline{X} = \frac{\sum fX}{N} = \frac{3,700}{50} = 74.00 \tag{3-3}$$

where each X is a midpoint value

The foregoing procedure for finding the mean from grouped data will be accurate in the degree to which the midpoint is adequately representative of the scores in the class interval. How safe is such an assumption? The reader is reminded of the discussion of grouping error in the previous chapter, where it was pointed out that using the midpoints will almost always give results which differ from those which would have been obtained had the original ungrouped scores been used; however, if the number of class intervals is over ten or twelve, the interval size will be reduced to the point where the error in the mean due to grouping should be negligible.

The Effects of Operations with Constants

In finding the mean using Form. (3-3), we were confronted with some large numbers in the process of multiplying, summing, and dividing. Such numbers invite error and, in any event, are awkward to manipulate. Happily, there is a procedure for computing the mean that reduces the size of the numbers involved. That procedure is based on an important principle regarding what happens to measures of central tendency when each original score is transformed by adding or subtracting a constant value, or by multiplying or dividing by a constant value. The principle deserves attention also, because it will be invoked in later chapters.

Consider the following scores: 10, 12, 13, 14, 16. The mean and median of the 5 scores are both 13. If we subtract the constant value 10 from each score, we have 0, 2, 3, 4, 6, the mean and median of which are 3. That is, the effect of subtracting the constant 10 from each score is to reduce the mean and median both by 10 points. If each original score is divided by the constant value 2, we have 5, 6, 6.5, 7, 8. The mean and median of these transformed scores are both 6.5—which is half of the original mean and median of 13. Similarly, as the reader can quickly demonstrate for himself with the above set of scores, the addition of a constant to each score increases the mean by the same amount, and the multiplication of each score by a constant increases the mean in the same way. To summarize the principle illustrated, *the application of a constant to every score*

*through addition, subtraction, multiplication, or division affects the mean
(as well as the median and mode) in precisely the same way as it affects
the individual scores.*

"Short" Method for Computing the Mean

The foregoing properties may be used to simplify the computation of
the mean. The most popular method for hand computation of the mean
actually involves both subtracting a constant from each score *and* dividing
the obtained amount by the size of the class interval. Although we do not
wish to advocate or encourage hand computing in this age of readily
available calculators, this "short" method will be illustrated for those who
may wish to use it. Consider the School *A* data again. The intervals and
frequencies are reproduced in Table 3-3. We shall reduce the size of our

Table 3-3

**Partial Computations for Determining the Mean
from Coded Midpoints, Utilizing "School A"
Data from Table 3-1**

Mental Age	X (midpoints)	f	d'	d	fd
100–104	102	1	55	11	11
95–99	97	0	50	10	0
90–94	92	1	45	9	9
85–89	87	2	40	8	16
80–84	82	7	35	7	49
75–79	77	14	30	6	84
70–74	72	12	25	5	60
65–69	67	6	20	4	24
60–64	62	5	15	3	15
55–59	57	1	10	2	2
50–54	52	0	5	1	0
45–49	47	1	0	0	0
		$N = 50$			$\sum fd = 270$

scores (the midpoints) by selecting one of the midpoints as an *arbitrary
origin* and subtracting that arbitrary origin from each midpoint. Let us
use the lowest midpoint as the arbitrary origin; this is 47. If we subtract
47 from the bottom midpoint, we get 0. Moving to the next midpoint,
we subtract the constant 47 from 52 to get 5, and so forth. The resulting
"coded" midpoints are labeled d' (read as "d prime") in Table 3-3. Now
let us make an additional simplification by dividing the coded midpoints
(d') by the interval size of 5 to obtain the *final* coded midpoints, which
are labeled d. Note that the d column is precisely what would have been

obtained if we simply started at the bottom interval and numbered each class interval from 0 through 11. We can find the mean for the d coded midpoints by applying a variation of Form. (3-3) for the mean of grouped data.

Using the data in Table 3-3, we find the mean d to be:

$$\bar{d} = \frac{\sum fd}{N} = \frac{270}{50} = 5.40 \qquad (3\text{-}4)$$

We are not, however, seeking the mean for the coded (d) midpoints. We wish the mean for the original midpoints. This is accomplished by "decoding" the mean coded score $(\bar{d})$ in order to obtain $\overline{X}$. The procedure for decoding should be easier to understand after examining the following summary of the operations performed so far.

Coding
1) Subtract the arbitrary origin (in this case 47) from each midpoint to obtain the coded midpoints (d').
2) Divide the coded midpoints (d') by the interval size (in this case 5) to obtain the final coded midpoints (d).
3) Find the mean for the d coded midpoints using Form. (3-4).

$$\bar{d} = \frac{270}{50} = 5.40$$

Since the mean of the distribution will be affected in the same way as the midpoints by Steps 1 and 2, the decoding procedure will involve first "undoing" Step 2 and then undoing Step 1.

Decoding
4) Multiply $\bar{d}$ by the interval size (this will undo Step 2).

$$5 \times 5.40 = 27.00$$

5) Then add the arbitrary origin (this will undo Step 1).

$$\overline{X} = 47.00 + 27.00 = 74.00$$

The student may feel that this method, far from being a short cut, is unnecessarily complicated; however, if the method is summarized, its simplicity will become apparent.

1) Select the midpoint of any interval as an arbitrary origin. It is recommended that the lowest interval be used, for then negative coded scores will be avoided.

2) Determine the d coded midpoints by calling the interval containing the arbitrary origin 0, the next interval 1, the next interval 2, and so on. The intermediate step of obtaining the d' coded midpoints is unnecessary

in practice. It was mentioned only to help clarify the basis for the "short cut" method.

3)   Find the mean ($\overline{X}$) with the following formula.

$$\overline{X} = \text{A.O.} + i\left(\frac{\Sigma fd}{N}\right) \tag{3-5}$$

where A.O. is the arbitrary origin and i is the interval size.

Using the data of Table 3-3:

$$\overline{X} = 47.00 + 5\left(\frac{270}{50}\right) = 47.00 + 27.00 = 74.00$$

Combining Means

Suppose we obtained the height in inches of 4 boys and 6 girls, with the following result.

Boys	Girls
47	43
51	45
52	46
54	46
$\Sigma X = 204$	47
	49
$\overline{X} = \dfrac{204}{4} = 51.0$	$\Sigma X = 276$
	$\overline{X} = \dfrac{276}{6} = 46.0$

Now, suppose that we wished to find the mean of the heights of boys and girls combined. Can we use the mean of the two means? That is, can we say that the combined mean is $(51 + 46)/2$? The answer is that we cannot because such a procedure gives the two means equal weights. The girls' mean should carry more weight than the boys' mean, since the former represents 6 scores against 4 for the boys. An appropriately weighted mean of the two means can be obtained by using the following formula, in which $\overline{X}_c$ represents the combined mean and $\overline{X}_1$ and $\overline{X}_2$ represent the means for the separate groups.

$$\overline{X}_c = \frac{N_1\,\overline{X}_1 + N_2\,\overline{X}_2}{N_1 + N_2} \tag{3-6}$$

Applying this formula to our example, we find:

$$\overline{X}_c = \frac{4\,(51) + 6\,(46)}{4 + 6} = \frac{480}{10} = 48.0$$

which is what is obtained if we add the 10 scores for boys and girls combined and divide by 10. The generalized formula, which applies to any number of means, can be written as:

$$\overline{X}_c = \frac{N_1 \overline{X}_1 + N_2 \overline{X}_2 + \ldots N_n \overline{X}_n}{N_1 + N_2 \ldots N_n} \tag{3-7}$$

When the separate means are based on the same N, of course, it is possible simply to sum the means and divide by the number of means.

COMPARISON OF THE MEASURES OF CENTRAL TENDENCY

Relationship to the Physical Characteristics of a Frequency Polygon

The three measures of central tendency can be compared in terms of the physical characteristics of a smoothed frequency polygon. The mode is perhaps the easiest to visualize. Since the vertical axis (abscissa) represents frequency, the mode will be the score under the highest point of the frequency curve. The median, also, is not difficult to understand in terms of a frequency curve if it is recalled that the proportion of cases falling below any point is equal to the proportion of the area below that point. Thus, the median would be the point which divides the area under the frequency curve exactly in half. These relationships are illustrated in Fig. 3.2.

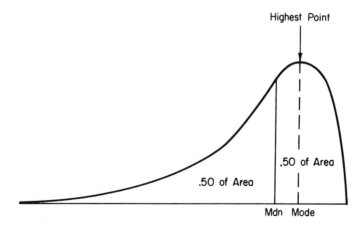

Figure 3-2. Comparison of the Mode and the Median

The relationship of the mean to the physical characteristics of a frequency curve depends on a property of the mean which has not yet been made explicit: *the algebraic sum of the score deviations from the mean is always equal to zero*. The deviation of a score from the mean is the difference between the score and the mean and is designated by a lower-case x (i.e., $x = X - \overline{X}$). This property may be illustrated with the following set of five scores.

X	x
2	-3
6	$+1$
8	$+3$
3	-2
6	$+1$
$\sum X = 25$	$\sum x = 0$

$$\overline{X} = \frac{25}{5} = 5$$

The reader may recall that the point of balance for a seesaw or lever is the point about which the algebraic sum of the *moments* is equal to zero.

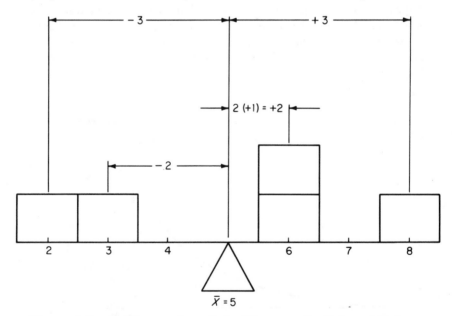

$$\overline{X} = 5$$

Figure 3-3. An Illustration of the Mean as the Point of Balance (Fulcrum) of a Lever, Assuming Each Score to Be of Equal "Weight"

If each of the scores can be considered of equal weight, the mean will be that point. Thus, the physical analogy to the mean is the point of balance. This is illustrated in Fig. 3-3 for the above set of scores. This analogy would also hold for a smoothed frequency curve cut out of some uniform material. The mean would be the point at which the curve would balance on edge.

It should be apparent by now that in a unimodal and symmetrical frequency distribution the mode, mean, and median coincide.

Effects of Extreme Scores

Consider the following set of nine scores which are arranged in order of size.

$$\begin{array}{l} 8 \\ 7 \\ 7 \\ 6 \\ 4 \\ 4 \\ 4 \\ 3 \\ \underline{2} \end{array} \qquad \begin{array}{l} \overline{X} = \dfrac{45}{9} = 5 \\ \\ \text{Mdn} = 4 \\ \text{Mode} = 4 \end{array}$$

$$\sum X = 45$$

Now suppose that an extremely high score, 155, is added to the set. The new measures of central tendency would be:

$$\overline{X} = \frac{\sum X}{N} = \frac{45 + 155}{10} = 20$$

$$\text{Mdn} = 5$$
$$\text{Mode} = 4$$

It can be seen that the addition of the extremely high score has had a substantial effect on the mean, a much smaller effect on the median, and no effect at all on the mode. This example is, of course, an artificial one constructed for demonstration purposes. Nonetheless, it does illustrate the fact that extreme scores usually have their greatest effect on the mean and their least effect on the mode. This principle can often be of great practical importance when one wishes to select that measure of central tendency which will be most representative of a distribution of scores. For instance, in a skewed distribution the mean will be "pulled" toward the extreme scores (or tail) of the distribution. In such a case, it may be far less representative of the bulk of scores than either the median or the mode. This is particularly true in those distributions of income in which most individuals have a moderate income and a few have very high incomes. Thus, we see that the three averages will usually not be equal to each other, since some skewness is present in most distributions of "real" data. In unimodal skewed distributions, the relative positions of the three averages are predictably what is illustrated in Fig. 3-4.

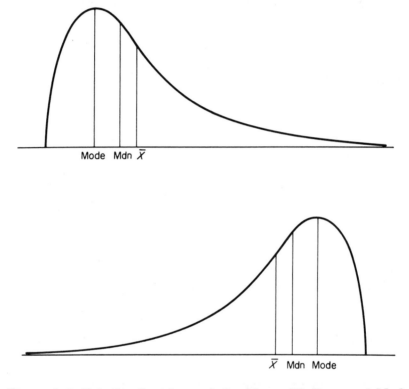

Figure 3-4. Relative Positions of the Mean, Median, and Mode in Unimodal Skewed Distributions

Other Bases for Comparison

1. *Sampling stability.* One fairly common task is that of estimating the central tendency of a population from a central tendency measure computed for a sample. An important consideration in deciding which sample measure to use is that of *sampling stability*. If a number of samples were selected from the population, we would certainly expect the sample

means to differ somewhat from one another and from the population mean because of the chance factors involved in selecting a sample. The extent to which the mean varies from sample to sample reflects the sampling stability (or instability) of the sample mean as an estimate. It can be shown that for a symmetric, unimodal distribution approaching the normal bell shape to be described in Chap. 5, the sample mean is a more stable estimate (i.e., it would vary less from sample to sample) than the sample median. The sample mode would be the least stable of the three.

2.   *Open-ended distributions.*   In cases in which the distribution of scores is highly skewed, the upper limit of the topmost interval or the lower limit of the bottom interval (depending on the direction of skewness) is sometimes eliminated. This is illustrated in Table 3-4 for a distribution of fam-

Table 3-4

***A Frequency Distribution of Annual Income
for a Group of 122 Families***

Annual Income	f
$10,000 and above	8
9,000–9,999	8
8,000–8,999	10
7,000–7,999	11
6,000–6,999	19
5,000–5,999	23
4,000–4,999	15
3,000–3,999	12
2,000–2,999	8
1,000–1,999	7
0–999	1
	$N = 122$

ily incomes. In order to avoid having to widen the intervals considerably or to increase the number of intervals to include several families with extremely high incomes, no upper limit has been indicated for the top interval. Since it is impossible to determine a reasonable midpoint for the top interval, an arithmetic mean can not be computed. The median, or perhaps the mode, would be used.

3.   *Use beyond the descriptive level.*   A final comparison of the mean, median, and mode concerns the degree to which each can be utilized in more advanced statistical procedures. Here the mean proves to be the most important, because of its mathematical properties. The great bulk of statistical theory and technique utilizes the mean as the basic measure

of central tendency. Consequently, if anything beyond mere description is contemplated the mean will usually be the most appropriate measure to use.

Exercises and Problems

1. Find the median for the distribution in Table 3-4. Is the mean higher, lower, or about the same? What would you expect? Why?
2. The median mental age for School *B* in Table 3-1 was found to be 71. Find the mean for School *B*. Why do the mean and median differ?
3. The Teachers' Association in an American city reported that "the average salary for our teachers is lower than the average salary for our garbage collectors." The Taxpayers' League, examining the same data, responded that the case was exactly the opposite—"the average for teachers is higher than that for garbage collectors." Both parties were correct. Explain.
4. In a particular college, the 1964–65 mean salary paid to the 210 members of the teaching staff was $9,550. What was the total amount paid to the teaching staff?
5. Suppose you were the coach of a baseball team and were interested only in improving the median batting average of the team. On which of the following players would you work hardest: (*a*) those with the lowest batting averages, (*b*) those with the highest, (*c*) those just below the median, or (*d*) those just above the median? Explain. On which players would you concentrate if you wished to improve the *mean?*
6. Consider the following statistics for three groups of people.

	Group A	Group B	Group C
N	20	10	30
Mean	12	15	13
Median	10	10	9

   a) What is the mean of all groups combined?
   b) What can you say about the median of all groups combined?
   c) What can you say about the shape of the distribution of all groups combined?
7. Give some possible interpretations for the following statement: More than half of American school children are below average in intelligence.
8. In connection with a reading investigation the reading speeds of ten adults were measured in terms of words per minute. The investigator, for ease in computation, subtracted 325 from each score. The ten "reduced" scores are as follows, in increasing order of size: 0, 2, 2, 3, 3, 3, 3, 75, 95, 135.
   a) What is the mean of the scores listed above? How can the mean of the

original scores be determined from the mean of the reduced scores? Explain.

    b) For descriptive purposes, which is the most informative measure of central tendency for these ten scores? Why?

9. For Group C of Table 2.6: (*a*) find the mean using Form. 3.3; (*b*) find the mean using coded midpoints; (*c*) find the median; (*d*) find the crude mode.

10. The following are the mathematics achievement test scores of a random sample of third-graders from a school. On the basis of these results, would you conclude that the distribution for all third-graders in this school is bimodal? Explain.

    24, 26, 29, 31, 31, 33, 33, 33, 34, 35, 35, 35, 39, 41, 43

Chapter 4

Variability

A set of scores, in all but the rarest of circumstances, will show some degree of "scatter" or spread. This variation in obtained scores is referred to as *variability* or *dispersion*, a distinctive and important property of frequency distributions. We have seen in Chap. 3 that frequency distributions can be described in terms of central tendency. In the present chapter, we shall consider how frequency distributions can be described in terms of *variability* or *dispersion*. As Table 4-1 illustrates, two distributions

Table 4-1

Estimated Number of Hours of Study per Week for Samples of Freshmen from Two Colleges

Hours of Study	College A f	College B f
33–35	1	2
30–32	0	3
27–29	2	8
24–26	7	8
21–23	15	9
18–20	24	12
15–17	12	9
12–14	8	9
9–11	1	6
6–8	0	4
	$N = 70$	$N = 70$

may be the same with regard to central tendency and yet differ considerably with respect to variability. The College A mean is 19.39, and the Col-

50

lege *B* mean is 19.43—not very different. Yet, an inspection of the two frequency distributions clearly reveals freshmen in College *B* are much more heterogeneous with respect to the number of hours studied weekly. That is, the College *B* distribution shows greater variability than that for College *A*.

Variability, then, is an important consideration in statistical description. We shall see later that it is also a basic concept in statistical inference. In the sections that follow, five widely used measures of variability will be discussed: the *range*, the *quartile deviation*, the *average deviation*, the *standard deviation*, and the *variance*.

RANGE

Perhaps the simplest way to indicate the variability of a distribution of scores is to use the range—the difference between the highest and lowest scores. In the case of College *A* (Table 4-1), the highest individual estimated that he studied 35 hours (before grouping), and the lowest estimated 9 hours. Thus the range is $35 - 9 = 26$ hours. For College *B*, the highest and lowest scores (before grouping) were 33 and 7, and the range is again 26 (i.e., $33 - 7 = 26$).

Although very simple to compute and understand, the range has several limitations as a measure of variability. First, since it is based only on the two most extreme scores, it does not fully reflect the variation present between these two scores. This point can be made clear by considering the two distributions of Table 4-1 again. The two ranges both cover twenty-six points. Yet the patterns of variability between the two extreme scores are markedly different for the two distributions.

When a sample range is used as an estimate of the range of the population from which the sample was selected two other limitations become important. First, a sample range will usually be an underestimation of the population range, and the degree of underestimation will tend to be greater for smaller samples. For purposes of illustration, let us consider that the 70 scores from College *A*, represented in Table 4-1, make up the entire group or population in which we are interested. If we select at random a sample of only 10 scores from the 70, it is rather unlikely that both extreme individuals would be included. Thus the sample range is likely to be less than the value of 26 obtained for all 70 scores. Furthermore, it should be apparent that the smaller the sample size which is used, the less extreme the highest and lowest scores in the sample are likely to be.

A second related limitation concerns the instability of a sample range. If, in our sample of size 10, the two most extreme scores were included, the range would be 26. If, however, the top score of 35 were not included (a likely possibility) the sample range would be at least 6 points less (there are no cases in the next lowest interval); if none of the three top scores were included, the range would be at least 9 points less ($35 - 26 = 9$). Thus, the value of the range for samples of size 10 might differ considerably for different samples.

QUARTILE DEVIATION

We have seen that the major limitations of the range as a measure of variability stem from the fact that it is based on the two extreme values. A partial reduction of these limitations may be achieved by using the range between values less extreme than the highest and lowest. One such approach utilizes what are known as the first and third *quartiles*. The three quartiles are the three score values which divide the total cases into four subgroups of equal size. That is, the first quartile (Q_1) is the point below which 25 per cent of the cases fall, the second quartile (Q_2) is the point below which 50 per cent of the cases fall, and the third quartile (Q_3) is the point below which 75 per cent of the cases fall. The attentive reader will recognize that Q_2 is the same as the median. The *quartile deviation*, or *semi-interquartile range*, as it is sometimes known, is defined as half the range between Q_1 and Q_3. This definition may be expressed in terms of the following formula, in which Q is the symbol for the quartile deviation.

$$Q = \frac{Q_3 - Q_1}{2} \tag{4-1}$$

The procedures for computing Q_1 and Q_3 from grouped data are analogous to those described in Chap. 3 for computing the median. These procedures will be illustrated with reference to the following data of Table 4-1 for College *A*.

Hours of Study	f
33–35	1
30–32	0
27–29	2
24–26	7
$Q_3 \rightarrow$ 21–23	15
18–20	24
$Q_1 \rightarrow$ 15–17	12
12–14	8
9–11	1
6–8	0

$N = 70$

$f_c = 9 \quad f_c = 45$

The first quartile, Q_1, is the score point below which the needed 17.5 cases fall ($1/4 \times 70 = 17.5$). The reader need not be concerned that a fractional number of cases is involved; for purposes of computation it is customary to carry along the fraction. In order to locate this score, we count up 17.5 cases from the bottom of the distribution. This places Q_1 somewhere in the interval 15–17. In order to determine exactly where, it will be assumed that the cases within the interval are spread evenly across the interval, as was assumed for computing the median from grouped data. There are 9 cases below the interval; therefore, we must count up 8.5 cases from the bottom of the interval to reach Q_1 (i.e., $17.5 - 9 = 8.5$). Since there are 12 cases within the interval, this amounts to .708 of the width of the interval ($8.5/12 = .708$). Multiplying the obtained proportion by the interval size (3) indicates that Q_1 must be 2.12 score points (.708 $\times$ 3 = 2.12) above the lower limit of 14.50. Thus, Q_1 equals 16.62 (i.e., $14.50 + 2.12 = 16.62$). These steps can be summarized in the following formula, which is a variation of Form. (3-1) for the median.

$$Q_1 = \text{L.L.} + i\left(\frac{\frac{N}{4} - fc}{f}\right)$$

where L.L. is the lower limit of the interval containing Q_1, fc is the cumulative frequency below the lower limit, and f is the frequency within the interval

Substituting the appropriate information from the distribution for College A:

$$Q_1 = 14.50 + 3\left(\frac{\frac{70}{4} - 9}{12}\right) = 16.62$$

In order to find Q_3 we count up 52.5 cases from the bottom ($3/4 \times 70 = 52.50$). This places Q_3 in the interval 21–23. Using the same reasoning as was used to determine Q_1, $Q_3 = 22.00$. Or a formula analogous to that for Q_1 could be used:

$$Q_3 = \text{L.L.} + i\left(\frac{\frac{3N}{4} - fc}{f}\right) = 20.50 + 3\left(\frac{\frac{3 \cdot 70}{4} - 45}{15}\right) = 22.00.$$

The quartile deviation may then be obtained.

$$Q = \frac{22.00 - 16.62}{2} = \frac{5.38}{2} = 2.69$$

The above value is easy to interpret if one keeps in mind the fact that the middle 1/2 or 50 per cent of the cases in any distribution fall between

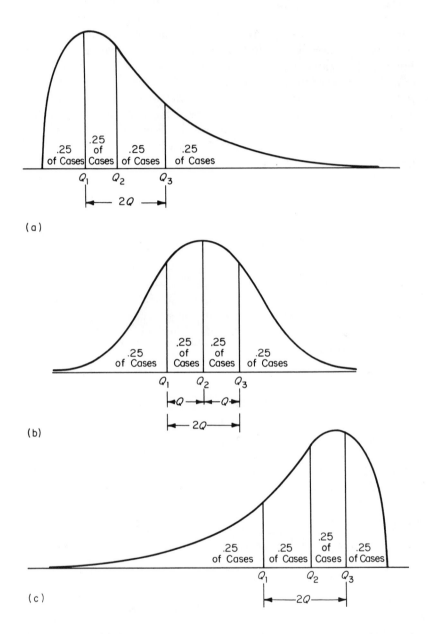

Figure 4-1. Positions of Q_1, Q_2, and Q_3 for Positively Skewed, Symmetric, and Negatively Skewed Distributions of Scores

54

Q_1 and Q_3. Since Q is 1/2 the range between Q_1 and Q_3, twice Q will be the range in score points for the middle 50 per cent of the cases. That is, the range in hours studied for the middle 50 per cent of the individuals in the College A distribution (Table 4-1) would be 5.38 (i.e., 2×2.69) score points, the distance between Q_1 and Q_3. If a distribution is symmetric, the median, or Q_2, will fall half-way between Q_1 and Q_3. In such a situation, the middle 50 per cent of the cases would fall between the median $+Q$ and the median $-Q$. If, however, the distribution is positively skewed, the median will not be half-way between Q_1 and Q_3; the distance $Q_3 - Q_2$ will be greater than $Q_2 - Q_1$. If the distribution is negatively skewed, $Q_3 - Q_2$ will be less than $Q_2 - Q_1$. This is illustrated in Fig. 4-1. The reader should keep in mind that .25 of the cases, and thus .25 of the area under the frequency curve, will fall between each quartile point regardless of the degree or direction of skewness.

THE AVERAGE DEVIATION

The quartile deviation does not eliminate the basic limitations of a reliance on only two values in describing variability. An early measure which takes into account all the cases in a frequency distribution is the *average deviation* (AD). Although the AD is no longer used, the reader may occasionally encounter some references to it, particularly in older research studies.

The average deviation is a measure of the degree to which the scores deviate from the mean of the distribution. Some of the computations necessary, for a set of five scores, are illustrated in Table 4-2.

Table 4-2

Computation of the Sum of Absolute Deviations About the Mean

1 X	2 $x = X - \bar{X}$	3 $|x|$
10	+3	3
8	+1	1
7	0	0
5	-2	2
5	-2	2
$\sum X = 35$	$\sum x = 0$	$\sum |x| = 8$

$$\bar{X} = \frac{35}{5} = 7$$

First, the deviation of each score from the mean is determined using the formula $x = X - \bar{X}$, where x is a *deviation score* and X is an original or *raw score*. For instance, for a raw score of 5, $x = -2$ (i.e., $5 - 7 = -2$). The deviation scores are listed in Col. 2. It would not be helpful to take an average of these deviations, because, as was pointed out in Chap. 3 during the discussion of the mean as the point of balance of a distribution, the sum of the deviations about the mean will always equal 0 (i.e., $\sum x = 0$). Thus, the average will equal 0. In determining the average deviation we ignore algebraic signs and use the *absolute* deviations from the mean, listed in Col. 3. The vertical bars indicate absolute value (i.e., value without regard to sign). The mean of the absolute deviations, or average deviation, can be obtained using the following formula.

$$AD = \frac{\sum |x|}{N} = \frac{8}{5} = 1.60 \tag{4-2}$$

It should be apparent that the more the scores in a group spread out from one another, the larger will be the absolute deviations from the mean and thus the larger the AD will be.

In addition to being easily understood, the average deviation does take into account all the scores in the distribution; however, the convenient device of ignoring the algebraic signs of the deviations leads to certain mathematical difficulties which preclude the use of the AD beyond the descriptive level. Consequently, it has been discarded in favor of an improved measure of variation, the *standard deviation*.

THE STANDARD DEVIATION

Probably the most important measure of variability, in terms of its usefulness for a variety of purposes, is the *standard deviation*, which is defined by the following formula.

$$S = \sqrt{\frac{\sum x^2}{N}} \tag{4-3}$$

where S is the symbol for the standard deviation and $\sum x^2 = \sum (X - \overline{X})^2$

It can be seen from the formula that S is based on deviations of all the scores in the group from the group mean, as was the AD; however, there is no need to ignore the signs of the deviation scores, because the squares of all the deviation scores (both positive and negative) will be positive. If the reader can recall, from elementary algebra, that the product of two negative numbers is always positive, he will see why this is so. The computation of the sum of squared deviations (i.e., $\sum x^2$) is illustrated in Table 4-3 with the same set of five scores for which the AD was determined earlier.

Table 4-3

Computation of the Sum of Squared Deviations about the Mean

1 X	2 $x = X - \overline{X}$	3 x^2
10	+3	9
8	+1	1
7	0	0
5	−2	4
5	−2	4
$\sum X = 35$	$\sum x = 0$	$\sum x^2 = 18$

$$\overline{X} = \frac{35}{5} = 7$$

The standard deviation can now be obtained using Form. (4-3).

$$S = \sqrt{\frac{\sum x^2}{N}} = \sqrt{\frac{18}{5}} = \sqrt{3.60} = 1.90$$

It should be apparent that the more the scores in a group deviate from the mean, the larger the squared deviations will be, and thus the larger S will be. If all five scores had been equal to a single value, such as 7, the mean would also be 7, the deviations would all be 0, and S would equal 0.

Computation: Raw-Score Methods

In practice, the computation of S using actual deviation scores can become quite cumbersome. Consider, for example, a group of twenty-six scores of which the sum equals 217 (i.e., $\sum X = 217$). The mean of these scores is 8.35 (i.e., $217/26 = 8.35$). Because of the fractional remainder for the mean, all twenty-six deviation scores will have fractional remainders; obtaining, squaring, and summing the deviations would involve a large amount of computational labor. Fortunately, it is possible to determine S directly from the original or raw scores without computing each individual deviation score. For example, the following raw-score formula may be used to obtain the sum of the squared deviation scores.

$$\sum x^2 = \frac{N \sum X^2 - (\sum X)^2}{N} \qquad (4\text{-}4)$$

The use of this formula is illustrated, with the same set of five scores, in Table 4-4.

Table 4-4

Computation of the Sum of Squared Deviations About the Mean Using Raw Scores

1 X	2 X^2
10	100
8	64
7	49
5	25
5	25
$\sum X = 35$	$\sum X^2 = 263$

$$\sum x^2 = \frac{5\,(263) - (35)^2}{5} = 18$$

The standard deviation can then be computed using Form. (4-3).

$$S = \sqrt{\frac{\sum x^2}{N}} = \sqrt{\frac{18}{5}} = \sqrt{3.60} = 1.90$$

It should be pointed out that many of the formulas to be presented in subsequent chapters of this text will involve the expression $\sum x^2$. It is our belief that such formulas are more easily understood than equivalent formulas which involve raw scores only; however, the reader should be aware that rarely, if ever, would one actually compute $\sum x^2$ using deviation scores. A raw-score formula such as Form. (4-4) can always be used instead.

The following formula for S, involving only raw scores, is obtained by combining the raw-score expression of Form. (4-4) with Form. (4-3).

$$S = \frac{1}{N} \sqrt{N \sum X^2 - (\sum X)^2} \tag{4-5}$$

Using the appropriate sums from Table 4-4, Form. (4-5) can be used to compute S for the five scores.

$$S = \frac{1}{5} \sqrt{5\,(263) - (35)^2} = \frac{1}{5} \sqrt{90} = 1.90$$

Computation of S from a Frequency Distribution

It is sometimes convenient to compute S after the individual scores have been grouped into a frequency distribution. The procedures involved will be illustrated with reference to the distribution shown in Table 4-1 for College A, for which a Q of 2.69 has already been obtained. This distribution is presented once again in Table 4-5 along with part of the computations necessary for obtaining S.

Table 4-5

Partial Computations for Determining S for the College A Distribution, Using Interval Midpoints

	f	1 X (midpoint)	2 fX	3 fX^2
33–35	1	34	34	1156
30–32	0	31	0	0
27–29	2	28	56	1568
24–26	7	25	175	4375
21–23	15	22	330	7260
18–20	24	19	456	8664
15–17	12	16	192	3072
12–14	8	13	104	1352
9–11	1	10	10	100
6–8	0	7	0	0
	$N = 70$		$\sum fX = 1357$	$\sum fX^2 = 27547$

As was done when computing $\overline{X}$ directly from a frequency distribution, each score is represented in the computation of S by the midpoint of the interval in which it falls. The respective midpoints are listed in Col. 1. Then, a variation of Form. (4-5), the raw score formula for S, is used. The quantities required for Form. (4-5) are the sums $\sum X$ and $\sum X^2$. It has already been pointed out in Chap. 2 that when each score in a class interval is represented by the midpoint of that interval, we shall think of X as standing for the midpoint. Thus, the sum of scores in each interval is arrived at by multiplying the midpoint by its associated frequency (fX). The total sum of scores is estimated by $\sum fX$. Similarly, the sum of the squared scores becomes $\sum fX^2$. Given the foregoing understandings, the appropriate variation of Form. (4-5) for grouped data is:

$$S = \frac{1}{N} \sqrt{N \sum fX^2 - (\sum fX)^2} \qquad (4\text{-}6)$$

Referring again to Table 4-5, the values in Col. 2 were obtained by multiplying the frequencies by the midpoints in Col. 1. The values in Col. 3 were obtained by multiplying the values in Col. 2 by the midpoints in Col. 1. The last step can be analyzed as follows.

$$\begin{array}{ccc} \text{Col. 1} \cdot \text{Col. 2} = & & \text{Col. 3} \\ (X) \cdot (fX) \;\; = (f)(X)(X) = & fX^2 \end{array}$$

The values in Col. 3 could also be obtained by first squaring each midpoint in Col. 1 and multiplying by the appropriate frequency; however, such an approach would involve an extra computational step, the squaring of the midpoints in Col. 1. The sums of Cols. 2 and 3 can be substituted in Form. (4-6) to obtain the value of S.

$$S = \frac{1}{70} \sqrt{70 (27547) - (1357)^2} = \frac{1}{70} \sqrt{86841} = 4.21$$

The Effects of Operations Using Constants

The foregoing procedure for computing S from a frequency distribution can be simplified somewhat by first coding the interval midpoints, as was done for computing the mean; however, if the reader is to understand the short-cut or coded method for computing S, he must first be aware of the effects on the value of S of applying a constant to each score through addition, subtraction, multiplication, or division. These effects will be illustrated with reference to the following group of four scores, which has a mean of 6 and a standard deviation of 2.

X	x	x^2
8	+2	4
8	+2	4
4	−2	4
4	−2	4
$\sum X = 24$		$\sum x^2 = 16$

$$\overline{X} = \frac{\sum X}{N} = \frac{24}{4} = 6$$

$$S = \sqrt{\frac{\sum x^2}{N}} = \sqrt{\frac{16}{4}} = 2$$

If the constant value 10 is added to each of the original scores, the new mean becomes 16, but the standard deviation is unchanged.

X	x	x^2
$8 + 10 = 18$	+2	4
$8 + 10 = 18$	+2	4
$4 + 10 = 14$	−2	4
$4 + 10 = 14$	−2	4
$\sum X = 64$		$\sum x^2 = 16$

$$\overline{X} = \frac{64}{4} = 16$$

$$S = \sqrt{\frac{16}{4}} = 2$$

A comparison of the two sets of scores shows that the distances between the new scores are exactly the same as the distances between the original scores. *Thus, adding a constant to all the scores in a group will not change the variability.* It should not be difficult to see that *if a constant were subtracted from every score, the distances between the scores, and thus the variability, would remain unchanged.*

Let us now examine the effects of *multiplying* or *dividing* by a constant value. If each of the four scores presented above is multiplied by 3, for instance, the new mean is 18 and the new standard deviation is 6.

X	x	x^2
$8 \times 3 = 24$	$+6$	36
$8 \times 3 = 24$	$+6$	36
$4 \times 3 = 12$	-6	36
$4 \times 3 = 12$	-6	36
$\sum X = 72$		$\sum x^2 = 144$

$$\overline{X} = \frac{72}{4} = 18$$

$$S = \sqrt{\frac{144}{4}} = \sqrt{36} = 6$$

Some insight into why the new standard deviation of 6 is three times what it was before can be obtained by again examining both sets of scores. The distances between the new scores are three times the distances between the original scores. Thus, *if all the scores in a group are multiplied by a constant, the new value of S can be found by multiplying the old value of S by the same constant.* On the other hand, *if all the scores in a group are divided by a constant, the new value of S can be found by dividing the old value by the same constant.* If, for instance, the four original scores above are divided by 2, the new scores will be half as far apart, and the new standard deviation will equal 1, or 1/2 of the original standard deviation.

If the reader will apply the above reasoning to the range, the average deviation, and the quartile deviation, it should be easy to see that the same rules will apply.

Computation of S: Short or Coded Method

In computing S by the short method, the intervals are coded in the manner utilized in Chap. 3 for computing $\overline{X}$. Then, the following variation of Form. (4-6) can be used to obtain the standard deviation for the coded midpoints.

$$S_{\text{(coded)}} = \frac{1}{N} \sqrt{N \sum fd^2 - (\sum fd)^2}$$

The computations necessary to obtain the sums for the above are illustrated in Table 4-6 for the data from College A.

Using the appropriate sums from Table 4-6, the standard deviation for the coded scores can be obtained.

$$S_{\text{(coded)}} = \frac{1}{70} \sqrt{70 \, (1331) - (289)^2} = 1.403$$

The next step is to "decode," that is, to convert $S_{\text{(coded)}}$ to S.

The two steps involved in moving from the interval midpoints to the coded scores were subtracting 7 (i.e., A.O.) and dividing by 3 (i.e., the interval size, i). The reader should review pp. 40–41 if this is not clear.

Table 4-6

Partial Computations for Determining S for the College A Distribution, Using "Coded" Interval Midpoints

	f	1 d	2 fd	3 fd²
33–35	1	9	9	81
30–32	0	8	0	0
27–29	2	7	14	98
24–26	7	6	42	252
21–23	15	5	75	375
18–20	24	4	96	384
15–17	12	3	36	108
12–14	8	2	16	32
9–11	1	1	1	1
6–8	0	0	0	0
	$N = 70$		$\sum fd = 289$	$\sum fd^2 = 1331$

Since subtracting a constant has no effect on S, decoding involves only multiplying by i. That is:

$$S = iS_{(coded)}$$

Using the data in Table 4-6, this would be:

$$S = 3(1.403) = 4.21$$

which is exactly the value obtained by using the interval midpoints. A single formula for S, which combines all the foregoing steps, is as follows.

$$S = \frac{i}{N}\sqrt{\sum fd^2 - (\sum fd)^2} \tag{4-7}$$

The Standard Deviation and Grouping Error

It is now appropriate to say something further about the error in S associated with grouping scores into class intervals. Consider Fig. 4-2, in which very large ($i = 10$) class intervals have been superimposed upon a distribution of scores with a mean of 100. The score points shown below the distribution can be considered the real limits of the intervals. After grouping, all of the cases in the interval 90–100 are represented by the midpoint, 95, and the deviation score, x, for each of the cases in the interval is -5. It can be seen, however, by comparing the area between 90 and 95 with the area between 95 and 100, that the majority of cases in that interval actually deviate less than 5 points from the mean of 100. Thus, the use of the interval midpoint results in deviations from the mean that, on the average, are too large. A similar conclusion would be reached for other intervals, including those above the mean. That is, the use of interval midpoints results in scores which deviate from the mean slightly more, on the average, than the original scores. *As a consequence, AD and S when computed from grouped data tend to be slightly larger than when computed from the original scores.* If the reader can visualize the scores of Fig. 4-2 grouped into much smaller intervals, say intervals of

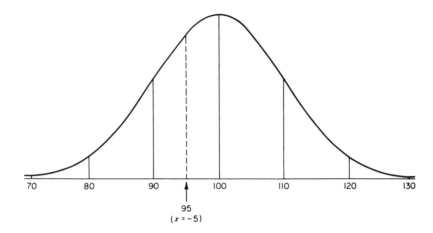

Figure 4-2. A Hypothetical Frequency Distribution of IQ Scores with Intervals of Size 10 Superimposed

size 2, he can understand why the systematic error in AD or S computed from grouped data will be smaller with smaller interval sizes. Normally, if more than 10 intervals are used, the interval size will be small enough, and the error due to grouping will be negligible; however, for distributions with less than 10 intervals, the following formula, known as *Sheppard's correction*, may be used to "correct" the obtained value of S.

$$S_{(corrected)} = \sqrt{S^2 - \left(\frac{i^2}{12}\right)} \qquad (4\text{-}8)$$

where S is the standard deviation computed from the frequency distribution and i is the interval size

Brief reference to grouping error was made in Chap. 3 during the discussion of the computation of the mean from grouped data. It should be pointed out here that the error in the mean due to grouping is not systematic in the same sense as the grouping error in S. That is, whereas S computed from grouped data tends to be systematically too large, $\overline{X}$ computed from grouped data is just as likely to be too small as too large. The reason is that, although the grouping error for the scores above the mean tends to pull the value of the mean upward, the grouping error for the scores below the mean tends to pull it downward. That is, the errors above the mean tend to be balanced by those below.

Variance

An additional measure of variability, *variance*, is the square of the standard deviation. It can be defined as:

$$\text{Variance} = S^2 = \frac{\sum x^2}{N} \tag{4-9}$$

Although the variance is little used for descriptive purposes (the standard deviation, S, is used instead), it is of great importance beyond the descriptive level, having certain useful mathematical properties that its square root (the standard deviation) does not. The variance is introduced here because it will be referred to from time to time throughout the text.

COMPARISON OF THE MEASURES
OF VARIABILITY

General Meaning

Of the variability measures discussed, the meaning of the range probably is most clear; it is easy to understand what is meant by the difference between the highest and lowest scores in the entire group. A quartile deviation, Q, is also easy to understand, if one keeps in mind that $2Q$ is the range for the middle 50 per cent of the cases regardless of the shape of the distribution. If the distribution is fairly symmetric, we know, in addition, that the middle 50 per cent of the cases fall approximately within one Q of the median (Q_2) of the distribution. These relationships are represented in Fig. 4-3(*a*) and (*b*). The reader should avoid the common mistake of assuming that, since the middle 50 per cent of the cases range over a distance of $2Q$, the entire group will range over a distance of $4Q$. Examination of Fig. 4-3 should indicate why this is not so.

Although the standard deviation is a more complicated measure than either the range or Q, it can usually be interpreted without much difficulty if one keeps several relationships in mind. First, if the distribution is roughly symmetric, sloping off to either side as in Fig. 4-3(*c*), a range of between four and five standard deviations will usually include all but a small proportion of the cases. Furthermore, if the distribution can be approximated by the normal "bell-shape" to be discussed in the next chapter, approximately 68 per cent of the cases will fall within one stand-

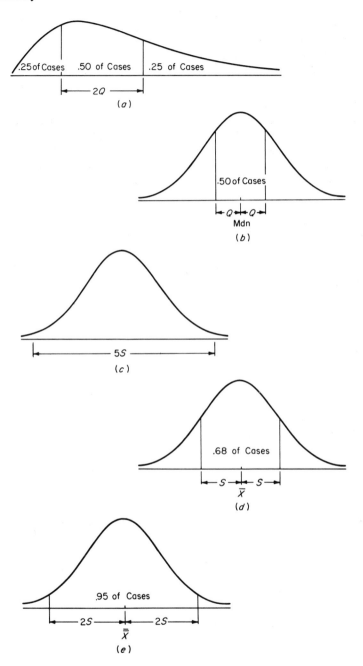

Figure 4-3. Illustration of Various Ways of Interpreting Q and S

ard deviation of the mean, and approximately 95 per cent will fall within two standard deviations of the mean. This is represented in Fig. 4-3(d) and (e). It should be apparent from this that S will usually be slightly larger than Q.

To see how an obtained value of S might be interpreted, consider a distribution of a large number of college-aptitude test scores which has a normal bell-shape and for which $\overline{X} = 50$ and $S = 10$. We know that all but a few of the cases will be included in a range of 50 points ($5S$), that approximately 95 per cent of the cases will fall between 30 and 70 (i.e., $\overline{X} - 2S$ and $\overline{X} + 2S$), and that approximately 68 per cent of the cases will fall between 40 and 60 (i.e., $\overline{X} - S$ and $\overline{X} + S$).

Effect of Extreme Scores

The range, of course, is most affected by extremely high or low scores, since it is based on the highest and lowest scores in the group. The standard deviation is also influenced by extreme scores, although to a lesser extent than the range. This can be illustrated with regard to the following five scores.

X	x	x^2
8	+4	16
4	0	0
3	−1	1
3	−1	1
2	−2	4
$\sum X = 20$		$\sum x^2 = 22$

$$\overline{X} = \frac{20}{5} = 4$$

$$S = \sqrt{\frac{\sum x^2}{N}} = \sqrt{\frac{22}{5}} = \sqrt{4.4} = 2.1$$

It can be seen that the one extreme score (8) contributes far more to the sum of squared deviations, and thus to the standard deviation, than all the other scores combined. Of the measures discussed, Q is least affected by extreme scores, since it is based on the middle 50 per cent of the cases only.

Other Bases for Comparison

1. *Sampling stability.* The notion of sampling stability was discussed briefly in connection with measures of central tendency. If a sample measure, such as the range, tends to vary considerably from sample to sample (for several samples selected from the same population of individuals) it is said to be relatively unstable in the sampling sense. Of the variability measures discussed, the range is by far the least stable, and,

for unimodal distributions of the type most often found in practice, the standard deviation is the most stable.

2. *Companion of measure of central tendency.* Both a measure of central tendency and a measure of variability should be presented in order to describe adequately a distribution of scores. If the median is used as the central-tendency measure, the quartile deviation, Q, will normally be used as the measure of variability, because both are based on the same kind of statistic, the quartiles [Mdn $= Q_2$; $Q = (Q_3 - Q_1)/2$]. On the other hand, if the mean is used, it is customary to use the standard deviation as the companion measure. The relationship between the mean and standard deviation becomes apparent if one recalls that the standard deviation is based on the sum of squared deviations *about the mean.*

3. *Open-ended distributions.* Distributions for which there is no upper limit to the topmost interval or no lower limit to the bottom interval were also mentioned in the last chapter. For such distributions, Q is the only feasible measure of variability. In computing a standard deviation from grouped data, every score within an interval must be represented by the midpoint of that interval; and, for an open-ended distribution, it would be impossible to locate the midpoint of the interval which has no limit. It should be apparent that a range could not be estimated from such a distribution.

4. *Use beyond the descriptive level.* The standard deviation (or its square, the variance) is a concept central to much statistical theory and practice. On the other hand, the quartile deviation and range are relatively little used beyond the descriptive level. As was pointed out earlier, because of the mathematical difficulties inherent in the convenient device of ignoring the algebraic signs of the deviations, the average deviation is no longer used.

Exercises and Problems

1. For the following scores, 3, 7, 8, 6, 1
    a) Compute AD.
    b) Compute $\sum x^2$ using deviation scores.
    c) Compute $\sum x^2$ directly from the raw scores.
    d) Use the answer from (a) or (b) above with formula (4.3) to determine S.
    e) Compute S directly from the raw scores using formula (4.5).

2. For the following scores: 6, 8, 8, 4, 5, 12, 9, 3, 11, 4
    a) Compute S from the ungrouped scores.
    b) Group the scores into a frequency distribution with 3–5 as the lowest
        interval. Compute S from the frequency distribution using formula
        (4.6). In practice, of course, one would rarely group so few scores into a
        frequency distribution. This exercise is presented merely to illustrate
        the various ways of computing S.
    c) Compute S from the frequency distribution using coded midpoints.
3. Compute Q for Group C of Table 2.6.
4. The following are based on a sample of 85 math achievement test scores:
    Mdn. $= 54.8$; $\overline{X} = 53.2$; $AD = 5.5$; $S = 7.0$; $Q = 4.9$; $Q_1 = 50.6$. What
    would be the new values for the above if
    a) Ten points were added to each of the original 85 scores?
    b) Each of the original 85 scores were multiplied by 3?
    c) 53.2 were subtracted from each of the original 85 scores?
    d) Each of the original 85 scores were divided by 7.0?
    e) If first 53.2 were subtracted from each of the original 85 scores and then
        the resulting scores were divided by 7.0?
5. Consider Table 4-1. We have already determined the following statistics for
    College A: Q, Q_1, Q_3, and S. Find the same statistics for College B. Utilizing
    the foregoing information, what statements can you make about how these
    two distributions differ in variability?
6. Which differences between Colleges A and B do you think would interest
    a college professor most, differences between the means or differences
    between the standard deviations? Why?
7. An instructor has scored a set of tests and identified Q, Q_1, Q_2, S, $\overline{X}$, the
    median, and the mode. He then learns that one of the scores in the bottom
    20 per cent of the distribution was in error; when corrected, it is slightly
    lower. Which of the statistics are affected by the correction? How?
8. Our investigator studying political orientation among college students, ad-
    ministered a test of "political liberalism-conservatism" to members of two
    fraternity groups. He summarized his results in the following form (high
    scores represent conservatism).

	Fraternity A	Fraternity B
Median	55.3	57.1
$\overline{X}$	55.1	57.5
S	12.2	6.2

    a) Which fraternity would you call the most conservative? Why?
    b) Does the difference in means appear to be very important? Explain.
9. Suppose we took two different random samples, each of the same size, of
    freshman in a given college and determined the ages of all persons selected.
    On which measure of central tendency would you expect the two samples
    to be most similar, the median or the mean? On which measure of variation
    would they most likely be similar, Q or S? Explain.

10. Would you expect the grouping error in Q to be systematic in the same way as the grouping error in S? Explain.

11. From the information in each of the following instances, what can be inferred about the distribution of scores?

a) $S = 5$

b) $\overline{X} = 53$; $S = 5$; and the distribution is approximately normal.

c) $Q_1 = 26$; $Q_2 = 30$; and $Q_3 = 38$.

d) $Q = 7.5$

e) $Q_2 = 69$ and $Q = 7.5$

f) $Q_2 = 69$; $Q = 7.5$; and the distribution is approximately symmetric.

Chapter 5

The Normal Curve

Frequency distributions, as we have noted earlier, can take on any of an infinite variety of shapes; they may differ in number of modes, skewness, and kurtosis ("flatness"). There is one particular shape that is of great interest to educators, psychologists, and statisticians. This is represented by the smooth bell-shaped curve of Fig. 5-1, called a *normal curve*.

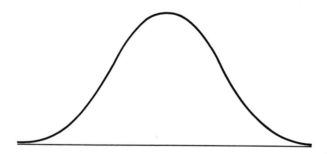

Figure 5-1. A Normal Curve

By definition, a normal curve is a graphical representation of any one of the group of mathematical functions defined by the rather complex and forbidding-looking general equation:

$$y = \frac{e^{-(X-\mu)^2/2\sigma^2}}{\sigma\sqrt{2\pi}}$$

where y is the height of the curve at any particular X score, e and

π are mathematical constants (2.7183 and 3.1416 respectively), and μ and σ are known as the *parameters* of the equation.

The level of mathematical sophistication required to understand and use this equation is far more than that required for readers of this text; however, it has been presented largely to help clarify two basic points concerning the nature of normal curves.

First, a normal curve is not itself a frequency distribution. It is a mathematical abstraction (albeit an extremely important one)—a representation of a mathematical function. Second, there is not one, but a whole family of normal curves. The equation given above is general in the sense that no particular numerical values were specified for what were referred to as *parameters*, μ and σ. If μ is replaced by any real number and σ by any real, positive number, the graphical representation of the resulting equation will be a normal curve. There are as many normal curves as there are different pairs of numerical values for μ and σ. Two specific normal curves ($\mu = 20$, $\sigma = 5$ and $\mu = 25$, $\sigma = 10$) are presented in Fig. 5-2. Although they appear to have different shapes they are both

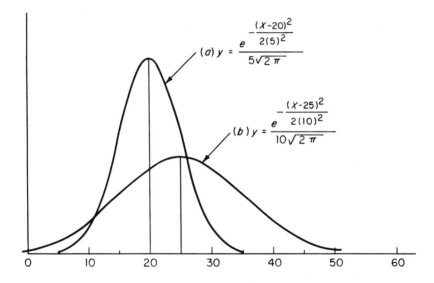

Figure 5-2. Two Normal Curves with Different Values for the Parameters μ and σ [for (a), $\mu = 20$ and $\sigma = 5$; for (b), $\mu = 25$ and $\sigma = 10$]

normal curves, because the functions they represent are variations of the general normal-curve function.

The Importance of the Normal-Curve Function

The reader may well ask why the normal-curve function, which after all is nothing more than a mathematical abstraction, is of such importance to those concerned with the theory behind or the application of statistical methods. The most important reason is its close fit to relative-frequency distributions obtained through the operation of "chance" factors. This relationship can be illustrated by an example. Suppose ten coins were flipped and the number of "heads" were counted. Since, for any single coin, obtaining heads and obtaining tails would be equally likely, one might expect five of the ten coins to come up heads; however, because of the operation of "chance" factors, only four heads or three heads, or even fewer, might be obtained if the ten coins were flipped. On the other hand, six or seven, or perhaps even more, heads might be obtained. It is even possible, although not very likely, that all ten coins might come up heads or that all ten might come up tails. Suppose now that the ten coins were flipped many times, and each time the number of heads were recorded. The relative-frequency distribution of the numbers of heads which would be obtained for many, many flips of a group of ten coins is represented by the histogram in Fig. 5-3. A normal curve has been superimposed on the histogram.

It can be seen that the normal curve is a fairly good approximation of the histogram. If twenty coins rather than ten were flipped each time, there would be twenty-one bars in the histogram, and the steps at the top of the histogram would be smaller. In such a circumstance, a normal curve would be an even better fit. If the group consisted of 100 coins, the top of the histogram would be almost indistinguishable from the best-fitting normal curve.

The relative-frequency distribution of Fig. 5-3 is one of a large class of relative-frequency distributions, called *sampling distributions*, which represent the operation of chance factors. Since the nature of sampling distributions will be discussed in great detail in later chapters, it will suffice here to point out that they play a basic role in statistical inference, the process of making inferences about a population on the basis of what is known about a random sample from that population. Many sampling distributions either can be approximated by a normal curve and/or are based upon an assumption of a normal shape for the frequency distribution of scores in the population.

It is no accident that so many chance distributions can be closely approximated by normal curves. In the eighteenth century, an English mathematician, Abraham De Moivre, recognized that as the number of

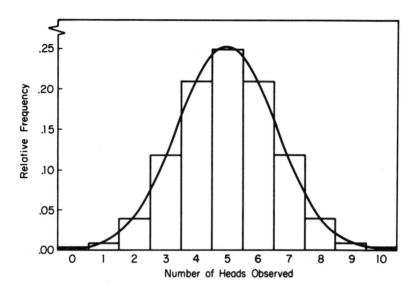

*Figure 5-3. Relative-Frequency Distribution of Number of Heads
Observed for Many, Many Flips of a Group of Ten Coins
(A normal curve has been superimposed.)*

coins in the group is increased, the top of a histogram, such as that represented in Fig. 5-3, approaches a smooth curve. He subsequently derived the general normal-curve function as the equation for this curve. Then, in the beginning of the nineteenth century, two famous mathematicians— a Frenchman, Pierre-Simon de Laplace, and a German, Carl Friedrich Gauss—derived the general normal-curve function as an approximation of chance distributions with which they were concerned. Their derivations were performed independently of each other and evidently without any knowledge of De Moivre's previous derivation.

The second reason for the importance of the normal-curve function concerns relative-frequency distributions of measurements obtained for large numbers of cases. Certain of these are closely approximated by normal curves. Examples are heights or weights or IQ scores for groups of individuals of the same sex with similar backgrounds, or the weights and physical dimensions of plants or animals of the same species raised under similar conditions. If a relative-frequency distribution of a group of scores on some variable can be approximated by a normal curve, the variable is said to be *normally distributed* for that group. A word of caution should, however, be given at this point. There is no "normal law" in the sense that a frequency distribution of any very large number of scores, whether they be from one of the physical sciences or social sciences or any other discipline, can be approximated by a normal curve. In fact, many frequency distributions of real data do not fit the normal-curve model.

Significance of the Parameters μ and σ

It is in the approximation of a relative-frequency distribution by a normal curve that the significance of the parameters of the normal-curve function can easily be understood. *For a normally distributed group of scores, the parameters, μ and σ, of the equation of the best-fitting normal curve will have values equal to the mean, $\overline{X}$, and the standard deviation, S, respectively, of that group of scores.* For instance, if the two normal curves of Fig. 5-2 were meant to be approximations of the relative-frequency distributions of two groups of scores, the means of the two frequency distributions would be 20 and 25, and the standard deviations would be 5 and 10. It should be pointed out that traditionally the symbols μ and σ have a broader meaning. In statistical-inference problems, μ represents the mean and σ represents the standard deviation of a population of scores *regardless* of the shape of its relative-frequency distribution. This will be amplified in the later sections on inference.

In order to avoid unnecessary confusion, no distinction will be made during the remainder of this chapter between the mean, $\overline{X}$, and the standard deviation, S, of a normally distributed group of scores and the corresponding parameters, μ and σ, of the best-fitting normal curve. Only the symbols $\overline{X}$ and S will be used, and the symbols μ and σ will be dropped until the chapters on statistical inference.

Properties of a Normal Curve

If the shape of a relative-frequency distribution of a group of scores can be approximated by a normal curve, then the relative-frequency distribution will have approximately the same properties as the best-fitting normal curve. Consequently, a knowledge of certain of the properties of normal curves is extremely useful in facilitating analyses of data which are known to be normally distributed. Fortunately, these properties have been determined by mathematical methods.

First, a normal curve is symmetric about its own mean; therefore, 1/2 or .50 of the area falls on each side of the mean. Second, a normal curve is asymptotic to the horizontal axis. That is, as the value of X is increased above the mean or decreased below the mean, the curve comes closer and closer to the horizontal axis but never quite reaches it, no matter how large or how small the value of X. The third property deals with the area relationships under a normal curve. Utilizing the methods of integral calculus, it has been determined that the total area under any normal curve as defined is equal to 1.00. Furthermore, it can be shown that the area between the mean and one standard deviation, S, above or below the mean is .3416 or approximately .34 of the total area; therefore, .16 (i.e., .50 − .34) of the area under the curve falls to the right of a point $1S$ above the mean and .16 falls to the left of a point $1S$ below the mean. These illustrative relationships, shown in Fig. 5-4, hold for any normal curve regardless of the values of the mean and standard deviation.

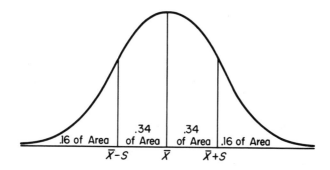

Figure 5-4. Some Area Relationships for Normal Curves

As was explained in Chap. 2, the proportion of area between two score values under the curve of any relative-frequency distribution of scores is equal to the proportion of cases falling between those two score values (if the reader feels uncomfortable with this point, he should reread pp. 22–25). For a group of normally distributed scores, therefore, .50 of the cases would fall above and .50 of the cases would fall below the mean, $\overline{X}$; .34 of the cases would fall between $\overline{X}$ and either $1S$ above or $1S$ below $\overline{X}$; and .16 of the cases would fall beyond $1S$ above or below $\overline{X}$.

Example 5-1. Suppose we had the IQ-test scores of 1,000 children between the ages of 5 and 6. Suppose furthermore that the scores tend to be normally distributed (i.e., the relative-frequency distribution can be approximated by a normal curve) with a mean of 100 and standard deviation of 15. How many children have IQs above 115?

A score of 115 is 15 score points, or 1 standard deviation, above the mean of 100. From Fig. 5-5 we see that .16 of the total number of cases fall above $\overline{X} + 1S$. Since .16 of 1,000 cases is 160 cases, approximately 160 children in this group have IQs above 115.

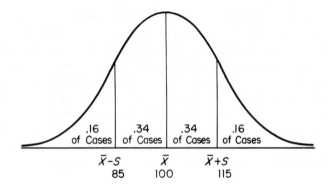

Figure 5-5. Relative-Frequency Distribution for 1,000 Normally Distributed IQ Scores ($\overline{X} = 100$, $S = 15$)

Example 5-2. How many children have IQs above 85? A score of 85 is 15 score points, or $1S$, below the mean of 100. From Fig. 5-5, we see that .34 of the cases fall between $\overline{X} - 1S$ and $\overline{X}$, and .50 fall above $\overline{X}$. One-half plus .34 equals .84, and .84 of 1,000 cases is 840 cases; therefore, approximately 840 children would have IQ scores above 85.

UTILIZING THE NORMAL-CURVE TABLE

The examples just solved are based on what is known about the area under a normal curve falling between $\overline{X} - 1S$ and $\overline{X} + 1S$. Utilizing the techniques of integral calculus, mathematical statisticians have been able to provide us with a far more detailed description of the area relationships. This detailed description is presented in tabular form in Appx. 2. From the table we can determine the proportion of area between the mean and any S-point up to $4.00S$ above the mean in increments of .01.

Column 1 of the normal-curve table is labelled "z or x/σ." It is the convention to let the letter z represent the number of standard deviations a score is above or below the mean. For instance, another way of indicating that a particular student's score is exactly $1.35S$ above the mean is to state that his score is equivalent to a z of $+1.35$. On the other hand, if a student's score is $1.35S$ *below* the mean, his score is equivalent to a z of -1.35. That is, if a score is above the mean, it will be equivalent to a positive z, whereas if a score is below the mean it will be equivalent to a negative z. If a score is exactly equal to the mean, it will be equivalent to a z of 0. Column 2 is labelled "Area between Mean and z," and Col. 3 is labelled "Area beyond z." Suppose we wanted to determine the area between $\overline{X}$ and $\overline{X} + 1.35S$. We first look down Col. 1 until we come to

1.35. In Col. 2 opposite 1.35 is the proportion .4115. This represents the proportion of area, and thus the proportion of cases, falling between $\overline{X}$ and a z of $+1.35$ (i.e., $\overline{X} + 1.35S$) in any normal distribution (see Fig. 5-6). The .0885 in Col. 3 indicates that .0885, or approximately 8.9 per cent, of the cases in a normal distribution fall above a z of $+1.35$. Notice that $.4115 + .0885 = .5000$; for any z, the numbers in Cols. 2 and 3 will always total .5000.

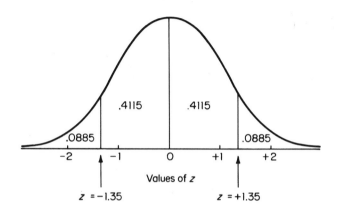

Figure 5-6. Area Relationships under a Normal Curve for $z = +1.35$ and $z = -1.35$

We have illustrated the use of the table for determining areas above the mean. Since all normal curves are symmetric about the mean, this table is also appropriate for areas below the mean. For instance, if we wish to determine the area between $\overline{X}$ and a z of -1.35, we look down Col. 1 until we come to 1.35. The .4115 opposite 1.35 is the proportion of area between $\overline{X}$ and a z of -1.35 as well as the proportion of area between $\overline{X}$ and a z of $+1.35$. The proportion of cases falling below a z of -1.35 is similarly found in Col. 3 of the table, since the area below a z of -1.35 is equal to the area above a z of $+1.35$.

Use of the Normal-Curve Table with Raw Scores

The examples in the previous section illustrate how to determine the proportion of cases or number of cases associated with a certain number of standard deviations above or below the mean in a normal distribution of scores. In this section we shall consider questions dealing with the proportion or number of cases above or below any *raw score* in a normal distribution of scores. In general, such questions are of two broad types: (1) we are given one or a pair of raw scores, and we are to find the number of cases above or below one of the raw scores or between the two raw scores; and (2) we are given a number or proportion of cases and we are to find the raw score below which the given number or proportion of cases falls. The following are some examples of the first type of question.

Example 5-3. We have 2,000 normally distributed scores with a mean of 45 and an S of 5. How many scores fall below 52.5?

Because Col. 1 in Appx. 2 must be entered with a value of z, we first must determine how far a score of 52.5 is above the mean, in terms of standard deviations. We can see that 52.5 is 7.5 raw-score points above the mean. Since $S = 5$, 7.5 raw-score points above the mean is $7.5/5 = 1.50S$ above the mean, or a z of $+1.50$. At this point we can enter Col. 1 of Appx. 2 and move down to 1.50. The entry in Col. 2 is .4332, indicating that approximately .43 of the scores fall between $\overline{X}$ and a z of $+1.50$ (i.e., between 45 and 52.5). Since 1/2 of the scores fall below 45, .9332 of the scores (.5000 + .4332) must fall below 52.5. Taking this proportion (.9332) of 2,000 cases gives us approximately 1,866 cases below 52.5. This and Ex. 5-4 are illustrated in Fig. 5-7.

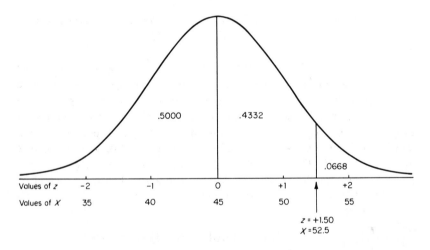

Figure 5-7. Relative-Frequency Distribution for 2,000 Normally Distributed Scores ($\overline{X} = 45$, $S = 5$)

The main steps used to determine the answer can be summarized as follows.

a) It was determined how far above or below the mean the raw score was in terms of standard deviations; that is, the value of *z* was determined.

$$z = \frac{X - \overline{X}}{S} = \frac{52.5 - 45}{5} = +1.50$$

b) In Col. 1 of Appx. 2 the value closest to the obtained *z* was located.

c) The proportion of cases between the score and the mean was obtained from Col. 1 and added to .5000 (i.e., .4332 + .5000 = .9332).

d) The total number of cases was multiplied by the obtained proportion to determine the number of cases below the score [i.e., .9332 (2000) = 1866].

Example 5-4. For the situation described in Ex. 5-3, how many scores fall above 52.5?

As was demonstrated in Ex. 5-3, a score of 52.5 is 1.50*S* above the mean (or *z* = +1.50). This time, however, we are interested in the scores above 52.5. The entry in Col. 3 indicates that .0668 of the scores fall *above* 52.5. If we take .0668 of 2,000, we find that approximately 134 scores fall above 52.5.

Example 5-5. For the same situation, how many scores fall below 42.5?

In this example, *z* is negative. That is, the score is below the mean.

$$z = \frac{X - \overline{X}}{S} = \frac{42.5 - 45}{5} = -.50$$

Looking down Col. 1 of Appx. 2, we find .50. We take the value .3085 from Col. 3 because we are interested in the cases falling below 42.5 rather than between 42.5 and the mean. Since .3085 of 2,000 cases is approximately 617, the latter is the number of cases falling below 42.5. This and the following example are illustrated in Fig. 5-8.

Example 5-6. How many cases fall between 42.5 and 52.5?

As was demonstrated in the foregoing examples, 52.5 is 1.50*S* above the mean (*z* = +1.50), and 42.5 is .50*S* below the mean (*z* = −.50). From the table we see that the proportion of cases between a score of 52.5 and 45 (i.e., between a *z* of +1.50 and $\overline{X}$) is .4332. Similarly, the proportion of cases between 42.5 and 45 (i.e., between a *z* of −.50 and $\overline{X}$) is .1915. The proportion of cases between scores of 42.5 and 52.5 is therefore .4332 + .1915, or .6247. Since .6247 of 2,000 is approximately 1,249, we can say that 1,249 cases fall between 42.5 and 52.5.

Example 5-7. In the distribution of scores of the above examples, how many cases fall between 47 and 52.5?

As we have shown, 52.5 is 1.50S above the mean ($z = +1.50$). We can also see that 47 is $(47 - 45)/5$, or $+.40S$, above the mean ($z = +.40$). This example is handled in a manner slightly different from that in Ex. 5-6 because both scores are on the same side of the mean. The Appx. 2 table

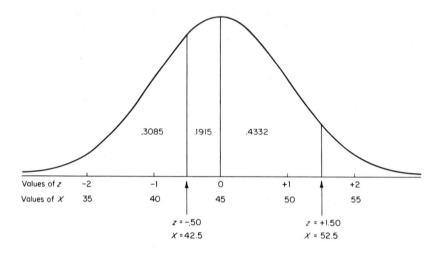

Figure 5-8. Relative-Frequency Distribution for 2,000 Normally Distributed Scores ($\overline{X} = 45$, $S = 5$)

tells us that .4332 of the scores fall between 52.5 and 45 (i.e., between a z of $+1.50$ and $\overline{X}$) and that .1554 of the scores fall between 47 and 45 (between a z of $+.40$ and $\overline{X}$). Therefore, the proportion of cases between 47 and 52.5 must be .4332 *minus* .1554, or .2778 (if this is not clear the reader should make a sketch like that in Fig. 5-8). Since .2778 of 2,000 is approximately 556, 556 cases fall between 47 and 52.5.

The foregoing examples should suffice to demonstrate the principles and techniques involved in determining the number of cases above or below a given raw score or between two given raw scores. Before attempting to solve this type of problem, it may be helpful for the reader to sketch a normal curve and to block out the relevant areas. With the help of such a figure, it is much easier to determine which column of Appx. 2 to use and how to combine the areas.

For the second general type of question we are given the number or proportion of cases and must find the corresponding raw score. This is really the converse of the first question. The following are examples.

Example 5-8. For 2,000 normally distributed scores the mean is 45 and the standard deviation is 5. Below what score do 65 per cent of the cases fall?

The score we are seeking must be above the mean since 65 per cent or .65 is greater than .50. Since .65 − .50 is .15, we can see that .15 of the cases fall between the mean of 45 and the score we are looking for. Looking down Col. 2 in Appx. 2, we find that .1517 is closest to .15. Opposite .1517 in Col. 1 is .39. This indicates that in any normal distribution approximately .15 of the cases fall between $\overline{X}$ and a z of +.39 (i.e., between $\overline{X}$ and .39S above the mean); therefore, the raw score we are looking for corresponds to a z of +.39. Since .39S above the mean is 1.95 (i.e., .39 × 5) raw-score points above the mean, the score we are seeking is 45 + 1.95, or 46.95. This is illustrated in Fig. 5-9. These steps described

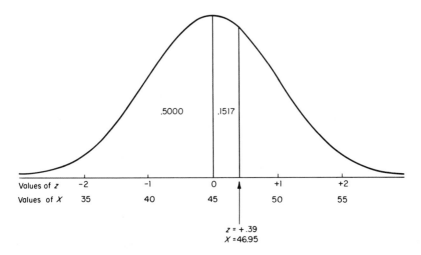

Figure 5-9. *Relative-Frequency Distribution for 2,000 Normally Distributed Scores* ($\overline{X}$ = *45, S* = *5*)

above can be summarized as follows.

a) The proportion of cases between the mean and the unknown score was determined.

b) The value closest to the proportion determined in step *a* was located in Col. 2 of the table. The value opposite in Col. 1 is the number of *S*'s the score is above the mean.

c) The number of raw-score points above the mean was determined by multiplying the *S* by *z*.

d) The result of step *c* was added to the mean to obtain the desired score.

Example 5-9. For the situation of Ex. 5.8, below what score do 600 of the cases fall?

Six hundred cases is .30 of the 2,000 (i.e., $600/2,000 = .30$). Since .30 is less than .50, the score we are looking for is *below* the mean (see Fig. 5-10).

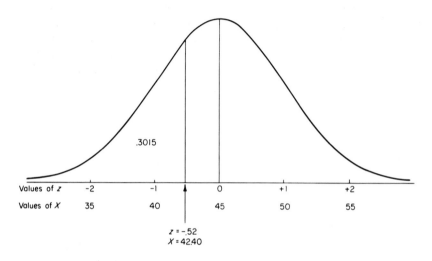

.3015

| Values of *z* | −2 | −1 | | 0 | +1 | +2 |
| Values of *X* | 35 | 40 | | 45 | 50 | 55 |

$z = -.52$
$X = 42.40$

Figure 5-10. Relative-Frequency Distribution for 2,000 Normally Distributed Scores ($\overline{X} = 45$, $S = 5$)

When the score we are looking for is below the mean, the steps can be summarized as follows.

a) Determine the proportion of cases below the unknown score ($600/2,000 = .30$).

b) Look down Col. 3 of the table to find the value closest to the proportion determined in the first step (.3015 is closest to .30). The value opposite in Col. 1 is the number of *S*'s the score is below the mean ($z = -.52$). Note that *z* is negative because the score is below the mean.

c) Determine the number of raw-score points below the mean by multiplying *S* by *z* (i.e., $-.52 \times 5 = -2.60$).

d) Subtract the appropriate number of raw-score points from the mean ($45 - 2.60 = 42.40$). The score below which approximately 600 of the cases fall is 42.40.

In each of the examples of the two general types of questions, a particular method of handling the problem was illustrated; however, as many readers already will have discovered, there are usually several equally good methods of solving such problems. The important thing, therefore, is not to memorize the steps outlined in the previous examples but to understand the general principles involved.

Exercises and Problems

1. In a normal distribution of scores, what per cent of the cases will fall (a) below a z of +1.00, (b) below a z of −1.00, (c) above a z of +1.00, (d) above a z of −2.25, (e) between a z of −.50 and a z of +.50, (f) between a z of −.50 and a z of −1.50?

2. In a normal distribution of 1,000 scores, how many fall (a) below a z of −.65, (b) below a z of +1.65, (c) above a z of +3.00, (d) between a z of +.25 and a z of +1.25, (e) between a z of −.75 and a z of +1.75?

3. In a normal distribution of 200 scores, how many fall (a) above z = +2.00, (b) below z = +.35, (c) between z = +.35 and z = +.85, (d) between z = −.35 and z = +.85, (e) between the mean and z = +1.00, (f) between the mean and z = +3.00?

4. In a normal distribution of college-aptitude test scores with a mean of 500 and a standard deviation of 100, what per cent of the cases fall (a) above a score of 600, (b) below a score of 550, (c) above a score of 300, (d) below a score of 400, (e) between 500 and 600, (f) between 600 and 700?

5. In a normal distribution of 100 final-exam scores with a mean of 70 and a standard deviation of 10, how many cases fall (a) above a score of 72, (b) below a score of 75, (c) below a score of 55, (d) between 55 and 75, (e) between 75 and 95, (f) between 65 and 85?

6. In a normal distribution of 5,000 IQ scores with a mean of 100 and a standard deviation of 16, how many cases fall (a) above a score of 104, (b) below 120, (c) below 88, (d) above 92, (e) between 132 and 140, (f) between 96 and 124?

7. In a normal distribution of scores, what is the z (a) above which 5 per cent of the cases fall, (b) above which 74 per cent of the cases fall, (c) below which 58 per cent of the cases fall, (d) below which 2 per cent of the cases fall? (e) Thirty per cent of the cases fall between the mean and what positive z value? (f) The middle 55 per cent of the cases fall between what two z values?

8. In a normal distribution of 10,000 scores, what is the z (a) above which 5,199 cases fall, (b) above which 968 cases fall, (c) below which 8,531 cases fall, (d) below which 2,576 cases fall? (e) The middle 6,046 cases fall

between what two z values? (f) The middle 8,064 cases fall between what two z values?

9. In a normal distribution of 300 scores, what is the z (a) above which 150 cases fall, (b) above which 18 cases fall, (c) below which 51 cases fall, (d) below which 222 cases fall, (e) above which 120 cases fall? (f) The middle 115 cases fall between what two z values?

10. In a normal distribution of college-aptitude test scores with a mean of 500 and a standard deviation of 100, what is the score (a) above which 21 per cent of the cases fall, (b) above which 83 per cent of the cases fall, (c) below which 90 per cent of the cases fall, (d) below which 4 per cent of the cases fall? (e) The upper 5 per cent and lower 5 per cent fall beyond what two scores? (f) The middle 50 per cent fall between what two scores? (g) The middle 95 per cent fall between what two scores?

11. In a normal distribution of 1,000 final-exam scores with a mean of 70 and a standard deviation of 10, what is the score (a) above which 18 cases fall, (b) above which 758 cases fall, (c) below which 115 cases fall, (d) below which 933 cases fall? (e) The middle 311 cases fall between what two scores? (f) The upper 55 cases and the lower 55 cases fall beyond what two scores?

12. In a normal distribution of 200 IQ scores with a mean of 100 and a standard deviation of 16, what two scores (a) enclose the middle 76 cases, (b) enclose the middle 184 cases, (c) enclose the middle 136 cases? (d) The upper 4 cases and the lower 4 cases fall beyond what two scores? (e) The upper 13 cases and the lower 13 cases fall beyond what two scores? (f) The upper 50 cases and the lower 50 cases fall beyond what two scores?

13. Suppose a distribution of 1,000 final-exam scores is normal with a mean of 156 and a standard deviation of 20. Consider the range to be (for practical purposes) about six standard deviations. If this range were divided into five equal parts, one for each letter grade:

a) How many students would obtain A's; how many, B's; how many, C's; how many, D's; and how many, F's?

b) What would be the limits in terms of final-exam scores for each of the letter grades?

Chapter 6

Derived Scores

A *raw score* is the score originally derived from the measurement used—one that has not been transformed or modified in any way. If a test is scored initially in terms of the number of correct responses, the raw score is "number right." The original, or raw, scores are often transformed into another set of scores, derived from the originals. The new scores are termed *derived scores* or *transformed scores.* An instance of such a transformation would be to give each pupil a *rank* based on his number of correct responses—or to score him as "above average," "average," or "below average." The necessity for transforming raw scores into derived scores arises partly because raw scores usually are difficult to interpret. Suppose, for example, that an English test and a mathematics test were administered to an entire eighth grade. Is John Jones, who scored "32 correct" in English and "65 correct" in math, better in math than in English? Not necessarily. Several questions must be considered:

1) *How many items were there on each test?* Suppose there were only fifty items in the English test, whereas the math test consisted of 150 items. John responded correctly to a larger percentage of the English items (64 per cent) than math items (43 per cent). This would suggest that he is better in English than in math, other things being equal.

2) *What was the mean score on each test?* Suppose that the eighth-grade mean score on the English test was 20 and the math-test mean was 45. John was 12 points above the mean in English but he was 20 points above the mean in math. This would suggest that he is better in math than in English.

3) *How much variability was there in each test?* Suppose that the English-test scores clustered very closely around the mean score of 20 and that John's score of 32 was one of the top scores. Suppose, further, that the math-test scores were dispersed very widely about the mean score of 45 and that many students exceeded John's score of 65. This situation would suggest that John is better in English than in math.

It should be evident from this discussion that raw scores by themselves are of little use. Additional information is necessary before they can be interpreted. One approach to this problem is to convert the raw scores into derived scores which incorporate the additional information needed for interpretation. Probably the most widely used derived scores in education and psychology are those involving a comparison of an individual with a reference group. Three types of such derived scores are described below: *percentile ranks, standard scores*, and *normalized scores*.

PERCENTILE RANKS

If all the individuals in the group are ranked from highest to lowest according to their raw scores, the *percentile rank* of a particular individual is the per cent of the total group who rank below him. If John Jones scores higher than 70 per cent of the entire group of eighth-graders on the English test, his percentile rank in English (relative to the reference group of eighth-graders) would be 70. Conversely, if we are told that Tom Smith's percentile rank on the English test is 22, we know that he scored higher than 22 per cent of the individuals in the reference group.

The term *percentile rank* may be applied to a score as well. *The percentile rank of a particular score will be defined as the per cent of the total reference group who obtain less than that score.* Later in the chapter this definition will be modified slightly for computational purposes; however, it will suffice at present. It should be pointed out that two other terms which mean the same thing as percentile rank have become fairly popular in recent years. These are *centile rank* and *centile score*.

Converting Raw Scores to Percentile Ranks: Graphic Approach

A very simple procedure for converting raw scores to percentile ranks is that which utilizes the graph of the cumulative per cents. The construction of a cumulative percentage curve or *ogive*, as it is commonly known, can be divided into four steps:

1) First, the scores are grouped in a frequency distribution with ten to twenty intervals. This is illustrated in Table 6-1, for a fictitious set of raw scores.

2) Next, the cumulative frequencies are computed. These are listed in Col. 2 of Table 6-1. For each interval, the number in the cumulative-

Table 6-1

Cumulative Frequency and Per Cent Distributions for 150 Test Scores

Scores	1 f	2 Cum. f	3 Cum. Per Cent
63–65	2	150	100
60–62	5	148	98.7
57–59	12	143	95.3
54–56	25	131	87.3
51–53	28	106	70.7
48–50	26	78	52.0
45–47	22	52	34.7
42–44	16	30	20.0
39–41	7	14	9.3
36–38	5	7	4.7
33–35	2	2	1.3

frequency column represents the total number of cases *up to and including* those in that interval. In other words, it represents the total number of cases below the upper limit of the interval. For example, the cumulative frequency through the interval 42–44, is 30, including the 16 cases in the interval. Therefore, there must be 30 cases below 44.5, which is the upper limit of the interval.

3) The cumulative frequencies are then transformed to cumulative percentages, as in Col. 3, Table 6-1. This is done by dividing the cumulative frequency for each interval by N (the total number of cases) and multiplying by 100. For example, the cumulative percentage for the interval 42–44 is 20.0.

$$\frac{\text{cum.} f}{N} \times 100 = \frac{30}{150} \times 100 = 20.0$$

This tells us that 20 per cent of the cases fall below the upper limit of 44.5.

4) Finally, the ogive or graph of the cumulative–per cent column may be constructed. It is customary to use the vertical axis for the cumulative per cents and the horizontal axis for the score intervals. Each per cent is plotted *at the upper limit* of the class interval rather than at the midpoint as for a frequency polygon. The reason for this is that we are representing the percentage of individuals who obtained scores below the *upper limit* of the interval. The plotted points may then be connected by straight lines. The ogive for the data in Table 6-1 is shown in Fig. 6-1.

We can determine, from the cumulative-percentage column of Table 6-1 the percentile rank for the upper limit of each interval. That is, the upper limit 35.5 would have a percentile rank of 1.3, the upper limit 38.5 would have a percentile rank of 4.7, and so forth. Now, using the ogive, we can easily approximate the percentile ranks for scores between the interval limits. Suppose, for instance, that we wish to find the percentile rank of a score of 42. We locate the position of this score on the baseline and proceed

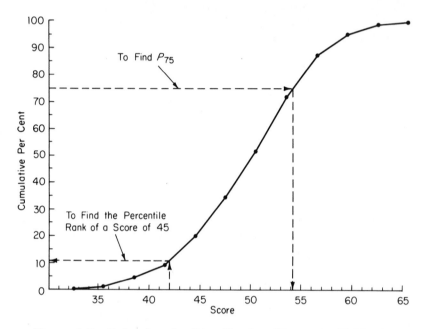

Figure 6-1. Ogive for the Distribution Shown in Table 6-1

vertically until the curve is intersected; from this intersection, we go horizontally to the vertical axis and estimate the cumulative-percentage point we strike. In this instance (see dotted lines in Fig. 6-1), we strike the vertical axis at approximately 11. Thus, we can say that the percentile rank of a score of 42 is 11; i.e., approximately 11 per cent of the examinees scored below 42. The percentile ranks of the remaining scores may be determined in the same manner. Needless to say, the ogive should be drawn very accurately. It is recommended that graph paper be used and that the scale be as large as possible so that fine discriminations can be made. It is also recommended that whole numbers on the score scale correspond to the vertical ruled lines on the graph paper and that the scores which are identified on the horizontal axis be whole numbers. This will make it easier to use the ogive for obtaining percentile ranks. Of course, regardless of how the score scale is laid out, the points for the ogive will always be plotted at the upper limits of the intervals.

Percentiles, Deciles, and Quartiles

The term *percentile* is often confused with the term *percentile rank*. Actually, percentile is the converse of percentile rank. *A percentile is a score point, not a per cent. It is the point below which a given per cent of cases fall.* If one uses the ogive of Fig. 6-1, a raw score of 57 has a percentile rank of 89. That is, approximately 89 per cent of the norm group fall below this raw score. Thus, a raw score of 57 would be the *eighty-ninth percentile*. The term *percentile* may be abbreviated by the symbol $P_\%$, in which $\%$ is the associated per cent. The eighty-ninth percentile, for instance, may be identified as P_{89}. Thus, $P_{89} = 57$.

A number of specific percentile points are also known by other names. The reader has already been introduced to the three *quartiles*, Q_1, Q_2, and Q_3, which would be P_{25}, P_{50}, and P_{75} respectively. The median, of course, is the same as Q_2 or P_{50}. In addition, reference is sometimes made to what are known as *deciles*. The deciles are the percentiles which divide the entire group of N individuals into ten equal groups of size $N/10$. The first decile is the same as the tenth percentile or P_{10}, the second decile is the same as P_{20}, and so on to the ninth decile, which is P_{90}. Thus, the point below which 50 per cent of the cases fall could be referred to either as the *fifth decile*, the *second quartile* (Q_2), the *fiftieth percentile* (P_{50}), or the median.

Percentiles also can be determined from an ogive, using the converse of the procedure for finding percentile ranks. For instance, suppose we wish to determine the seventy-fifth percentile (i.e., P_{75} or Q_3) from the ogive of Fig. 6-1. We locate the 75 per cent point on the vertical axis, move horizontally to the ogive and downward to the horizontal axis. The raw score of 54 (approximately) read from the horizontal axis is P_{75}; it is the score below which 75 per cent of the reference group fall.

Determining Percentile Ranks and Percentiles: Arithmetic Method

When scores are grouped into class intervals, the graphic approach to determining percentile ranks and percentiles is quite simple and gives results of sufficient accuracy for most purposes; however, if automatic calculating equipment is available, the arithmetic method may be preferred. This method involves the interpolation process utilized in Chaps. 3 and 4 for finding the median and the quartiles from grouped data. Let us find, for example, the percentile rank of a score of 42 in the distribution given in Table 6-1. The following steps are appropriate.

1) Determine, by interpolation, the number of cases falling between the score and the lower limit of the interval in which the score lies.

A score of 42 is .5 of a score point above 41.5, the lower limit of the interval 42–44. A distance of .5 of a score point represents .167 of the total interval width of 3 (i.e., $.5/3 = .167$). Assuming the 16 cases to be spread evenly throughout the interval, we find that 2.67 cases fall between 42 and the lower limit of 41.5 [i.e., $.167 (16) = 2.67$].

2) Add the number of cases determined in Step 1 to the number of cases which fall below the lower limit in order to find the number of cases falling below the score.

It can be seen that 14 cases fall below the lower limit of 41.5. Thus, a total of 16.67 cases fall below a score of 42 (i.e., $14 + 2.67 = 16.67$).

3) Divide the number of cases below the score by the total number of cases and multiply by 100. This will give the per cent falling below the score and, thus, the percentile rank.

Based on the number of cases determined in Step 2, the percentile rank of a score of 42 is 11.1 [i.e., $(16.67/150) 100 = 11.1$].

It should be noted that the answer, 11.1, is within 1/10 of a per cent of the answer (11) obtained earlier from the ogive. If it had been possible to read the vertical axis to the nearest 1/10 of a per cent, an answer of exactly 11.1 would have been obtained from the ogive as well, because, barring difficulties in making fine discriminations, the two methods give identical results. The arithmetic method can also be used to determine percentiles. It will not be illustrated here, however, since the procedures are identical with those presented earlier for determining the median, Q_1, and Q_3 (see pp. 52–53).

Determining Percentile Ranks and Percentiles: Midpoint Percentile Method

When scores are not grouped into class intervals, the most widely used procedure for determining percentile ranks is what will be called the *midpoint percentile method*. This method involves treating a score value as an interval of size 1 and determining the percentage of cases which fall below the midpoint of the interval. The assumption is made that half the cases in the interval fall above the midpoint and half fall below. For instance, a raw score of 15 would be considered an interval of size 1 with limits of 14.5 and 15.5 and a midpoint of 15. The number of cases falling below the *midpoint* 15 would be the number who obtained scores of less than 15 plus half those who obtained scores of 15. This leads to the following formula for obtaining the percentile rank of a raw score.

$$\text{Percentile Rank} = 100 \left[\frac{\text{cum.} f(\text{below}) + .5f}{N} \right] \qquad (6\text{-}1)$$

where cum. f(below) is number of cases below the given score and f is number obtaining the score

The midpoint percentile method is illustrated in Table 6-2, for a dis-

Table 6-2

Illustration of the Mid-percentile Method for Determining Percentiles and Percentile Ranks ($N = 199$)

1 Raw Score	2 f	3 Cum. f	4 Cum. f (below) + .5f	5 Percentile Rank
28	1	199	198.5	99.7
27	0	198	198	99.5
26	2	198	197	99.4
25	6	196	193	97.0
24	8	190	186	93.5
23	15	182	174.5	87.7
22	26	167	154	77.4
21	29	141	126.5	63.6
20	38	112	93	46.7
19	19	74	64.5	32.4
18	18	55	46	23.1
17	12	37	31	15.6
16	9	25	20.5	10.3
15	6	16	13	6.5
14	5	10	7.5	3.8
13	2	5	4	2.0
12	3	3	1.5	0.8

tribution of 199 raw scores. The cum.f column is a straightforward cumulative frequency distribution, with the cumulation to the upper limit of each class interval. The novel step is in Col. 4, labeled "cum. f(below) + .5f." Here we indicate, for each score value, the number of cases below that particular score plus half those obtaining that score. Consider again a raw score of 15. The cumulative frequency *below* it is 10. The frequency associated with a score of 15 is 6. Thus:

$$\text{cum.} f(\text{below}) + .5f = 10 + .5(6) = 13$$

The percentile rank for each score (Col. 5) is determined by dividing the entry in Col. 4 by N and multiplying by 100. Hence, for a raw score of 15, the percentile rank is 6.5.

$$100 \left(\frac{13}{199} \right) = 100 (.065) = 6.5$$

A Limitation of Percentile Ranks

A percentile rank generally has the advantage of easy interpretation and communication. It indicates fairly simply the status of an individual in terms of an unambiguous reference, or norm, group. A difficulty arises, however, in the interpretation of differences between percentile ranks.

Consider, as an illustration, a situation in which an algebra achievement test is administered to all eighth-grade students at the beginning of the school year and again at the end of the school year. Student *A* obtains percentile ranks of 50 on the intial test and 60 on the final test. Student *B* obtains corresponding percentile ranks of 89 and 99. Observe that both *A* and *B* improved ten percentile points, relative to their classmates. Did they improve equally in algebra competence?

To answer this question, let us consider the frequency distributions of raw scores, from which the percentile ranks were derived. If the test had enough "bottom" and "top" in both situations, each distribution probably would be unimodal and fairly symmetric. In order for student *A* to move from a percentile rank of 50 to a percentile rank of 60, he would have to surpass an additional 10 per cent of his classmates. This additional 10 per cent is represented as an area under the frequency distribution shown in Fig. 6-2. Since the frequency distribution is highest in the center,

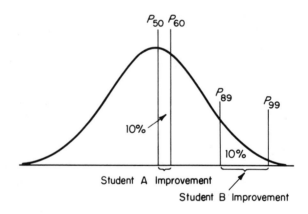

Figure 6-2. Comparison of 10-Percentile-Point Differences in the Middle and Tail of a Frequency Distribution

he does not have to improve a great deal in terms of raw score in order to surpass 10 per cent of his classmates; however, the frequency distribution is much lower in either tail (few students obtain extremely high or extremely low scores). Consequently, student *B* has to improve far more in terms of raw scores in order to surpass an additional 10 per cent of his classmates. The point of this example is that a difference between percentile ranks in the middle of the distribution means less than a similar difference in percentile ranks at either extreme. It is very important to keep this in mind when using percentile ranks to compare two or more individuals on the same variable or to compare a single individual's performance on one variable (e.g., an English test) with his performance on another (e.g., a math test).

The foregoing point has another implication. It is usually difficult to interpret the results of any arithmetic operations involving percentile ranks. For instance, the arithmetic mean of several percentile ranks is obtained by adding the ranks and dividing by the number. The mean of the percentile ranks would rarely be the same as the percentile rank for the mean of the raw scores from which they were derived.

The Shape of a Frequency Distribution of Percentile Ranks

It has been shown that differences in percentile ranks near the center of a distribution mean less than differences at either extreme. This can also be illustrated by comparing a frequency distribution of percentile ranks with the frequency distribution of raw scores from which they were derived. Suppose every individual who took the algebra test mentioned earlier had his score converted to a percentile rank. Ten per cent of the individuals would have percentile ranks less than 10, 10 per cent would have percentile ranks between 10 and 20, 10 per cent would fall between 20 and 30, and so forth. Thus, *regardless of the shape of the frequency distribution of raw scores, the frequency distribution of percentile ranks would have a flat or rectangular shape, as in Fig. 6-3*. Each bar of the histogram of percentile ranks contains 10 per cent of the total area, and each division under the distribution of raw scores contains 10 per cent of the total area. It can be seen that transforming scores to percentile ranks tends to "squeeze" together the individuals at the extremes and to spread out the individuals near the center.

STANDARD SCORES

Standard scores comprise another commonly used type of derived score. A standard score, denoted by z, is obtained by the formula:

$$z = \frac{X - \overline{X}}{S} = \frac{x}{S} \qquad (6\text{-}2)$$

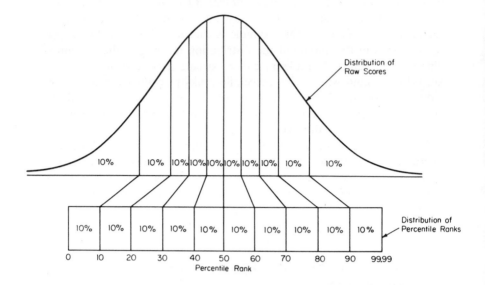

Figure 6-3. Comparison of a Distribution of Percentile Ranks with the Distribution of Raw Scores

As was pointed out in Chap. 5, a standard score indicates how far a given raw score departs from the mean, in terms of standard-deviation units. If the raw score is above the mean, z will be positive; if the raw score is below the mean, z will be negative.

Before examining further the nature of standard scores, we shall review what effects adding, subtracting, multiplying, and dividing by a constant have on the mean and standard deviation of a frequency distribution. (These effects were discussed earlier in Chaps. 3 and 4.)

1) If a constant amount is added to every original score, the mean and standard deviation of the new distribution of derived scores are obtained as follows:

$$\overline{X}_{new} = \overline{X}_{original} + \text{constant}; \qquad S_{new} = S_{original}$$

2) If a constant is subtracted from every original score:

$$\overline{X}_{new} = \overline{X}_{original} - \text{constant}; \qquad S_{new} = S_{original}$$

3) If every original score is multiplied by a constant:

$$\overline{X}_{new} = (\text{constant})(\overline{X}_{original}); \qquad S_{new} = (\text{constant})(S_{original})$$

4) If every original score is divided by a constant:

$$\overline{X}_{new} = \frac{X_{original}}{\text{constant}}; \qquad S_{new} = \frac{S_{original}}{\text{constant}}$$

On the basis of these rules, what would be the mean and standard deviation of a distribution of z-scores? For example, if every raw score in a distribution with a mean of 76 and a standard deviation of 8 were converted to a z-score, what would be the values of the mean and standard deviation of the resulting distribution of z-scores? Let us consider the effects of the two computational steps involved in the conversion.

a) First the deviation scores (x) would be determined by subtracting the constant 76 from every original score ($x = X - \overline{X} = X - 76$). Using Rule 2 above, the mean of the x-scores would be 0 (i.e., $\overline{X}_{new} = 76 - 76 = 0$), and the standard deviation would be unchanged (8).

b) The z-scores then would be determined by dividing each x-score by the constant 8, (i.e., $z = x/S = x/8$). Using Rule 4, the mean of the z-scores would be 0 (i.e., $\overline{X}_{new} = 0/8 = 0$), and the standard deviation would be 1 (i.e., $S_{new} = 8/8 = 1$).

If any other original mean and standard deviation had been used, the results would be the same. That is, *the mean and standard deviation of any distribution of z-scores in which $z = (X - \overline{X})/S$ are 0 and 1 respectively.*

Standard scores do not have the major limitation of percentile ranks in that a difference between standard scores, in any distribution, has the same meaning (in terms of raw scores) regardless of whether the difference is in the center of the distribution or in either tail. This is illustrated in Fig. 6-4, which represents a distribution of scores in which $\overline{X} = 76$

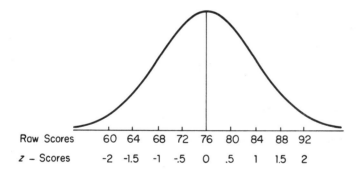

Figure 6-4. A Distribution of Scores Showing Raw-Score Points and Corresponding z-Score points ($\overline{X} = 76$, $S = 8$)

and $S = 8$. A difference of .5 standard-score points is equivalent to a difference of 4 raw-score points throughout the entire range of scores.

Standard scores are extremely useful in comparing performance on two different tests or scales, when the distributions are fairly similar. Consider, for instance, our earlier reference to John Jones, who obtained a higher score in math (65) than he did in English (32). We could not say that his performance in math was better than his performance in English, because the means and standard deviations of the two distributions were different. If, however, both distributions were converted to standard scores, his performances on the two tests could be compared, because the mean and standard deviation of each distribution of derived scores would be equal to 0 and 1 respectively. These two distributions, if of the same shape, could be superimposed on each other, as in Fig. 6-5; and John

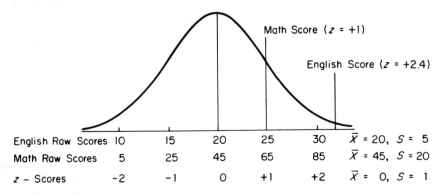

English Raw Scores	10	15	20	25	30	$\bar{X}$ = 20, S = 5
Math Raw Scores	5	25	45	65	85	$\bar{X}$ = 45, S = 20
z – Scores	-2	-1	0	+1	+2	$\bar{X}$ = 0, S = 1

Figure 6-5. Comparison, in Terms of z-Scores, of Performances on Two Different Tests with Similar Distributions

Jones's performances could be compared in terms of his standard scores on the two tests.

$$\text{Math:} \qquad z = \frac{65 - 45}{20} = +1.00$$

$$\text{English:} \qquad z = \frac{32 - 20}{5} = +2.40$$

This comparison of z-scores indicates that his performance was relatively better in English than in math.

Z-scores (Transformed Standard Scores)

There are at least two objections to using z-scores as derived scores. First, since the mean of a distribution of z-scores is equal to 0, many of the scores are negative. This can be bothersome if further computations involving the derived scores are to be performed. Second, z-scores have to be carried to at least 1 decimal place to provide any discrimination. Since the standard deviation of a distribution of z-scores is 1, the effective range is usually 6 or less (-3 to $+3$). Consequently, if whole numbers were used, only 6 or 7 values would be possible.

In order to eliminate negative numbers and fractions, z-scores themselves are often transformed to derived scores with a larger mean and standard deviation. The conversion procedure is very simple. Suppose, for instance, that we wish to convert a distribution of z-scores to a new distribution of derived scores with a mean of 50 and a standard deviation of 10. The two basic steps are merely applications of Rules 3 and 1 on page 94.

a) First, multiply each z-score by the new standard deviation, 10. The mean and standard deviation of the resulting distribution of scores would be 0 and 10 respectively [$\overline{X}_{new} = 10\,(0) = 0$, $S_{new} = 10\,(1) = 10$].

b) Then add 50 to each score obtained in step a to obtain the distribution of derived scores with a mean of 50 and a standard deviation of 10 (i.e., $\overline{X}_{new} = 0 + 50 = 50$, $S_{new} = S_{original} = 10$).

Scores obtained from z-scores in this way are often denoted by Z.

The most commonly used values for the mean and standard deviation of a distribution of Z-scores are 50 and 10 respectively; however, the same procedure could be used to convert a distribution of z-scores to a distribution of Z-scores with any desired mean and standard deviation. A general formula describing the conversion procedure follows.

$$Z = \overline{X}_Z + S_Z\,(z) \qquad\qquad (6\text{-}3)$$

where $\overline{X}_Z$ is the desired mean of the Z-scores and S_Z is the desired standard deviation of the Z-scores

For example, John Jones obtained z-scores of $+2.4$ and $+1.0$ in English and math respectively. If the z-scores from both tests were converted to Z-scores with a mean of 150 and a standard deviation of 25, John's Z-scores would be obtained as follows.

$$Z_{English} = 150 + 25\,(2.4) = 150 + 60 = 210$$
$$Z_{math} = 150 + 25\,(1.0) = 150 + 25 = 175$$

If many raw scores are to be converted to Z-scores, it is not necessary to go through the intermediate step of computing z-scores. The Z-scores can be computed directly from the raw scores using the following formula.

$$Z = \left(\frac{S_Z}{S_{raw\ scores}}\right) X + \overline{X}_Z - \frac{S_Z \cdot \overline{X}_{raw\ scores}}{S_{raw\ scores}} \qquad\qquad (6\text{-}4)$$

The mean and standard deviation of the English test taken by John Jones were 20 and 5 respectively. Using the above formula, a computation formula can be developed for converting raw scores on the English test directly to Z-scores with a mean of 150 and a standard deviation of 25.

$$Z = \left(\frac{25}{5}\right) X + 150 - \frac{25 \cdot 20}{5} = 5X + 50$$

John Jones's raw score of 32 could be converted directly to a Z-score.

$$Z = 5\,(32) + 50 = 160 + 50 = 210$$

The Shape of a Frequency Distribution
of Standard Scores

It has been pointed out that a difference between standard scores has the same meaning (in terms of raw scores), whether the difference is in

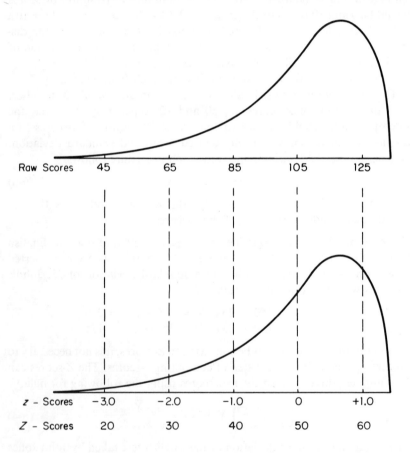

Figure 6-6. Comparison of the Shapes of a Distribution of Raw Scores ($\overline{X} = 105$, $S = 20$) and the Distributions of Standard Scores

the center of the distribution or in either tail. For the distribution represented in Fig. 6-4, a difference of .5 standard-score points is equal to a
difference of 4 raw-score points no matter where that difference is taken.
Because of this, transforming a distribution of raw scores to a distribution of standard scores (z) or transformed standard scores (Z) does not
change the shape of the distribution. That is, a distribution of standard
scores will always have the same shape as the distribution of raw scores
from which it is derived. This is demonstrated in Fig. 6-6, in which each
score for a negatively skewed distribution of raw scores ($\overline{X} = 105$, $S = 20$)
has been transformed into a z-score ($\overline{X} = 0$, $S = 1$) and then into a Z-score
($\overline{X} = 50$, $S = 10$). It can be seen that each of the indicated raw scores is
represented with exactly the same relative position and distance in both
the z-score and Z-score distributions. The shape of the distribution is
unchanged.

Limitations of Standard Scores

The fact that a distribution of standard scores has exactly the same
shape as the distribution of raw scores from which it was derived raises
problems of interpretation in many situations. We have seen that raw
scores from two different tests are ordinarily not comparable, because
the two distributions of raw scores will usually have different means and
standard deviations. If both distributions of raw scores are converted
to standard scores with the same mean and standard deviation, the resulting distributions of standard scores, under some conditions, may be
superimposed on each other, and performance on one test can be compared directly with performance on the other; however, in order to super-
impose one distribution on another and have it fit, *both distributions must
have the same shape* as well as the same mean and standard deviation.

If the distributions of raw scores on the two tests have different shapes,
the distributions of standard scores will also have different shapes. When
superimposed on each other, they will not fit; consequently a standard
score from one of the tests will not be comparable to a standard score
from the other. This situation is illustrated in Fig. 6-7. The scores from a
difficult math test (positively skewed distribution of raw scores) and an
easy English test (negatively skewed distribution of raw scores) have been
converted to standard scores with a mean of 50 and a standard deviation
of 10. Even though their means and standard deviations are identical,
the two distributions of standard scores are skewed in opposite directions.

The conclusion is that standard scores from two different distributions
are comparable only if the distributions have the same shape. Unless
two raw-score distributions are both approximately normal, they rarely

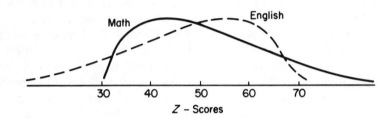

Figure 6-7. Illustrating Non-comparability of Z-Scores Derived from Dissimilar Distributions

have the same shape. Consequently, standard scores are usually not used as derived scores unless the raw-score distribution is approximately normal.

NORMALIZED STANDARD SCORES

The partial limitations of both percentile ranks and standard scores have led to the development of "normalized" scores. Meaningful comparisons can be made between normalized scores based on raw-score distributions of various shapes; and yet, unlike percentile ranks, normalized scores do not distort the importance of differences in the middle of the distribution relative to those in either tail.

Normalized scores are derived scores which have been "forced" into a normal distribution. A raw-score distribution of practically any shape can be transformed to a normal distribution of derived scores with any desired mean and standard deviation. Essentially three steps are involved in the process.

1) The raw scores are converted to percentile ranks.

2) Using the normal-curve table, the percentile ranks are converted to normalized scores with a mean of 0 and a standard deviation of 1 (i.e., normalized z-scores).

3) The distribution of normalized scores obtained in Step 2 can be converted to a normal distribution with any desired mean and standard deviation.

Any of the procedures described in the section on percentile ranks might be used for Step 1. Step 2 is the key step, for it involves the basic logic behind the normalizing procedure. Once the percentile ranks are obtained, the question is asked: If these percentile ranks were based on a normal distribution, what would be the corresponding z-score for each? Appx. 2 is utilized here. For instance, suppose Bill Williams obtains a percentile rank of 38 on an arithmetic test. Using Appx. 2, it could be determined that 38 per cent of the cases in a normal distribution fall below a z of $-.31$. Therefore, Bill's z-score (assuming a normal distribution) would be $-.31$. The distribution of z-scores obtained in this way would be normal and would have a mean of 0 and a standard deviation of 1.

The procedure for the third step, converting z-scores to Z-scores, has already been covered. It would involve the following variation of formula 6.3.

$$Z_{normal} = \overline{X}_Z + S_Z (z_{normal}) \qquad (6\text{-}5)$$

where $\overline{X}_Z$ is the desired mean and S_Z is the desired standard deviation

The common practice in educational measurement is to express normalized Z-scores in terms of an $\overline{X}$ of 50 and an S of 10. It is also a common practice to symbolize this type of Z-score as T. That is:

$$T = 50 + 10 (z_{normal}) \qquad (6\text{-}6)$$

Bill Williams' T-score, with a mean of 50 and standard deviation 10, can be obtained by using the above formula.

$$T = 50 + 10 (-.31) = 50 - 3.1 = 46.9$$

Tables for Deriving T-Scores

The direct computation of T-scores, although simple and straightforward, is rather burdensome and time-consuming. It is more convenient to use a special conversion table to convert percentile ranks directly to T-scores. Several such tables are available and may be found in most reference books on measurement and statistics. An example is given in Table 6-3, showing the appropriate T-score (and normal z-score) for each percentile rank. This particular conversion table does not give T-score values above 80 or below 20. The omission is of no great moment, however, since the indicated range covers almost all possible cases—from $P_{0.1}$ to $P_{99.9}$.

Stanines

One type of normalized standard score which has become popular in recent years is the stanine. The nature of the stanine scale can best be illustrated with reference to the normal curve of Fig. 6-8. Although, theoretically, a normal curve has an infinite range (i.e., it never reaches the horizontal axis), a range of 4.5 standard deviations ($\overline{X} \pm 2.25S$) will include all but 2.44 per cent of the cases. If we now divide this "effective" range of 4.5 standard deviations into nine equal intervals, each interval

Table 6-3

Conversion Table for z-Scores, T-Scores and Percentile Ranks, Assuming a Normal Distribution of Scores

Percentile Ranks	z-Scores	T-Scores	Percentile Ranks	z-Scores	T-Scores
99.9	3.0	80	50	0.0	50
99.8	2.9	79	46	−0.1	49
99.7	2.8	78	42	−0.2	48
99.6	2.7	77	38	−0.3	47
99.5	2.6	76	34	−0.4	46
99.4	2.5	75	31	−0.5	45
99.2	2.4	74	27	−0.6	44
99	2.3	73	24	−0.7	43
99	2.2	72	21	−0.8	42
98	2.1	71	18	−0.9	41
98	2.0	70	16	−1.0	40
97	1.9	69	14	−1.1	39
96	1.8	68	12	−1.2	38
96	1.7	67	10	−1.3	37
95	1.6	66	8	−1.4	36
93	1.5	65	7	−1.5	35
92	1.4	64	5	−1.6	34
90	1.3	63	4	−1.7	33
88	1.2	62	4	−1.8	32
86	1.1	61	3	−1.9	31
84	1.0	60	2	−2.0	30
82	0.9	59	2	−2.1	29
79	0.8	58	1	−2.2	28
76	0.7	57	1	−2.3	27
73	0.6	56	0.8	−2.4	26
69	0.5	55	0.6	−2.5	25
66	0.4	54	0.5	−2.6	24
62	0.3	53	0.4	−2.7	23
58	0.2	52	0.3	−2.8	22
54	0.1	51	0.2	−2.9	21
50	0.0	50	0.1	−3.0	20

will be half a standard deviation wide ($4.5S/9 = .5S$). The middle interval will run from a z of $-.25$ to a z of $+.25$, and the limits of each successive interval above and below the middle will be $.5S$ apart with two exceptions. In order to include all the cases, we will ignore the upper limit of the highest interval ($z = +2.25$) and extend that interval to include all cases above a z of $+1.75$; similarly, the lowest interval will be extended to include all cases below a z of -1.75. The nine intervals as described make up the *stanine* (*sta*ndard *nine*-point) scale with the lowest interval being stanine 1 and the highest interval being stanine 9. The percentile ranks for the limits of each stanine can easily be determined from Appx. 2, and then the proportion of cases falling within the stanine can be determined by subtraction.

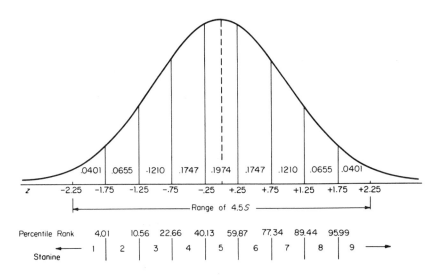

Figure 6-8. An Illustration of the Stanine Scale

Converting a distribution of raw scores to stanines is a very simple process. First, each raw score is transformed to a percentile rank using any of the methods discussed. Then each of the resulting percentile ranks is transformed to a stanine using the stanine limits of Fig. 6-8. For instance, if John Jones obtains a percentile rank of 72, his score on the stanine scale is 6. The resulting distribution of stanine scores will be approximately normal with a mean of 5 and a standard deviation of 1.96. The main advantage of stanines over other normalized scores, such as the T-scores discussed in the previous section, is that they will fit in a single column of a punched card. The main disadvantage concerns the lack of discrimination at the extremes. Because there is no upper limit to stanine 9, individuals obtaining a stanine score of 9 may differ widely from one another with regard to the variable being measured. A similar problem exists with stanine 1; however, for most practical purposes, the scale discriminates adequately among those individuals who fall between stanines 1 and 9.

IMPORTANCE OF THE NORM, OR REFERENCE, GROUP

All the derived scores discussed in this chapter are based on a reference (or norm) group and can be interpreted only with reference to that norm group. It is essential, therefore, that the norm group used be an appropriate one and that it be described in sufficient detail. For instance, it is not sufficient to say that a college student's T-score on a particular test is 60. If the scores were based on a group of students attending a highly selective school, a score of 60 would have a meaning different from the same T-score based on a group of students from all colleges or less selective colleges. This caution is also important when comparing scores from one test with scores from another. It should be obvious that if the derived scores used in the comparison are not based on the same or equivalent norm groups comparison is difficult or impossible.

Exercises and Problems

1. The scores on a test are normally distributed with a mean of 60 and a standard deviation of 8. Determine the percentile ranks for the following raw scores: (a) 52, (b) 78, (c) 64, (d) 40.

2. For the test of Prob. 1, determine the following percentiles: (a) 20, (b) 38, (c) 60, (d) 95.

3. Construct an ogive for the frequency distribution of test scores presented below. Use an $8\frac{1}{2}$ in. by 11 in. sheet of graph paper, and construct the ogive carefully. The ogive will be used to obtain answers in succeeding problems.

score	f		
57–59	12		
54–56	25		
51–53	28		
48–50	33		
45–47	18	$\overline{X} = 45.0$
42–44	20	$S = 9.0$
39–41	18	Mdn $= 47.2$
36–38	10	$Q = 6.47$
33–35	14		
30–32	6		
27–29	6		
24–26	10		
	200		

4. Use the ogive of Prob. 3 to determine (a) the first decile, (b) Q_2, (c) P_{60}, (d) P_{70}, (e) P_4, (f) P_{28}.

5. For the frequency distribution of Prob. 3 determine by interpolation (a) the first decile, (b) Q_2, (c) P_{60}, (d) P_{70}, (e) P_4, (f) P_{28}.

6. Use the ogive of Prob. 3 to determine the percentile rank for a score of
   (a) 27, (b) 30, (c) 48, (d) 25, (e) 37, (f) 50.
7. For the frequency distribution of Prob. 3, determine by interpolation the
   percentile rank for a score of (a) 27, (b) 30, (c) 48, (d) 25, (e) 37, (f) 50.
8. Use the ogive of Prob. 3 to verify the value of Q which is given.
9. If each of the following operations were performed on all of the scores
   of the distribution of Prob. 3, what would be the resulting values of $\overline{X}$, S,
   Mdn, and Q?

   a) Add 20 points.   d) Divide by 9.
   b) Subtract 45 points.   e) Divide by 2; then add 10.
   c) Multiply by 5.   f) Subtract 45; then divide by 9.

10. Transform each of the following raw scores from the distribution of
    Prob. 3 to standard (z) scores: (a) 27, (b) 30, (c) 48, (d) 25, (e) 37, (f) 50.
11. Determine, for the distribution of scores in Prob. 3, the raw score cor-
    responding to a z-score of (a) $+.3$, (b) -1.6, (c) -2.0, (d) $+.5$, (e) $+1.5$,
    (f) $+1.9$.
12. Transform each of the following raw scores from the distribution of Prob. 3
    to standard (Z) scores with a mean of 50 and a standard deviation of 10:
    (a) 27, (b) 30, (c) 48, (d) 25, (e) 37, (f) 50.
13. Determine, for the distribution of scores in Prob. 3, the raw score cor-
    responding to a Z-score (mean = 50; standard deviation = 10) of (a) 53,
    (b) 34, (c) 30, (d) 55, (e) 65, (f) 69.
14. Transform each of the following raw scores from the distribution of Prob. 3
    to Z-scores with a mean of 100 and a standard deviation of 15: (a) 27,
    (b) 30, (c) 48, (d) 25, (e) 37, (f) 50.
15. Use the ogive of Prob. 3 and appropriate tables to transform each of the
    following raw scores to normalized standard (T) scores with a mean of 50
    and a standard deviation of 10: (a) 27, (b) 30, (c) 48, (d) 25, (e) 37, (f) 50.
16. Use the ogive of Prob. 3 and appropriate tables to transform each of the
    following raw scores to normalized standard scores with a mean of 100
    and a standard deviation of 15: (a) 27, (b) 30, (c) 48, (d) 25, (e) 37, (f) 50.
17. Use the ogive of Prob. 3 and appropriate tables to determine the raw score
    corresponding to a T-score (mean = 50; standard deviation = 10) of (a)
    40, (b) 65, (c) 55, (d) 38.
18. Use the ogive of Prob. 3 and appropriate tables to determine the raw score
    corresponding to a normalized standard score (mean = 100; standard
    deviation = 15) of (a) 85, (b) 110, (c) 95, (d) 135.
19. Use the ogive of Prob. 3 and appropriate tables or figures to transform
    each of the following raw scores to stanines: (a) 27, (b) 30, (c) 48, (d) 25,
    (e) 37, (f) 50.
20. Use the ogive of Prob. 3 and appropriate tables or figures to find the raw-
    score limits for the following stanines: (a) 1, (b) 3, (c) 5, (d) 7.
21. John and Bill obtain percentile ranks of 89 and 45, respectively, on a
    nationally standardized arithmetic-achievement test. After a month of in-

tensive tutoring, they are given the same test. This time they receive percentile ranks of 99 and 55, respectively. Have they made equal gains in terms of arithmetic skill? Explain.

22. The first midterm in elementary psychology proves to be quite difficult for a large lecture section of 500 students. The second midterm, however, proves to be quite easy. Which would you use to compare a student's performance on the first midterm with his performance on the second, standard scores, percentile ranks, or normalized standard scores? Why?

Chapter 7

Correlation

Thus far, we have largely considered only the analysis of scores on a single variable. That is, we have addressed ourselves to describing and analyzing *a* distribution of scores. Problems in the professions and the behavioral sciences, however, frequently involve the *simultaneous* analysis of scores on two or more variables. The most common instance of such analyses occurs when we are interested in the *relationship* between two variables. Here we ask not only for the characteristics of X- and Y-scores independently, but how X- and Y-scores are related to each other—i.e., how they *co-relate*.

A simple representation of the relationship between two variables is presented in Fig. 7-1. The ten dots in the figure represent the ten pupils whose scores on two tests (X and Y) are listed in Table 7-1. Each pupil

Table 7-1

Scores of Ten Pupils on Two Tests

Pupil	X-Score	Y-Score
A	2	1
B	1	3
C	4	4
D	7	5
E	7	7
F	5	6
G	3	7
H	9	8
I	5	9
J	7	10

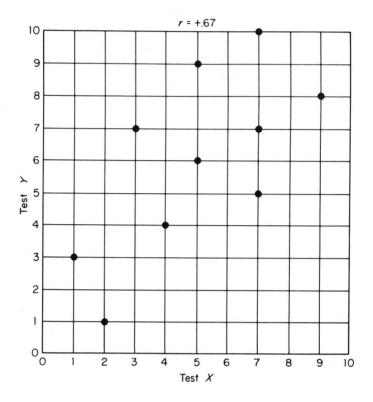

Figure 7-1. A Scattergram Illustrating a Positive Relationship between Two Tests (See Table 7-1.)

has a pair of scores, one for X and one for Y. If any pupil missed either test, he would not be listed. The horizontal axis of the *scattergram* in Fig. 7-1 is used to represent scores on test X and the vertical axis, scores on test Y. For instance, consider pupil D who has a score of 7 on test X and a score of 5 on test Y. He is represented by a dot above 7 on the X axis and opposite 5 on the Y axis. The remaining dots, each representing a pupil, have been similarly placed. When the range of scores on either variable is large and a relatively large number of cases is involved, a scattergram of the sort illustrated in Fig. 7-2 will be appropriate. It depicts the relationship between the number of correct answers on a test of scholastic aptitude and freshman grade-point average for fifty-seven students at a local college. The scores have been grouped into class intervals, and each case has been indicated by a tally. The tallies have been counted and the resulting frequency indicated for each cell.

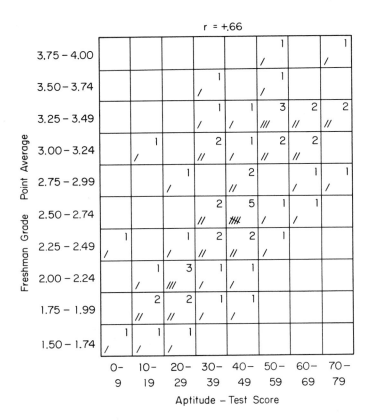

Figure 7-2. Scattergram Illustrating the Relationship between
Scores on a Scholastic-Aptitude Test and Freshman Grade-
Point Averages at a Local College

Inspection of Figs. 7-1 and 7-2 reveals an important fact about the
nature of the relationships represented: although there are specific exceptions such as pupil G in Fig. 7-1, there is a general tendency in both
figures for the pattern of dots or tallies to go from the lower left to the
upper right. Those who score high on one variable tend to score high on
the other. Such a tendency indicates a *positive* relationship between the
variables. If, on the other hand, high scores on one variable tend to be
associated with low scores on the other as in Fig. 7-3, the relationship is
said to be *negative*. In Fig. 7-4, where there is no apparent trend, the
variables may be said to have little or no relationship.

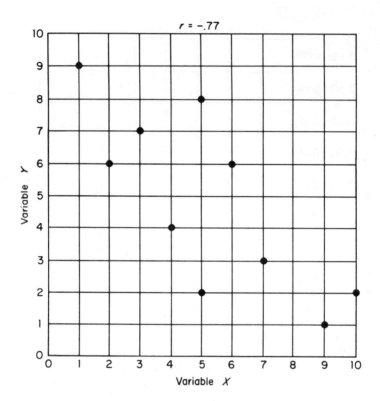

Fig. 7-3. A Scattergram Illustrating a Negative Relationship between Two Variables

THE PEARSON COEFFICIENT
OF CORRELATION

Early in the history of statistical analysis there was considerable interest in finding some simple way of indicating the degree of relation between a pair of variables. Late in the nineteenth century, Karl Pearson popularized the most widely used measure of relationship, the *correlation coefficient*. This index of relationship is almost universally symbolized by the letter *r*, and it is frequently called the *Pearson r*. It is helpful to use subscripts to identify the pair of variables correlated, when more than two variables are being studied. In such an instance, the correlation between tests *X* and *Y* would be written precisely as r_{xy}; however, when we are concerned with only two variables, it will be sufficient to use the letter *r* without subscripts.

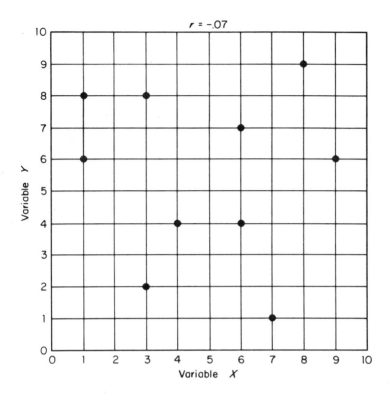

Figure 7-4. A Scattergram Illustrating the Virtual Absence of a Relationship between Two Variables

Basic Characteristics of r

The value of r ranges from -1.00 to $.00$ to $+1.00$, with -1.00 and $+1.00$ indicating perfect relationships between the two variables and $.00$ indicating no relationship. The numerical *value* of r indicates the *degree* of relationship, and the *sign* of r indicates the *kind* of relationship. If there is a tendency for high values of X to be associated with high values of Y, the sign of r is positive; if there is a tendency for high values of X to be associated with low values of Y, the sign of r is negative. The larger the value of r, whether negative or positive, the greater the degree of relationship between X and Y. That is, coefficients of $+.90$ and $-.90$ represent the same degree of relationship but in opposite directions; they represent a greater degree of relationship than coefficients of $+.80$ or $-.80$.

The "meaning" of r as a numerical index of the degree of relationship may be better understood by examining the sample scattergrams in Figs.

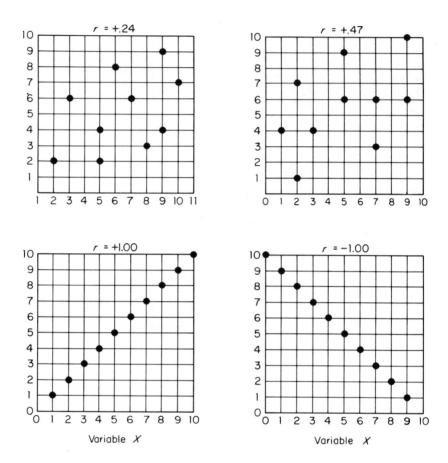

Figure 7-5. Scattergrams Illustrating Varying Degrees of Correlation between Variables

7-1 through 7-5. The dots or tallies represent the joint position of various individuals on two different scales. The value of r is given for each case. Note that perfect correlations (i.e., -1.00 or $+1.00$) indicate that all the dots fall along a straight line. Although the use of X and Y to label, respectively, the horizontal and vertical scales is traditional, it is usually best to identify both variables by name, as in Fig. 7-2.

Definition of r

The Pearson coefficient of correlation may be defined as:

$$r_{xy} = \frac{\sum xy}{NS_x \, S_y} \qquad (7\text{-}1)$$

where r_{xy} is the Pearson coefficient of correlation between X and Y, N is the number of pairs of values of X and Y, S_x and S_y are the two standard deviations; $x = X - \overline{X}$, and $y = Y - \overline{Y}$

Formula (7-1) contains the deviation scores, x and y, in the numerator and S_x and S_y in the denominator. In Chap. 6 it was pointed out that the standard score for any given value of X may be defined as $z_x = x/S_x$. Similarly, $z_y = y/S_y$. If these expressions are substituted into Form. (7-1), an alternate formula for r is the result.

$$r_{xy} = \frac{\sum z_x z_y}{N} \tag{7-2}$$

Formulas (7-1) and (7-2) introduce the new terms $\sum xy$ and $\sum z_x z_y$. An expression of the form $\sum xy$ or $\sum z_x z_y$ is called a "sum of cross-products." That is, each x or z_x value is multiplied by the y or z_y value for the same individual, and the resulting products are summed. The use of the two formulas will be illustrated with the scores of the ten students of Table 7-1. The scores are presented again in Table 7-2 along with part of the necessary computations. It should perhaps be pointed out that the values in Cols. 6 and 7 of Table 7-2 were obtained by dividing the values

Table 7-2

Computation of the Values Used in Forms.
(7-1) and (7-2) for Obtaining r
(Test Scores from Table 7-1)

Pupil	Test Scores X	Y	1 x	2 y	3 xy	4 x^2	5 y^2	6 z_x	7 z_y	8 $z_x z_y$
A	2	1	-3	-5	15	9	25	-1.24	-1.89	2.34
B	1	3	-4	-3	12	16	9	-1.66	-1.13	1.88
C	4	4	-1	-2	2	1	4	-.41	-.75	.31
D	7	5	2	-1	-2	4	1	.83	-.38	-.32
E	7	7	2	1	2	4	1	.83	.38	.32
F	5	6	0	0	0	0	0	0	0	0
G	3	7	-2	1	-2	4	1	-.83	.38	-.32
H	9	8	4	2	8	16	4	1.66	.75	1.25
I	5	9	0	3	0	0	9	0	1.13	0
J	7	10	2	4	8	4	16	.83	1.51	1.25
	50	60	0	0	43	58	70	0.00	0.00	6.71
	$\sum X$ $\overline{X} = 5$	$\sum Y$ $\overline{Y} = 6$			$\sum xy$	$\sum x^2$	$\sum y^2$			$\sum z_x z_y$

$$S_x = \sqrt{\frac{\sum x^2}{N}} = \sqrt{\frac{58}{10}} = 2.41, \qquad S_y = \sqrt{\frac{\sum y^2}{N}} = \sqrt{\frac{70}{10}} = 2.65$$

in Cols. 1 and 2 by the values of S_x and S_y respectively. The correlation can now be determined using either Form. (7-1) or (7-2) with the appropriate values from the table.

$$r = \frac{\sum xy}{NS_x \, S_y} = \frac{43}{(10)\,(2.41)\,(2.65)} = +.67$$

$$\text{or} \quad r = \frac{\sum z_x z_y}{N} = \frac{6.71}{10} = +.67$$

Additional understanding of Forms. (7-1) and (7-2) can be gained by examining the two cross-product columns (3 and 8) of Table 7-2. Consider individuals E, H, and J, who are high (above the mean) on both variables. Their deviation scores (x and y) and standard scores (z_x and z_y) for both variables are positive; consequently their cross-products (xy and $z_x z_y$) are positive. Now consider individuals A, B, and C who are low (below the mean) on both variables. Their deviation scores and standard scores are negative, but their cross-products are still positive (the product of two negative quantities will always be positive). It is only when an individual, such as individual G, is low on one variable and high on the other that his two deviation scores will be of different signs and his cross-product, either xy or $z_x z_y$, will be negative. Consequently, when the relationship is positive (as is the case for the two variables of Table 7-2) the positive cross-products will predominate, and the cross-product sums will be positive. Thus, the correlation coefficient obtained from either Form. (7-1) or Form. (7-2) will be positive.

On the other hand, when the relationship is negative as in Fig. 7-3, individuals who are high on one variable tend to be low on the other. Thus, the negative cross-product terms will predominate, the cross-product sums will be negative, and the correlation will be negative. If there is little or no trend, as in Fig. 7-4, the positive cross-products will tend to balance the negative cross-products, the cross-product sums will be close to zero, and the correlation coefficient obtained using either Form. (7-1) or Form. (7-2) will be close to zero.

Fortunately, in practice, the computation of r does not require explicit computation of each individual's deviation score or standard score as is necessary if Form. (7-1) or Form. (7-2) is used. Several practical methods for computing r from either ungrouped or grouped data will be discussed in the following two sections.

Computation of r: Raw-Score Methods

Formula (7-1) may be simplified as follows.

$$r = \frac{\sum xy}{NS_x \, S_y} = \frac{\sum xy}{N \sqrt{\dfrac{\sum x^2}{N}} \sqrt{\dfrac{\sum y^2}{N}}}$$

$$r = \frac{\sum xy}{\sqrt{\sum x^2} \, \sqrt{\sum y^2}} \qquad (7\text{-}3)$$

Then each of the sums necessary for Form. (7-3) may be computed using a raw-score formula. Raw-score formulas for obtaining $\sum x^2$ and $\sum y^2$ were first presented in Chap. 4. They are presented below along with a raw-score formula for obtaining $\sum xy$.

$$\sum x^2 = \frac{N \sum X^2 - (\sum X)^2}{N} \tag{4-4}$$

$$\sum y^2 = \frac{N \sum Y^2 - (\sum Y)^2}{N}$$

$$\sum xy = \frac{N \sum XY - (\sum X)(\sum Y)}{N} \tag{7-4}$$

Note that it is especially important to distinguish between upper-case X and Y, which denote raw scores, and lower-case x and y, which denote deviation scores.

The set of scores found in Tables (7-1) and (7-2) is presented once again in Table 7-3 along with the computations required for obtaining the necessary sums based on raw scores. These sums can then be substi-

Table 7-3

Computation of the Raw-Score Sums Necessary for Obtaining r
(Test Scores from Table 7-1)

	Test Scores		1	2	3
Pupil	X	Y	XY	X^2	Y^2
A	2	1	2	4	1
B	1	3	3	1	9
C	4	4	16	16	16
D	7	5	35	49	25
E	7	7	49	49	49
F	5	6	30	25	36
G	3	7	21	9	49
H	9	8	72	81	64
I	5	9	45	25	81
J	7	10	70	49	100
	50	60	343	308	430
	$\sum X$	$\sum Y$	$\sum XY$	$\sum X^2$	$\sum Y^2$

tuted in Forms. (4-4) and (7-4), and the correlation coefficient can be computed using Form. (7-3).

$$\sum x^2 = \frac{10\,(308) - (50)^2}{10} = \frac{3080 - 2500}{10} = 58$$

$$\sum y^2 = \frac{10\,(430) - (60)^2}{10} = \frac{4300 - 3600}{10} = 70$$

$$\sum xy = \frac{10\,(343) - (50)\,(60)}{10} = \frac{3430 - 3000}{10} = 43$$

$$r = \frac{\sum xy}{\sqrt{\sum x^2}\sqrt{\sum y^2}} = \frac{43}{\sqrt{58}\sqrt{70}} = \frac{43}{(7.62)(8.37)} = +.67$$

A further simplification can be accomplished by substituting the raw-score expressions of Forms. (4-4) and (7-4) in Form. (7-3). The following single raw-score formula for r is the result.

$$r = \frac{N\sum XY - (\sum X)(\sum Y)}{\sqrt{[N\sum X^2 - (\sum X)^2][N\sum Y^2 - (\sum Y)^2]}} \qquad (7\text{-}5)$$

The sums from Table 7-3 can be substituted directly into this formula to obtain r.

$$r = \frac{10(343) - (50)(60)}{\sqrt{[10(308) - (50)^2][10(430) - (60)^2]}} = +.67$$

Formula (7-5) may, at first glance, appear more forbidding than Form. (7-1) and (7-2); however, as was pointed out in Chap. 4, computations involving the direct use of deviation scores or standard scores are particularly cumbersome when N is large or when the means and standard deviations have fractional remainders (the usual case). Thus, the use of raw-score formulas such as Form. (7-5) will usually minimize both computational labor and "rounding" errors. Furthermore, the sums required, $\sum X$, $\sum Y$, $\sum X^2$, $\sum Y^2$ and $\sum XY$, can be obtained easily and directly if an electric desk calculator is available.

Computation of r: Coded-Scattergram Method

The raw-score methods presented in the previous section are particularly appropriate for use with an electric desk calculator if the sample size is less than 75 or 100, or with an electronic computer, if one is available. However, when the computations must be performed manually, or when an electric desk calculator is available but the sample is extremely large, a further short cut is sometimes helpful.

In order to understand the method to be presented, the reader should be familiar with the following property of r: *The value of a correlation coefficient is not affected by adding a constant to or subtracting a constant from the scores on either or both variables. Neither is it affected by multiplying or dividing the scores by a constant.* This principle can be rationalized by referring to a basic characteristic of standard (z) scores. Performing any of the above operations on a distribution of scores does not change the shape of the distribution; the individuals in the distribution will remain relatively the same distance apart. Thus, each individual will have exactly the same standard score (z) afterward as he had before, although both the mean and the standard deviation of the distribution may have been altered by the operations. The reader should review the sections on standard scores in Chap. 6 if this point is not clear. Once it is clear, he need only examine Form. (7-2), the standard-score formula for r, to see that the value of r will not be affected, because the standard scores themselves will not be affected.

This property provides the basis for a method of computing r similar to the coded methods presented in Chaps. 3 and 4 for computing means and standard deviations. Essentially, the method involves grouping the scores into class intervals on both variables, assigning the intervals coded values, and computing the correlation from the coded values using the following variation of Form. (7-5).

$$r = \frac{N \sum fd_x\, d_y - (\sum fd_x)(\sum fd_y)}{\sqrt{[N \sum fd_x^2 - (\sum fd_x)^2][N \sum fd_y^2 - (\sum fd_y)^2]}} \qquad (7\text{-}6)$$

where d_x and d_y are coded scores on variables X and Y, respectively

The coded sums required by this formula can be determined directly from a scattergram as is illustrated in Table 7-4. The necessary computations can be divided into the following steps.

1) Assign the coded values (d_x or d_y) to the class intervals on each variable, starting with 0 for the lowest interval and increasing by 1 for each successive interval.

2) Determine the frequency, f_y, for each interval on the Y variable, by adding the frequencies in each row. Record these row sums in column f_y at the right of the table. Similarly, determine the frequency, f_x, for each interval on the X variable by adding the frequencies in each column and record in row f_x at the top of the table. $\sum f_x$ and $\sum f_y$ should both equal N.

3) Multiply the f_y column by the d_y column to obtain the values in the fd_y column. Now, multiply the fd_y column by the d_y column to obtain the values in the fd_y^2 column.

4) Similarly, multiply the f_x row by the d_x row to obtain the values in the fd_x row. Multiply the fd_x row by the d_x row to obtain the values in the fd_x^2 row. The reader should recognize the operations in Steps 3 and 4 above as those described earlier in Chap. 4 in the discussion of the coded method for computing S.

5) The process of obtaining the values in the fd_x column is slightly more complex. For each row, multiply the frequencies by the coded values of the columns in which they fall and add the resulting products. For

Table 7-4

Computation of Sums for Determining the r between Scores on a Test of Scholastic Aptitude and Freshman Grade-Point Average (Data from Fig. 7-2)

fd_x^2	0	5	32	90	208	225	216	196	972 Σfd_x^2					
fd_x	0	5	16	30	52	45	36	28	212 Σfd_x					
f_x	2	5	8	10	13	9	6	4	57 N					
d_x	0	1	2	3	4	5	6	7						
Freshman Grade-Point Average									d_y	f_y	fd_y	fd_y^2	fd_x	$fd_x d_y$
3.75–4.00						1		1	10	2	20	200	12	120
3.50–3.74				1		1			9	2	18	162	8	72
3.25–3.49				1	1	3	2	2	8	9	72	576	48	384
3.00–3.24		1		2	1	2	2		7	8	56	392	33	231
2.75–2.99			1		2		1	1	6	5	30	180	23	138
2.50–2.74				2	5	1	1		5	9	45	225	37	185
2.25–2.49	1		1	2	2	1			4	7	28	112	21	84
2.00–2.24		1	3	1	1				3	6	18	54	14	42
1.75–1.99		2	2	1	1				2	6	12	24	13	26
1.50–1.74	1	1	1						1	3	3	3	3	3
Aptitude-Test Score	0 to 9	10 to 19	20 to 29	30 to 39	40 to 49	50 to 59	60 to 69	70 to 79		57 N	302 Σfd_y	1928 Σfd_y^2	212 Σfd_x	1285 $\Sigma fd_x d_y$

instance, consider the row for the grade-point-average interval 3.25 – 3.49. The value of fd_x for that row was obtained as follows.

$$(f\cdot d_x + f\cdot d_x + f\cdot d_x + f\cdot d_x + f\cdot d_x)$$
$$(1\cdot 3) + (1\cdot 4) + (3\cdot 5) + (2\cdot 6) + (2\cdot 7) = 3 + 4 + 15 + 12 + 14 = 48$$

The computations performed in this step can be checked by comparing the sum of the fd_x *column* with the sum of the fd_x *row*. They should be equal.

6) Multiply the fd_x column by the d_y column to obtain the values in the $fd_x\, d_y$ column.

7) Substitute the appropriate sums into Form. (7-6).

$$r = \frac{57\,(1285) - (212)\,(302)}{\sqrt{[57\,(972) - (212)^2]\,[57\,(1928) - (302)^2]}} = +.66$$

The method used to code the grade-point averages is identical to that used earlier in Chaps. 3 and 4. The reader will recall that such a method of coding is equivalent to subtracting a constant (the midpoint of the lowest interval) from each interval midpoint and dividing the result by a constant (the interval size, i). It has already been pointed out that such operations as these will not affect the size of the obtained correlation coefficient. Consequently, the value of r—obtained using the coded scores, d—will be exactly the same as that which would have been obtained had the interval midpoints been used instead; however, it will not be exactly the same as the value of r obtained for the original X- and Y-scores because of the errors produced by grouping (i.e., representing each score by its interval midpoint). Usually, if more than ten intervals are used and N is not too small, the effects of grouping will be negligible. If very few intervals are used, the value of r obtained using the coded method may substantially underestimate the "exact" value.

Several advantages of the scattergram method should be mentioned. First, inspection of the scattergram may reveal several things about the relationship—such as a marked degree of curvilinearity (discussed below) —which could not be determined from the correlation coefficient alone. Also, an inspection of the scattergram can act as a rough check on the computed value of r. Finally, when the sample is extremely large, and a scattergram is to be constructed anyway, the computational labor in-volved in determining r is considerably less than for the other computa-tional methods discussed.

FACTORS AFFECTING THE SIZE OF r

Non-linearity

The basic assumption underlying the use of a Pearson r to describe a relationship between two variables is that of *linearity of regression*. Al-though the meaning of this cannot be fully understood without some knowledge of the concept of regression itself (Chap. 8), an attempt will be made here to describe what will happen if the assumption is not ful-filled by the data. Actually, it is possible to compute a Pearson r even if the relationship to be described is markedly non-linear; the problem we are concerned with here is one of interpretation rather than computation.

The scattergrams presented thus far in this chapter exhibit, in general,

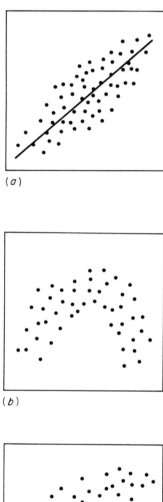

(a)

(b)

(c)

Figure 7-6. Scattergram Sketches Illustrating Linearity and Curvilinearity

"linearity." That is, it is possible to represent the general trend illustrated in each of the scattergrams of Figs. 7-1–7-5 by a *straight line*. This is also true of the scattergram in Fig. 7-6(*a*), where a straight line has been super-imposed on the pattern of dots. But what if the scattergram took the form shown in Fig. 7-6(*b*)? In this case, there seems to be a close relationship between the X variable and the Y variable, but it is not a linear one. There is a marked tendency for Y values to go up as X values increase *until* one arrives at medium values along the X axis, at which point the Y values begin to drop. Thus, the line that best "fits" this scattergram is not straight but curved, and the relationship would be described as *curvilinear*. An example of two variables which might show this general type of relationship would be chronological age (X) and scores on a finger-dexterity test (Y). That is, there is a general tendency for finger dexterity to improve with increasing age *until* muscular coordination begins to deteriorate as in very old persons. The relationship represented in Fig. 7-6(*c*) would also be considered curvilinear, although the departure from linearity is not as great as in Fig. 7-6(*b*).

The use of a Pearson r would be inappropriate for describing the relationship of either Fig. 7-6(*b*) or 7-6(*c*), because the resulting coefficients would be too low. *That is, a Pearson r, when used with data which show a curvilinear trend, will be an underestimate of the actual degree of relationship.* The amount of underestimation may be substantial in cases in which the trend is markedly curvilinear, as in Fig. 7-6(*b*); a Pearson r, computed for that figure, would be close to zero. A discussion of the reason for this must be deferred until the next chapter. In view of these facts concerning curvilinearity, one would be well advised to construct and inspect a scattergram before using a Pearson r if there is any doubt about the nature of the trend to be described. Fortunately, there are other types of correlation coefficients, such as η (the Greek letter *eta*), which are appropriate for use in those instances in which the trend cannot be considered linear. (For a discussion of η, the reader should consult a more advanced text.)

Heterogeneity of the Group Used

One must be very cautious in generalizing about a correlation coefficient obtained from a particular group of individuals. One reason for this concerns the relation between the degree of heterogeneity of the group used and the size of a Pearson r. Consider again the scattergram of Fig. 7-2, showing the relationship between aptitude scores and grade-point averages for a group of high-school students. For the entire group, an r of .66 was obtained (coded method). Suppose, however, that the college had used the aptitude test as a basis for admission and had admitted only those students with aptitude scores of 50 or more. Furthermore, suppose that the teachers at the college used the same standards for grading the selected or restricted group as they would have used had the entire group been granted admission (admittedly an unlikely possibility). The scattergram showing the relationship between aptitude and grade-point average for the restricted group of nineteen students is presented in Fig. 7-7. The reader should note

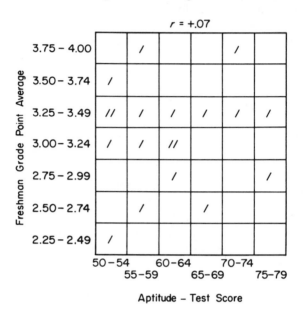

Figure 7-7. Scattergram for the Nineteen Students of Fig. 7-2
Whose Aptitude Scores Are above Fifty
(Smaller Intervals Have Been Used for Aptitude)

that Fig. 7-7 is merely that portion of the scattergram of Fig. 7-2 above the aptitude cut-off score of 50, although it has been drawn to a larger scale for illustrative purposes and smaller class intervals have been used for the aptitude-test scores because of the narrower range of Fig. 7-7. It should be apparent from comparing the two scattergrams that the Pearson r based on the restricted group of Fig. 7-7 would be a good deal less than that for the entire group of Fig. 7-2. In fact, the r for Fig. 7-7 is only + .07 (coded method).

The above example illustrates the principle that *if other factors are held constant, the size of the correlation between two variables will depend on the heterogeneity of the group used (with regard to the variables being studied).*

The more homogeneous the group, the smaller will be the obtained coefficient.
One would expect, therefore, that the correlation between two variables
such as yearly income and measured intelligence would be less for male
college graduates than it would be for adult males in general. Or, one would
expect that correlations between measures of creativity and intelligence
would be a good deal less if based on groups of successful professional
men than if they were based on adult males in general. Both college graduates and professional men would certainly be more homogeneous with
regard to intelligence and income than adult males in general.

Combining Two or More Groups with Different Means

Suppose we wished to determine the correlation between score on a
numerical-aptitude test and grade in a course in elementary statistics
(grades to be assigned according to the following scale: 8 for an *A*, 7 for
an *A*−, 6 for a *B*, 5 for a *B*−, etc.). The total group consists of twenty
students, ten from Dr. Smith's class and ten from Dr. Jones's class. The
range of aptitudes is about the same in each class, and the correlation

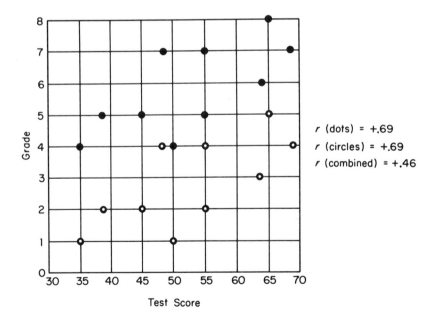

r (dots) = +.69
r (circles) = +.69
r (combined) = +.46

Figure 7-8. Scattergram Illustrating the Relationship between
Numerical-Aptitude Scores and Grades in Elementary Statistics
for Two Classes of Ten Students

between aptitude and grade for each class, considered separately, is equal to .69. Suppose, however, that Dr. Jones is a much more stringent grader; that is, he tends to give lower grades than Dr. Smith for the same level of performance. This hypothetical situation is represented in the scatter-gram of Fig. (7-8). The dots are for Dr. Smith's class, and the circles are for Dr. Jones's class. The reader can see that the scattergram for the combined groups shows less of a trend, and thus less a correlation, than if each group were considered separately. In fact, the correlation for the combined group is only .46, considerably less than the .69 for each group separately. Although this example is a hypothetical one, it is not unrealistic, for some instructors undoubtedly have higher standards than others.

It would appear, then, that one should exercise caution in interpreting a correlation based on a combination of two or more groups. If the group means differ substantially on either or both variables, a spuriously low, or

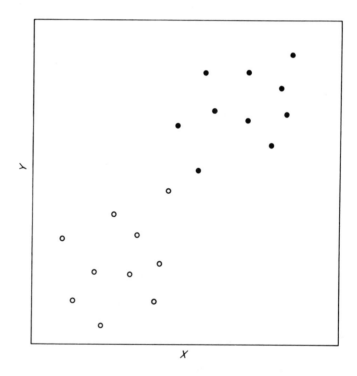

Figure 7-9. A Scattergram Illustrating the Relationship between Two Variables for a Combination of Two Groups with Very Different Means on Both Variables

in some instances a spuriously high coefficient might result. The latter case is illustrated by the scattergram of Fig. 7-9 in which the correlation for the two groups combined is much greater than that for either group taken separately.

The Use of Extreme Groups

Often, the size of the group used in an investigation is relatively small because of limitations on the time and money available for research. Occasionally, when this is true, only individuals who have extremely high scores or extremely low scores on the major variable being investigated are included in the analysis; the great bulk of individuals who fall toward the center are not used. The high and low groups can then be compared with regard to a variety of other variables. For instance, a high-aptitude group could be compared with a low-aptitude group to see how the groups differ on one or more non-intellective personality variables.

If a correlational analysis is utilized with extreme groups of this type, spuriously high coefficients may result. For example, let us again refer to Fig. 7-2, eliminating all of the cases between aptitude scores of 20 and 60. The correlation between aptitude score and grade-point average computed for the remaining extreme cases is substantially higher than the value of .66 obtained for the entire group.

INTERPRETING r IN TERMS OF VARIANCE

When one has obtained a numerical value for r, the question arises: what does an r of this size mean? In the present section, an attempt will be made to explain one common and important way of interpreting the size of a Pearson r. It will be helpful if we can again move to a consideration of the relationship between scores on a scholastic-aptitude test and grade-point averages at a particular institution. Individuals will usually vary with regard to their grade-point averages from very low to perhaps as high as a straight A. These individual differences in grades are associated with a variety of factors. We can be fairly certain, for instance, that different individuals obtain different grade-point averages partly because their intellectual potentials for scholastic work differ. We can be equally sure however, that at least a portion of the individual differences in grades is associated with differences in some non-intellective factors, such as motivation or health. Additional factors, over which the student may have little or no control, such as grading errors or the different standards of different instructors, also play a part.

Suppose we were interested in determining just what portion of the individual differences in grades could be associated with individual differences in intellectual potential as measured by our scholastic-aptitude test. One approach to doing this involves considering individual differences in terms of variance. The reader will recall that the variance, S^2, is the square of the standard deviation, S, and consequently is a numerical measure of the variability or dispersion of a group of scores. If the individuals' scores differ widely from one another, S and thus S^2 will be large; if the scores are relatively homogeneous, S^2 will be relatively small; and if everyone obtains the same score, S^2 will equal zero.

Let us use, then, S^2 as a measure of the individual differences in grade-point averages for the students represented in Fig. 7-2. The standard deviation, S, of the grade-point averages of the total group, obtained using the methods of Chap. 3, equals .60 of a grade point. Thus, the variance, S^2, equals $(.60)^2$ or .36. Now, consider only those students in a single class interval on aptitude, say the interval 50–59. The grade-point average variance, S^2, for these students alone, equals .19 (corrected for grouping). That the grade-point average variance for these students would be less than the variance for the entire group should be apparent just by inspection of Fig. 7-2. We would of course expect it to be less, because all of the students in the interval have approximately the same aptitude scores; there would be no variation in grades due to differences in aptitude, as it is measured by our test. The variation in grades that remains, then, is associated with other factors such as motivation, chance, etc. On the other hand, the grade-point-average variance of the total group is a function of individual differences in aptitude as well, since, when the group as a whole is considered, those with higher aptitudes tend to obtain higher grades. In fact, the grade-point-average variance for the entire group can be partitioned into two additive components as shown below.

$$S_y^2 \begin{bmatrix} \text{total } GPA \\ \text{variance} \end{bmatrix} = S^2 \begin{bmatrix} \text{portion associated with} \\ \text{individual \quad differences} \\ \text{in aptitude} \end{bmatrix} + S^2 \begin{bmatrix} \text{portion associ-} \\ \text{ated with other} \\ \text{factors} \end{bmatrix}$$

If the reader has followed the argument thus far, he perhaps can see that the higher the correlation is between two variables, the more the individuals with high X-scores will tend to differ on Y from those who have low X-scores, and the larger will be that portion of the total variance of the Y variable which can be associated with individual differences (variance) in the X variable. This relationship is a very precise one and can be expressed in terms of an equation.

$$r^2 = \frac{S^2 \text{ (associated with individual differences in } X)}{S_y^2 \text{ (total } Y \text{ variance)}}$$

That is, *the square of the correlation coefficient, r, equals the proportion of the total variance in Y which can be associated with individual differences in X*. This can be illustrated with reference to the r of .66 for Fig. 7-2. The square of .66 equals .44. Thus, 44 per cent of the grade-point-average variance can be associated with individual differences in aptitude as measured by the test. The remainder of the individual differences in grades $(1.00 - .44 = .56)$ would be associated with other factors. In this sense, then, an obtained correlation of $+.50$ or $-.50$ would indicate a relationship 1/4 as high as a perfect relationship $(-1.00$ or $+1.00)$, since $-.50^2 = +.50^2 = .25$. An obtained correlation would have to be at least .71 before it could be said that half the variance on the Y variable can be associated with variance on the X variable $(.71^2 = .50)$.

In these terms, correlations of less than .50 would appear to be quite low, because they would indicate that less than 25 per cent of the Y variance is associated with X. For instance, a correlation of .30 would indicate that less than 10 per cent of the variance in Y is associated with X (i.e. $.30^2 = .09$); however, the reader should be cautioned that correlation coefficients can be interpreted in other ways as well, some of which will be discussed in the next chapter. Furthermore, for some purposes, a correlation as low as .30 might indicate a relationship of practical or theoretical importance.

Correlation and Causality

Lest the reader obtain a mistaken impression from some of the examples used, a few comments should be made concerning the distinction between *correlation* and *causality*. If we know that two variables are positively correlated we know that individuals with high scores on the first variable tend to have high scores on the second also; however, we can not tell from the correlation coefficient whether or not those individuals who are high on the second variable are high *because* of their being high on the first. It may seem reasonable to assume that the correlation between aptitude and achievement reflects a causal relationship (i.e., some people obtain high grades *because* they have high intellectual potential). Nevertheless, we can not make this inference on the basis of the correlation coefficient alone; we need to consider, in addition, the nature of the two variables involved. This point can be made clearer by considering the r, obtained for a group of high-school seniors, between the grade-point average for all English courses and the grade-point average for all social-studies courses. Which of the two variables may be considered the cause and which the effect in this case?

Thus, when interpreting the size of a correlation in terms of variance, one should think of the variance in one variable *associated* with (not *due to*) variation in the other.

RANK-ORDER CORRELATION

In certain instances, an investigator may wish to obtain a measure of relationship between two variables, one or both of which are not scored on a numerical scale. Since a Pearson r requires numerical scores on both variables, it obviously can not be used in this type of situation; however, if the individuals involved can be ranked from high to low on the non-scaled variable or variables, it is possible to compute what is known as a rank-order correlation coefficient. The most commonly used of such coefficients is usually represented by the symbol ρ (Greek letter *rho*) and is often referred to as a *Spearman ρ*, after the British statistician who developed it.

The procedure for obtaining ρ is illustrated in Table 7-5. The data presented are for fifteen psychology graduate students, whose grade-point averages have been listed from high to low in Col. 1. In Col. 2, their ranks

Table 7-5

Computation of $\sum D^2$ for Determining Rho between Grade-Point Average and Research Potential

Student	GPA	Rank on GPA	Rank on Research Potential	D	D²
	1	2	3	4	5
A	4.00	1.5	3	−1.5	2.25
B	4.00	1.5	4	−2.5	6.25
C	3.90	3	2	1.0	1.00
D	3.80	4	1	3.0	9.00
E	3.75	5	7	−2.0	4.00
F	3.65	6	5	1.0	1.00
G	3.50	8	8	0.0	0.00
H	3.50	8	10	−2.0	4.00
I	3.50	8	6	2.0	4.00
J	3.33	10	11	−1.0	1.00
K	3.25	11	15	−4.0	16.00
L	3.20	12	9	3.0	9.00
M	3.10	13	13	0.0	0.00
N	3.00	14	12	2.0	4.00
O	2.75	15	14	1.0	1.00
					62.50
					$\sum D^2$

are listed, from 1 to 15, obtained on the basis of their grade-point averages. The grade-point averages have been converted to ranks because, in order to compute a Spearman ρ, the scores on both variables must be expressed in these terms. In Col. 3 are listed the ranks assigned to the students according to their potentials for doing worthwhile independent research. These ranks are based on the combined judgments of a faculty committee.

Careful study of Col. 2 will reveal how rank numbers are assigned. It makes no difference whether the ranks are assigned from high to low or vice versa, provided both sets of ranks are assigned in the same direction. If two or more individuals share the same rank position, each is assigned the average rank of the group. For example, there are two students with 4.00 averages, and hence these students share ranks 1 and 2. The mean of these two ranks is $(1 + 2)/2 = 1.5$. Further down the list are three students with 3.50 averages, sharing rank positions 7, 8, and 9; these students have been assigned a rank of 8 [that is, $(7 + 8 + 9)/3$].

Computation of the Spearman ρ coefficient requires the sum of the squared differences between the ranks for each individual. The difference, D, for each student is obtained by subtracting his rank on research potential from his rank on grade-point average. The differences, D, and the squared differences, D^2, are listed in Cols. 4 and 5 respectively. The sum of Col. 5, $\sum D^2$, is then used in the following formula, in which N, as usual, designates the number of cases.

$$\rho = 1 - \frac{6 \sum D^2}{N(N^2 - 1)} \tag{7-7}$$

For the data of Table 7-5, ρ will equal $+.89$.

$$\rho = 1 - \frac{6(62.50)}{15[(15)^2 - 1]} = +.89$$

An interesting insight into the nature of ρ can be obtained by using the ranks on the two variables as the X- and Y-scores and computing the Pearson r (for the ranks) using any of the methods presented earlier. For instance, let us use the raw-score method. The sums required for Form. (7-5) are obtained in Table 7-6. The numbers in Cols. 1 and 2 of that table are the ranks from Table 7-5, Cols. 2 and 3. Using Form. (7-5), a Pearson r of $+.89$ is obtained.

$$r = \frac{N \sum XY - \sum X \sum Y}{\sqrt{[N \sum X^2 - (\sum X)^2][N \sum Y^2 - (\sum Y)^2]}}$$
$$= \frac{15(1207.5) - (120)(120)}{\sqrt{[15(1237.5) - (120)^2][15(1240.0) - (120)^2]}} = +.89$$

This illustrates the fact that the Spearman ρ coefficient for any two sets of ranks is the same as the Pearson r obtained using the ranks as scores.

The above relationship does not mean, however, that a Spearman ρ computed from the ranks on two variables both of which are scores on a

Table 7-6

Computations Necessary for Determining r
Using the Ranks of Table 7-5 as Scores

Student	1 GPA Rank (X)	2 Research Potential Rank (Y)	3 XY	4 X^2	5 Y^2
A	1.5	3	4.50	2.25	9.00
B	1.5	4	6.00	2.25	16.00
C	3	2	6.00	9.00	4.00
D	4	1	4.00	16.00	1.00
E	5	7	35.00	25.00	49.00
F	6	5	30.00	36.00	25.00
G	8	8	64.00	64.00	64.00
H	8	10	80.00	64.00	100.00
I	8	6	48.00	64.00	36.00
J	10	11	110.00	100.00	121.00
K	11	15	165.00	121.00	225.00
L	12	9	108.00	144.00	81.00
M	13	13	169.00	169.00	169.00
N	14	12	168.00	196.00	144.00
O	15	14	210.00	225.00	196.00
	120	120	1207.5	1237.5	1240.0
	ΣX	ΣY	ΣXY	ΣX^2	ΣY^2

numerical scale will have exactly the same value as the Pearson r computed from the *original* scores. The reason for this can be seen by examining Cols. 1 and 2 of Table 7-5. The reader will notice that the difference between the grade-point averages of students K and L is .05, while the difference for pupils N and O is .25. In both cases, however, the difference between the rank scores is 1. Thus, in going from original or raw scores to ranks, the relative distances between pairs of individuals are distorted, and the Pearson r computed for the raw scores will usually not equal that computed for the ranks (i.e., the Spearman ρ).

Nonetheless, it has been shown that if the scores on two variables, the distributions of which are approximately normal, are converted to ranks and a Spearman ρ is computed, the ρ will be only slightly (usually less than .02) less than the r computed from the original scores; therefore, a Spearman ρ can be interpreted, in much the same way as r, as a measure of the degree of relationship between two variables. Although it is not immediately apparent from Form. (7-7), ρ can vary from -1.00 to 0 to $+1.00$, as can r. As for r, the values -1.00 and $+1.00$ indicate perfect relationships, and 0 indicates no relationship at all. A ρ of $+1.00$ would be obtained if all individuals had the same ranks on both variables; whereas a ρ of -1.00 would be obtained if the orderings on the two variables were exactly reversed—that is, if the highest individual on X were the lowest on Y, the second highest on X the second lowest on Y, and so forth.

Exercises and Problems

1. The following are the scores for six students on two tests, X and Y.

Student	1	2	3	4	5	6
Score on X	4	3	5	3	2	1
Score on Y	5	4	8	10	1	2

   a) Compute $\sum x^2$, $\sum y^2$ and $\sum xy$, using deviation scores.
   b) Compute $\sum x^2$, $\sum y^2$ and $\sum xy$, using raw scores.
   c) Compute r, using the answers from (a) or (b) above.

2. The following are the scores for six students on two measures, U and V.

Student	1	2	3	4	5	6
Score on U	7	2	1	6	5	3
Score on V	7	6	12	4	3	10

   a) Compute r, using deviation scores.
   b) Compute r directly from the raw scores.

3. a) Construct a scattergram for the data in Table 7-7. Use 20–24 as the lowest interval for X and 12–13 as the lowest interval for Y.
   b) Compute $\overline{X}$ and S_X, using the coded method.
   c) Compute $\overline{Y}$ and S_Y, using the coded method.
   d) Compute r_{XY}, using the coded scattergram method.

4. The following are the summary data for 100 fourth-graders on an aptitude test (X) and an arithmetic achievement test (Y).

   $$\sum X = 5200 \qquad \sum X^2 = 272{,}312 \qquad \sum XY = 166{,}931$$
   $$\sum Y = 3200 \qquad \sum Y^2 = 102{,}683$$

   a) Compute $\overline{X}$, $\overline{Y}$, S_X, and S_Y.
   b) Compute $\sum xy$.
   c) Using the answers to (a) and (b), compute r.
   d) Compute r directly from the data given.

5. The following is a summary of the data from two measures administered to a group of 200 individuals.

Measure X	$\overline{X} = 51.2$	$S_X = 12.3$	$r_{XY} = .60$
Measure Y	$\overline{Y} = 62.8$	$S_Y = 10.1$	

   a) What is the value of $\sum xy$?
   b) What is the value of $\sum z_x z_y$?

6. A psychology professor administers two personality scales he has just constructed to a large lecture section of elementary-psychology students. The following is a summary of the results in terms of raw scores.

Test A $\overline{X}_A = 37.32$ $S_A = 8.71$ positively skewed
Test B $\overline{X}_B = 61.82$ $S_B = 12.59$ positively skewed $r_{AB} = +.53$

For each of the following, indicate whether or not the correlation would be affected by the specified operation. Where it is possible to determine how the correlation would be affected, indicate this as well.
a) Multiply the scores on test A by 2.
b) Convert the scores on both tests to Z-scores with means of 50 and standard deviations of 10.
c) Subtract 50 points from the scores on test A (yes, this will result in negative scores for most of the students).
d) Multiply the scores, on test A only, by -1.
e) Multiply the scores on both tests by -1.
f) Convert the scores on both tests to stanines.
g) Include only honor students in the analysis.
h) Exclude from the analysis all students who obtained scores on A between 31 and 43.

7. The correlation between a new academic-aptitude test and freshman grade-point average is .61 for last year's freshman class at a large state university. In the absence of additional information, would you guess the correlation between the same aptitude test and freshman grade-point average to be higher, about the same, or lower for the freshman class at a highly selective private university? Why?

8. The correlation between an intelligence test and a certain personality test is equal to .40. On the basis of this correlation, the statement is made: "A major reason why some people score higher than others on the personality test is that they are more intelligent." Do you agree with this statement? Explain your answer.

9. For the entire group of students who completed their freshman year at State University last spring, the correlation between their college freshman grade-point averages and their four-year high-school grade-point averages was .48.
a) Can you think of any reasons why the correlation is not any higher? Explain. (Hint: Consider, among other things, the variation in grading practices for different high schools.)
b) Consider for a moment the large group of students who went to State University last year from Jefferson High School in the city. Would you guess the correlation between college freshman grade-point average and high-school grade-point average, computed for this group of students only, to be greater than, less than, or about equal to the .48 obtained for the entire freshman class? Why?

Correlation   133

10. Suppose that by revising two tests, U and V, you are able to increase their correlations with variable Y. The following are the correlations before and after revision.

Before	After
$r_{UY} = .20$	$r_{UY} = .40$
$r_{VY} = .40$	$r_{VY} = .60$

 a) Did the process of revision double the relationship between test U and variable Y? Explain.
 b) Were the relationships between the two tests and variable Y increased an equal amount by the revision? Explain.
11. Compute the Spearman ρ for the following data.

Case	1	2	3	4	5	6	7	8	9
Variable X	8	6	6	8	9	3	7	5	2
Variable Y	6	9	4	12	10	3	7	9	4

12. a) Suppose the rank-order correlation between X and Y based on 10 individuals is equal to $+1.00$. Suppose furthermore that r_{XY} for the same 10 individuals is equal to $+.80$. What must be true about the relationship between X and Y (at least for the 10 individuals involved)?
 b) We know that it is possible to obtain a value for r anywhere between -1.00 and $+1.00$ inclusive. Does this imply anything about the possible range of values for ρ? Explain.

Table 7-7

The Scores of Fifty Students on a Vocabulary Test (X) and a Reading Test (Y)

Student	X	Y	Student	X	Y	Student	X	Y
1	36	18	18	38	17	35	36	15
2	46	24	19	37	22	36	36	20
3	45	28	20	43	26	37	53	31
4	32	20	21	50	29	38	54	23
5	36	23	22	48	23	39	38	29
6	50	28	23	38	26	40	28	19
7	43	20	24	39	22	41	34	21
8	21	12	25	30	15	42	39	15
9	30	13	26	33	22	43	38	25
10	47	19	27	39	18	44	40	17
11	40	22	28	42	21	45	58	29
12	57	25	29	44	23	46	44	18
13	41	23	30	48	22	47	49	26
14	39	20	31	47	25	48	49	29
15	35	19	32	44	27	49	34	23
16	43	16	33	31	25	50	52	25
17	37	14	34	34	19			

Chapter 8

Regression and Prediction

The preceding chapter dealt with methods of describing the degree and kind (positive or negative) of relationship between two variables in terms of what is called a *coefficient of correlation*. In many instances, a description is all that is desired—as when we are investigating how scores on a certain attitude measure are related to such variables as age, intelligence, or number of years of schooling. On the other hand, another practical reason for analyzing the relationships between variables is to develop a method of predicting an unknown value from a known one. We may wish to predict, for instance, how much a particular pupil is likely to learn in third-grade arithmetic as measured by an achievement test given at the end of the school year. If we knew nothing about the pupil, our safest guess would be that he would do about average on the achievement test; however, if there were a high relationship between scores on the final achievement test and scores on an aptitude test given at the beginning of the third grade, and if we knew the student's score on the aptitude test, we would be in a position to make a better guess. The present chapter is concerned principally with how such informed guesses are made, using what are called *regression* (more specifically, linear regression) *methods*.

Before scores on one variable, Y, can be predicted with any accuracy from scores on another variable, X, an analysis of the relationship between these two variables must be undertaken for a sample of individuals whose scores on both variables are known. The specific prediction procedures developed in the course of the analysis can then be used with other individuals whose Y-scores are unknown. A basic assumption is that the same relationship between the two variables will hold for these

134

new individuals. To the extent that this assumption is incorrect, additional
error will be included in our predictions.

THE PREDICTION OF SCORES ON Y
FROM SCORES ON X

The data we require are the same as those used in the determination
of the correlation coefficient. The scores of ten pupils on an aptitude test,
X, (the *predictor* or *independent variable*) and an achievement test, Y, (the
criterion or *dependent variable*) are shown in Table 8-1, and the scattergram for these ten pairs of scores is shown in Fig. 8-1. These are the same
data presented earlier in Fig. 7-1 and Table 7-1. The scattergram suggests

Table 8-1

Scores of Ten Pupils on Two Tests

| | Test Scores | | | | |
| | Aptitude | Achievement | 1 | 2 | 3 |
Pupil	X	Y	XY	X^2	Y^2
A	2	1	2	4	1
B	1	3	3	1	9
C	4	4	16	16	16
D	7	5	35	49	25
E	7	7	49	49	49
F	5	6	30	25	36
G	3	7	21	9	49
H	9	8	72	81	64
I	5	9	45	25	81
J	7	10	70	49	100
	50	60	343	308	430
	ΣX	ΣY	ΣXY	ΣX^2	ΣY^2

a generally positive relationship between the two variables; there is a
tendency for high scores on X to be associated with high scores on Y and
for low scores on X to be associated with low scores on Y. The degree of
relationship can be determined again by substituting the appropriate sums
from Table 8-1 into Form. (7-5).

$$r = \frac{N \sum XY - (\sum X)(\sum Y)}{\sqrt{N \sum X^2 - (\sum X)^2}\sqrt{N \sum Y^2 - (\sum Y)^2}}$$

$$= \frac{10(343) - (50)(60)}{\sqrt{10(308) - (50)^2}\sqrt{10(430) - (60)^2}} = .675$$

It would appear reasonable, because of the positive nature of the relationship, to predict that a pupil who is high on X will probably be high
on Y and that a pupil who is low on X will probably be low on Y. In order

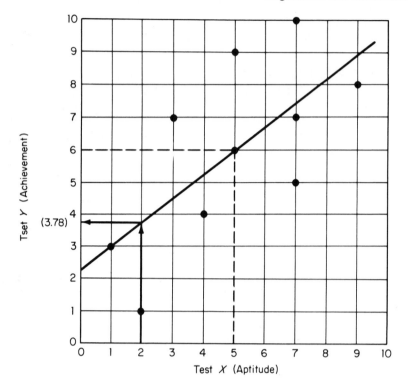

Figure 8-1. The Scattergram for the Ten Pairs of Scores of Table 8-1

to determine exactly what the predicted Y value should be, *we shall assume that the relationship is linear.* That is, we shall assume that the trend suggested by the scattergram can best be represented by a slanting straight line, such as the one indicated in Fig. 8-1. This line is called a *regression line.*

Now let us see how the regression line of Fig. 8-1 can be used to predict an achievement-test score from an aptitude score. Consider pupil A, who has an aptitude score, (X), of 2. First, we move vertically from 2 on the X axis until we meet the regression line. Then we move horizontally to the left and read the predicted score on the Y axis. It can be seen, by following the arrows in Fig. 8-1, that the predicted score on the achievement test would be close to 4. For the moment, let us suppose that we are able to read the values on the Y axis accurately to two decimal places and that the predicted score equals exactly 3.78. This may be written as $Y' = 3.78$, Y' being the symbol used for indicating a predicted score on variable Y.

The same procedure can be used to determine the predicted achievement score for each of the remaining nine pupils of Table 8-1. The predicted scores which would be obtained for all ten students, using the regression line of Fig. 8-1, are listed in Table 8-2, Col. 1.

The Criterion of Least Squares

Close examination of the scattergram of Fig. 8-1 may suggest to the reader that other lines, perhaps differing only slightly from the one that has been drawn, might also serve as fairly "accurate" representations of the trend. How can one decide which of the many possible lines should be used in making predictions? We need some overall measure for comparing one line with another with regard to the accuracy of prediction each line permits.

Such a measure can be illustrated by the computations of Table 8-2. The predicted score of each pupil on Y (i.e., Y') has been subtracted from his actual score to obtain the discrepancy $Y - Y'$. These discrepancies, sometimes referred to as *errors of prediction*, are listed in Col. 2. At first

Table 8-2

The Computation of Errors of Prediction
for the Ten Pupils of Table 8-1

Pupil	Test Scores X	Y	1 Y'	2 $Y - Y'$	3 $(Y - Y')^2$	4 $(Y')^2$
A	2	1	3.78	−2.78	7.73	14.29
B	1	3	3.04	−.04	0.00	9.24
C	4	4	5.26	−1.26	1.59	27.67
D	7	5	7.48	−2.48	6.15	55.95
E	7	7	7.48	−.48	.23	55.95
F	5	6	6.00	.00	.00	36.00
G	3	7	4.52	2.48	6.15	20.43
H	9	8	8.96	−.96	.92	80.28
I	5	9	6.00	3.00	9.00	36.00
J	7	10	7.48	2.52	6.35	55.95
	50	60	60.00	0.00	38.12	391.76
	ΣX	ΣY	$\Sigma Y'$	$\Sigma (Y - Y')$	$\Sigma (Y - Y')^2$	$\Sigma (Y')^2$

glance, it might seem that an average of these errors would be a good measure of the accuracy of prediction using the line; however, for a line which passes through the middle of the scattergram pattern, such an average would have little meaning, because the negative errors would tend to balance the positive. It can be seen that the sum (and thus the mean) of the errors of prediction in Col. 2 is equal to zero, even though the predictions are all somewhat in error.

It would be possible to avoid the balancing effect of positive and negative errors by ignoring algebraic sign; but a far more useful and widely
accepted approach utilizes the squared errors, listed in Col. 3. By squaring
the errors, negative signs are eliminated, and yet the problems created by
ignoring algebraic signs are avoided. For a line which is a good fit, the
sum of the squared errors, $\sum (Y - Y')^2$, will be relatively small. Utilizing
the techniques of differential calculus, procedures have been developed
which will allow one to locate, for any set of data, the line for which the
sum $\sum (Y - Y')^2$ is a minimum. This line, sometimes referred to as the
line of least squares, is the one most commonly used for predictive purposes. Before the procedures for locating the least-squares line are presented and their use illustrated, a brief review of certain general notions
concerning straight lines may be helpful.

The Equation of a Straight Line

The equation of any straight line drawn on the space defined by two
coordinate axes, X and Y, can be written in the general form:

$$Y = bX + a$$

where b is the *slope* of the line and a is what is known as the
intercept

For instance, the solid line of Fig. 8-2 has a slope, b, of $+2$ and an intercept, a, of $+1$. Thus, its equation is $Y = 2X + 1$. If several values are
substituted for X in this equation, the corresponding values of Y are
obtained.

a) If $X = 1$, then $Y = 2(1) + 1 = 3$
b) If $X = 2$, then $Y = 2(2) + 1 = 5$
c) If $X = 0$, then $Y = 2(0) + 1 = 1$
d) If $X = 3$, then $Y = 2(3) + 1 = 7$

These pairs of X and Y values can now be plotted as points, as in Fig. 8-2.
The point $X = 1$, $Y = 3$ is located above the value 1 on the X axis and
opposite the value 3 on the Y axis. The other three points are similarly
located. Notice that all four points fall exactly on the line, as would any
points obtained by substituting values for X in the equation and solving
for Y. It should be apparent that the line could have been drawn after only
two points had been plotted.

The value of the slope, b, is a function of the angle between the line
and horizontal or X axis. Using the line as one side, let us form the smaller
right triangle of Fig. 8-2 by starting on the line at the point $(X = 1, Y = 3)$,
moving horizontally 1 unit to the right, and then moving vertically until
we meet the line again. Let us now form the large triangle by starting at

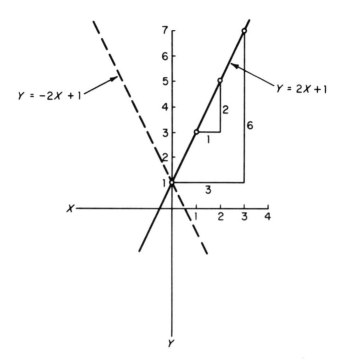

Figure 8-2. Graphs of the Equations for Two Straight Lines with the Same Intercept but Slopes of Opposite Sign

another point on the line, $X = 0$, $Y = 1$, moving horizontally 3 units to the right, and then moving vertically until we meet the line again. Notice that the ratio of the length of the vertical side to the length of the horizontal side is equal to 2 for both triangles.

$$\frac{\text{vertical}}{\text{horizontal}} = \frac{2}{1} = \frac{6}{3} = 2$$

This ratio is the slope of the line and would be the same for any other right triangle formed in similar fashion, using the line as the hypotenuse. The sign of the slope in this case is positive, which indicates that the line slopes upward to the right. A line with a negative slope would slope upward to the left. This is illustrated in Fig. 8-2 by the dotted line, which has an equation of $Y = -2X + 1$; the dotted line shows the same degree of slope as the solid line, but in a different direction.

The intercept, a, is the value at which the line crosses the Y axis; that is, it is the value of Y when $X = 0$. It can be seen that both lines of Fig. 8-2 cross the Y axis at $+1$. Thus the intercepts for both are equal to $+1$.

DETERMINATION OF THE LEAST-SQUARES REGRESSION LINE

The regression line indicated in Fig. 8-1 is the line of least squares for the scattergram represented there. That is, if any other line were used to obtain predicted scores for the sample of ten pupils, the sum of the squared errors of prediction, $\sum (Y - Y')^2$, would be larger than the 38.12 obtained in Table 8-2.

The specific procedures used to locate the line of least squares may now be described.

The equation for the least-squares regression line can be determined from the values of $\overline{X}$, $\overline{Y}$, S_x, S_y, and r. A correlation of .67 has already been computed for the scattergram of Fig. 8-1, and the values of $\overline{X}$, $\overline{Y}$, S_x and S_y can easily be computed using the appropriate sums from Table 8-1. Formula (4-5) is that used in the computation of S_x and S_y.

$$\overline{X} = \frac{50}{10} = 5.00; \quad S_x = \frac{1}{N} \sqrt{N \sum X^2 - (\sum X)^2} = \frac{1}{10} \sqrt{10\,(308) - (50)^2}$$

$$= 2.408$$

$$\overline{Y} = \frac{60}{10} = 6.00; \quad S_y = \frac{1}{N} \sqrt{N \sum Y^2 - (\sum Y)^2} = \frac{1}{10} \sqrt{10\,(430) - (60)^2}$$

$$= 2.646$$

Now, the values for the slope and the intercept can be computed using Forms. (8-1) and (8-2).

$$b = \frac{S_y}{S_x} r \tag{8-1}$$

$$a = -b\overline{X} + \overline{Y} \tag{8-2}$$

For the pupils of Fig. 8-1

$$b = \frac{2.646}{2.408}\,(.675) = .741$$

$$\text{and} \quad a = -(.741)\,(5.00) + 6.00 = 2.30$$

The equation of the regression line of least squares, is, then, $Y' = .741X + 2.30$. This is referred to as the *regression equation*. For purposes of minimizing the effects of rounding error in several illustrations later in the chapter, these and other results based on the scores of Table 8-1 are carried out to more decimal places than would be justified by the original data.

The obtained value for b may be confirmed by constructing a triangle (see Fig. 8-1) and obtaining the ratio of two sides as described earlier; the obtained value of a can be confirmed by noting where the line crosses the Y axis.

Constructing the line on the scattergram is quite simple: merely locate two points which satisfy the regression equation and draw a straight line through these points. One such point will always be easy to locate, because the least-squares regression line will always pass through the intersection of $\bar{X}$ and $\bar{Y}$. For the scattergram of Fig. 8-1, that would be the point $X = \bar{X} = 5.00$, $Y = \bar{Y} = 6.00$, as indicated by the intersection of the dotted lines. The intercept can be used as the second point if the range of scores is such that the Y axis (i.e., the vertical axis erected at $X = 0$) is included in the scattergram. If it is not, as is the case in the scattergram of Fig. 7-2, another point may be located by substituting a convenient value for X into the regression equation. For instance, if a value of 2 were substituted for X in the equation of the line of Fig. 8-1, a Y' of 3.78 would be obtained $[Y' = .741 (2) + 2.30 = 3.78]$.

It should be apparent that either the line or its equation can be used to obtain the predicted or Y' values. In fact, the Y' values listed in Table 8-2 were really determined using the equation rather than the line. That is why it was possible to obtain predicted values to two decimal places.

An additional formula for computing the slope directly from the raw-score sums of Table 8-1 should be mentioned.

$$b = \frac{N \sum XY - \sum X \sum Y}{N \sum X^2 - (\sum X)^2} \tag{8-3}$$

Using the sums of Table 8-1:

$$b = \frac{10 (343) - (50) (60)}{10 (308) - (50)^2} = .741$$

This formula involves fewer computational steps than Form. (8-1), and its use will reduce errors due to rounding.

Equivalent Forms of the Regression Equation

The equation for the line of Fig. 8-1 was written as $Y' = .741X + 2.30$. This is commonly referred to as the *raw-score form* of the regression equation, since it is expressed in terms of original or raw scores. A general formula for the raw-score form can be developed by incorporating the expressions for b and a of Forms. (8-1) and (8-2), respectively, into a single expression, as follows.

$$Y' = \overbrace{\left(\frac{S_y}{S_x}r\right)}^{b} X - \overbrace{\left(\frac{S_y}{S_x}r\right)\overline{X} + \overline{Y}}^{a} \qquad (8\text{-}4)$$

By subjecting Form. (8-4) to some very simple algebraic operations, the regression equation can be rewritten in terms of deviation scores.

$$Y' - \overline{Y} = \left(\frac{S_y}{S_x}r\right)(X - \overline{X})$$

If we allow y' to represent $(Y' - \overline{Y})$ and x to represent $(X - \overline{X})$, the foregoing becomes:

$$y' = \left(\frac{S_y}{S_x}r\right)x$$

If we now divide both sides of the above by S_y, the regression equation will be in *standard-score form*.

$$\frac{y'}{S_y} = r\left(\frac{x}{S_x}\right)$$

$$z'_y = rz_x \qquad (8\text{-}5)$$

The use of Form. (8-5) can be illustrated with reference to pupil B of our sample of ten pupils (Tables 8-1 and 8-2). His standard score on the ability test (X) is -1.66.

$$z_x = \frac{1 - 5}{2.408} = -1.66$$

We would, therefore, predict a standard score on the achievement test (Y) of -1.12.

$$z'_y = (.675)(-1.66) = -1.12$$

That is, we predict that pupil B will fall 1.12 standard deviations below the mean on the achievement test. This is equivalent to 2.96 raw-score points below the mean $[z'_y \cdot S_y = -1.12(2.65) = -2.96]$, or a raw score of 3.04 (i.e., $6.00 - 2.96 = 3.04$). The same answer is obtained directly by using the raw-score form of the regression equation.

$$Y' = (.741)(1) + 2.30 = 3.04$$

DETERMINING THE ACCURACY
OF PREDICTION

The use of a least-squares regression line or its equation will minimize errors of prediction, but it will not eliminate them. Predictions would be perfectly accurate only if the correlation (Pearson r) between the variables were equal to -1.00 or $+1.00$, in which case the dots on the scattergram would fall exactly on a straight line, and, since that line would be the regression line, the actual Y-scores would equal the predicted (i.e., Y') scores. In practice, perfect correlations are not found, and most of the cases fall above or below the regression line. That is, most individual predictions are erroneous in some degree.

It is important, then, in interpreting a predicted value, to have some notion of how large the error is likely to be. Assume, for example, that on the basis of his score on a test taken in ninth grade, it is predicted that a particular student will obtain a score of 550 on a certain college-aptitude test to be administered in grade 12. Before using this predicted value as a basis for any conclusions about the student, it is as important to know something about the possible accuracy of the prediction: is it likely to be within just a few points of the actual value, or might it be off by as much as 100 or 200 points? To this matter we now turn.

Linearity and Homoscedasticity

Consider the scattergram in Fig. 8-3, in which the relationship between two other tests, X and Y, is represented, this time for a larger sample of 100 individuals. Notice that the scores have been grouped into intervals of size 3 on both variables. The number in each cell represents the frequency or number of cases obtaining that particular combination of X- and Y-scores, and the solid line represents the least-squares regression line. Consider the array above $X = 18$. (The term *array* as used here refers to the column formed by extending a class interval on the X variable up through the scatter diagram.) We could, if we wished, determine the mean and standard deviation of the distribution of Y-scores for that array (i.e., for individuals who obtained an X-score in interval 17–19). Using methods discussed in Chaps. 3 and 4, we obtain an array mean of 23.10 and an array standard deviation of 6.24. Similarly, we can obtain the means and standard deviations of all the other arrays, with the results shown in Table 8-3.

Notice that the ten array means, as indicated by the pluses in Fig. 8-3, tend to fall roughly along the regression line. This will always be the case if the general trend represented in the scattergram does not depart greatly from linearity. Notice, also, that the values listed in Table 8-3 for the array standard deviations do not differ widely. The latter phenomenon is referred to as *homoscedasticity:* to the extent that the array standard deviations are similar in value, the scattergram can be said to show homoscedasticity. For a non-fictional sample, one would never expect the array means to fall exactly on the regression line nor the array standard deviations to be

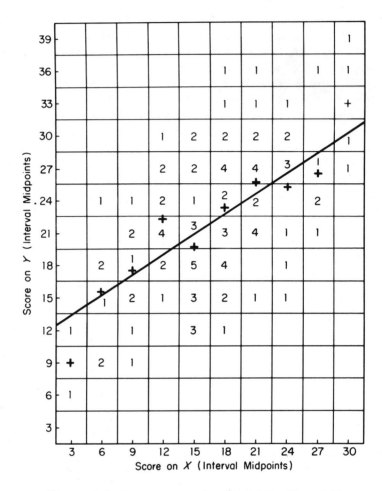

Figure 8-3. Scattergram for Variables X and Y
(Pluses indicate the positions of the array means.)

exactly equal, partly because of the influence of chance factors. That is,
which individuals are included in the sample group and what scores these
individuals actually obtain on the two tests would to some extent be functions of chance.

Let us now make two assumptions with regard to the situation represented in Fig. 8-3: *if the chance effects associated with our particular sample
could be eliminated, (1) all of the array means would fall exactly on the regression line (assumption of linearity), and (2) all of the array standard
deviations would be equal (assumption of homoscedasticity).* We are in-

Table 8-3

Mean and Standard Deviation of Y-Scores in Each Vertical Array of Fig. 8-3

Array Midpoint (X)	Mean Y	Y Std. Dev.*
30	33.00	4.66
27	26.40	5.09
24	25.32	5.61
21	25.59	5.17
18	23.10	6.24
15	19.59	5.55
12	22.26	4.05
9	16.89	4.65
6	15.51	5.24
3	9.00	2.87

* Corrected for grouping error

terested in the situation which would obtain if these chance effects were eliminated, because we wish to predict for individuals beyond the present sample. It seems reasonable to assume that our obtained regression line is a good estimate of what would occur with "chance" factors removed. It is also reasonable to assume that a good estimate for the array standard deviations (barring chance) will be a value near the average of the obtained array standard deviations. The particular estimate used is called the *standard error of prediction*—sometimes also referred to as the *standard error of estimate*—and is represented by the symbol $S_{y \cdot x}$.

The Computation and Use of $S_{y \cdot x}$

The following values can be computed from the data of Fig. 8-3, using the scattergram method discussed in the previous chapter.

$$\overline{X} = 16.89 \qquad \overline{Y} = 22.23$$
$$S_x = 6.23 \qquad S_y = 6.85$$
$$r_{xy} = .571$$

Once S_y and r_{xy} have been determined, the estimated value for the array standard deviations (assuming linearity and homoscedasticity) can be obtained with the following formula.

$$S_{y \cdot x} = S_y \sqrt{1 - r^2} \tag{8-6}$$

For the data in Fig. 8-3:

$$S_{y \cdot x} = 6.85 \sqrt{1 - (.571)^2} = 5.6$$

The value of $S_{y \cdot x}$ can be extremely useful in determining the amount of error resulting from use of the regression line or its equation for predicting values of Y from values of X. In order to illustrate this, let us now obtain the regression equation of the line in Fig. 8-3.

The slope (b) and the intercept (a) for the regression line can be computed using Forms. (8-1) and (8-2).

$$b = \frac{S_y}{S_x} r = \frac{6.85}{6.23} (+.571) = .628$$

$$a = -b\overline{X} + \overline{Y} = -(.628)(16.89) + 22.23 = 11.62$$

The regression equation becomes:

$$Y' = bX + a = .63X + 11.6$$

Here, of course, the assumption of linearity is important. It would make little sense to use a line for predicting if the scattergram shows a wide departure from linearity. Now suppose we know that a particular individual has an X-score of 24, but we do not know his Y-score. If this individual can be considered to be from a group similar to the group from which the sample in Fig. 8-3 was selected, it is reasonable to obtain his predicted score on variable Y, using the regression equation.

$$Y' = .63(24) + 11.6 = 26.7$$

We would expect that the predicted value of 26.7 is somewhat in error; that is, we expect it to differ somewhat from the score the individual would obtain if he were actually administered test Y.

In order to obtain an idea of the amount of error to be expected, we will make a further assumption: *if the effects of chance were eliminated, the scores within each array would be normally distributed about the regression line.* This is shown schematically in Fig. 8-4, for the array above $X = 24$. The distribution, as represented for that array, is normal; it centers at the predicted Y' of 26.7; it has a standard deviation of $S_{y \cdot x} = 5.6$. We therefore expect that approximately 68 per cent of the individuals with an X-score of 24 will obtain a Y-score between 21.1 and 32.3 (i.e., $Y' - S_{y \cdot x} = 21.1$, $Y' + S_{y \cdot x} = 32.3$) and that approximately 95 per cent will obtain a Y-score between 15.5 and 37.9 (i.e., $Y' - 2S_{y \cdot x} = 15.5$, $Y' + 2S_{y \cdot x} = 37.9$). The reader should note that, although the middle 95 per cent of the cases in a normal distribution fall between $\overline{X} - 1.96S$ and $\overline{X} + 1.96S$, it is common practice to round the value 1.96 and use 2 instead. In this sense then, we can be approximately 95 per cent "sure" or "confident" that an individual with an X-score of 24 would obtain a Y-score somewhere between 15.5 and 37.9 if he were actually administered the Y test. It should be evident from this why $S_{y \cdot x}$ is referred to as the *standard error of prediction;* it gives us an indication of the amount of

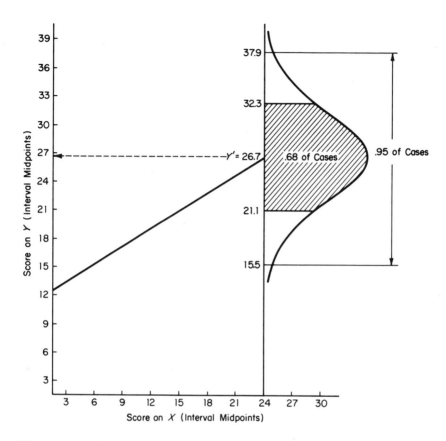

Figure 8-4. Schematic Representation of the Distribution of Scores in the Array X = 24 of Fig. 8-3

error to be expected. Similar statements can be made for individuals with other X-scores. For instance, the predicted Y'-score for an individual with an X-score of 9 is 17.3 [i.e., .63 (9) + 11.6 = 17.3]. We may be 68 per cent confident that such an individual would obtain a score somewhere between 11.7 and 22.9 (i.e., $Y' - S_{y \cdot x}$ and $Y' + S_{y \cdot x}$) or 95 per cent confident that he would obtain a score between 6.1 and 28.5 (i.e., $Y' - 2S_{y \cdot x}$ and $Y' + 2S_{y \cdot x}$) if he were administered test Y.

It should be emphasized that the procedure described for obtaining the Y' values is based only upon the assumption of linearity. However, the use of $S_{y \cdot x}$ to obtain 68 per cent or 95 per cent *confidence limits* (as in the previous paragraph) is based upon the additional assumptions of homoscedasticity and normality within arrays. The reader may well wonder about the realism of these assumptions; how often can we expect to find an actual situation in which they would be fulfilled? Strictly speaking, the answer is probably "seldom" or "never"; however, the important practical consideration is whether or not the data come *close* enough to meeting the assumptions so that results of sufficient accuracy are obtained with the foregoing techniques. Fortunately, there is a wide variety of situations in which this is the case.

Let us summarize what has been said by referring to an example mentioned earlier. Suppose, on the basis of his score on a test (X) taken in the ninth grade, it is predicted that a particular student will obtain a score of 550 on a certain college-aptitude test (Y) to be administered in grade 12. Suppose, furthermore, that for the sample upon which the regression line (or equation) is based, $r_{xy} = .60$, and $S_y = 75$. Using Form. (8-6), $S_{y \cdot x}$ may be obtained.

$$S_{y \cdot x} = 75 \sqrt{1 - (.60)^2} = 75\,(.80) = 60$$

If the data roughly fulfill the assumptions of linearity, homoscedasticity, and normality within arrays, we can be roughly 68 per cent confident that such a student will obtain a score somewhere between 490 and 610 ($Y' - S_{y \cdot x}$ and $Y' + S_{y \cdot x}$) were he to take the college-aptitude test.

Further Comments Concerning $S_{y \cdot x}$

Thus far, $S_{y \cdot x}$ has been described as an estimate of the array standard-deviation value which would have been obtained if the relationship were truly linear and homoscedastic and if the effects of chance were removed. Additional discussion concerning the nature of $S_{y \cdot x}$ may be helpful.

Let us refer once more to the data of Table 8-2. An error score ($Y - Y'$) is computed for each individual and is shown in Col. 2. These error scores are then squared and added to obtain $\sum (Y - Y')^2$, the sum that is minimized in the course of determining the least-squares line. *The standard error of prediction*, $S_{y \cdot x}$, can be obtained from this sum, as follows.

$$S_{y \cdot x} = \sqrt{\frac{\sum (Y - Y')^2}{N}} \qquad (8\text{-}7)$$

For the data of Table 8-2:

$$S_{y \cdot x} = \sqrt{\frac{38.12}{10}} = 1.952$$

This value is equal to the one which is obtained with Form. (8-6) for the same set of scores.

$$S_{y \cdot x} = S_y \sqrt{1 - r^2} = 2.65 \sqrt{1 - (.675)^2} = 1.952$$

By examining Form. (8-7), it can be seen that $S_{y \cdot x}$ is a measure of the degree to which the actual scores on Y spread out around the predicted or Y' values. A relatively small value for $S_{y \cdot x}$ indicates that the actual values are close to the predicted values and that relatively accurate predictions can be made. We will show below that $S_{y \cdot x}$, obtained from Form. (8.7), is the standard deviation of the error $(Y - Y')$ scores.

The reader will note once again that the sum of the error scores in Col. 2 of Table 8-2 is zero. This will be true for any set of data, because the least-squares regression line is located in such a way that the cases below the line exactly balance those above. Thus, the mean of the error scores will always equal zero.

$$\frac{\sum (Y - Y')}{N} = \frac{0}{N} = 0$$

Using this fact, a formula for the standard deviation of the error scores may be developed from the basic deviation score formula for the standard deviation.

$$S_{(\text{error scores})} = \sqrt{\frac{\sum (\text{error score} - \text{mean error score})^2}{N}}$$

$$= \sqrt{\frac{\sum [(Y - Y') - 0]^2}{N}} = \sqrt{\frac{\sum (Y - Y')^2}{N}} \qquad (8\text{-}8)$$

By comparing the final expression for $S_{(\text{error scores})}$ with that of Form. (8-7), it can be seen that the standard deviation of the error scores and the standard error of prediction are one and the same.

Additional Sources of Error in Predicted Values

Thus far, we have been concerned mainly with errors in prediction that are attributable to the fact that relationships between variables are usually far from perfect. As a consequence, few points on a scattergram will fall exactly on the regression line; most will cluster about the line. The value $S_{y \cdot x}$ is a measure of how closely they cluster. There are two additional sources of error in prediction which stem from the fact that the estimated regression line and the estimate $(S_{y \cdot x})$ of the array standard-deviation value must necessarily be based on a particular sample group for which both X- and Y-scores are available. First, the estimated regression line and $S_{y \cdot x}$ will usually be somewhat in error because of the chance effects mentioned earlier. Fortunately, these effects can be kept to a minimum by using a large number of cases in the sample group. A further possibility of error arises when predictions are made in a new situation for individuals somewhat different from those included in the sample group. For example, if the composition of the student body at college A has been gradually changing over the years, a regression equation based on a freshman class of several years ago might give somewhat erroneous results when used with current freshmen; and the equation might be completely inappropriate for making predictions at college B.

THE PEARSON CORRELATION COEFFICIENT: FURTHER CONSIDERATIONS

It should now be apparent that correlation and regression really involve two sides of the same coin and that the Pearson r is closely related to the least-squares regression line. Certain aspects of this relationship will now be examined in order to shed additional light on the meaning of the Pearson r.

The Variance Interpretation of r

In the previous chapter an attempt was made to explain how the correlation coefficient can be interpreted in terms of the proportion of variance in one variable which is associated with variance in the other. It would be helpful for the reader to review that discussion. The relationships upon which this interpretation is based can now be specified in greater detail, in terms of concepts introduced in the present chapter.

Consider once again the data in Table 8-2. The standard deviation of the ten Y-scores and the standard deviation of the ten error scores in Col. 2 have already been determined ($S_y = 2.646$, and $S_{error} = S_{y \cdot x} = 1.952$). The standard deviation of the predicted scores in Col. 1 can also be determined, using the appropriate sums from Table 8-2 and the raw-score Form. (4-5) for computing a standard deviation.

$$S_{y'} = \frac{1}{N} \sqrt{N \sum (Y')^2 - (\sum Y')^2} = \frac{1}{10} \sqrt{10 \, (391.76) - (60.00)^2} = 1.782$$

If the three standard deviations are squared, the corresponding variances are obtained.

$$S_y^2 = (2.646)^2 = 7.00 \quad \text{(total variance of the } Y\text{-scores)}$$
$$S_{y'}^2 = (1.782)^2 = 3.18 \quad \text{(variance of the predicted } (Y') \text{ scores)}$$
$$S_{y \cdot x}^2 = (1.952)^2 = 3.81 \quad \text{(variance of the error } (Y - Y') \text{ scores)}$$

Notice that $3.18 + 3.81 = 6.99$ or, within limits of rounding error, 7.00. That is, the total Y variance (S_y^2) can be divided into two parts.

$$S_y^2 = S_{y'}^2 + S_{y \cdot x}^2 \tag{8-9}$$

If we look closely at what the two variances on the right above represent, the meaning of this relationship may become apparent. The variance S_y^2 represents the total variation in the scores on the Y variable. Since an individual's predicted or Y'-score is obtained from his X-score, using the regression equation, the term $S_{y'}^2$ must represent that portion of the total Y variance which is associated with individual differences or variance on X. On the other hand, an individual's error score, $Y - Y'$, cannot be predicted; it is unrelated to his score on X; therefore, the term $S_{y \cdot x}^2$ must represent that portion of the total Y variance which cannot be predicted from X and thus that portion which is unrelated to individual differences or variance on X.

It can be seen, then, that the relationship among the three variances S_y^2, $S_{y'}^2$, and $S_{y \cdot x}^2$, is the one described earlier. That is:

$$S_y^2 \text{ (total } Y \text{ variance)} = S_{y'}^2 \left(\begin{array}{c} \text{portion associated with indi-} \\ \text{vidual differences in } X \end{array} \right)$$

$$+ S_{y \cdot x}^2 \text{ (portion associated with other factors)}$$

As was also pointed out earlier, the higher the correlation coefficient, the larger is that portion of the total variance of Y which can be said to be associated with individual differences or variance in X. This relationship can now be specified in terms of the above variances.

$$r^2 = \frac{S_{y'}^2}{S_y^2} \tag{8-10}$$

For the data of Tables 8-1 and 8-2.

$$(.675)^2 = .455$$

Thus, it can be said that, for the ten pupils of Tables 8-1 and 8-2, .455, or approximately 45 per cent of the total variance on achievement (Y), can be predicted from or is associated with aptitude (X).

Interpreting r in Terms of Slope

The relationship between r and the slope of the least-squares regression line can be reviewed by considering, once again, Form. (8-1).

$$b = \left(\frac{S_y}{S_x} \right) r$$

The slope is merely the correlation corrected for differences between the standard deviations of the two variables. Thus, for any given values of S_x and S_y, the value of r is directly proportional to the slope. A correlation of .60, for instance, indicates a slope twice that of $r = .30$. If the standard deviations were equal, the ratio (S_y/S_x) would equal 1, and the slope would equal the correlation.

When the correlation is 0, the slope also is 0 [i.e., $b = (S_y/S_x)\cdot 0 = 0$], indicating a perfectly horizontal regression line. This point can be used to illustrate how a correlation close to 0 may be obtained from a scattergram showing a high relationship between the two variables but with a marked degree of curvilinearity. Consider the scattergram sketch in Fig. 7-6(b). The best fitting *straight* line for such a scattergram would be perfectly horizontal. Consequently, both the slope and the Pearson r would be 0.

Interpreting r in Terms of Errors in Prediction

Two equivalent formulas for the standard error of prediction have been presented. One of them, Form. (8-6), which is commonly used in practice for determining $S_{y\cdot x}$, involves the Pearson r.

$$S_{y\cdot x} = S_y \sqrt{1 - r^2} \qquad (8\text{-}6)$$

The formula suggests that the higher the correlation, the smaller will be the value for $S_{y\cdot x}$. For correlations of 1.00 or -1.00, $S_{y\cdot x}$ is equal to 0:

$$S_{y\cdot x} = S_y \sqrt{1 - (\pm 1)^2} = S_y \sqrt{1 - 1} = S_y (0) = 0$$

and for a correlation of 0, $S_{y\cdot x}$ equals S_y.

$$S_{y\cdot x} = S_y \sqrt{1 - (0)^2} = S_y \sqrt{1} = S_y$$

Thus, the possible values for $S_{y\cdot x}$ vary between 0 and S_y, depending on the size of r.

For correlations of the size usually obtained in practice, $S_{y\cdot x}$ will be greater than 0 and less than S_y. That is, it will be equal to some fraction of S_y. The term $\sqrt{1 - r^2}$, sometimes called the *coefficient of alienation*,

Table 8-4

Values of the Coefficient of Alienation and of $S_{y\cdot x}$ (Assuming $S_y = 10$) for Various Values of r

r	$\sqrt{1 - r^2}$	$S_{y\cdot x}$
1.000	.000	0.00
.950	.312	3.12
.900	.436	4.36
.866	.500	5.00
.800	.600	6.00
.600	.800	8.00
.400	.916	9.16
.200	.980	9.80
.000	1.000	10.00

is that fraction. In Table 8-4, values of the coefficient of alienation and values of $S_{y \cdot x}$ (assuming, for illustrative purposes, that $S_y = 10$) have been listed for several values of r.

It can be seen that the correlation must be greater than .866 if the standard error of prediction, $S_{y \cdot x}$, is to be less than 1/2 of its maximum value. With correlations of .400 or less, predictions will be only slightly more accurate than with a correlation of 0.

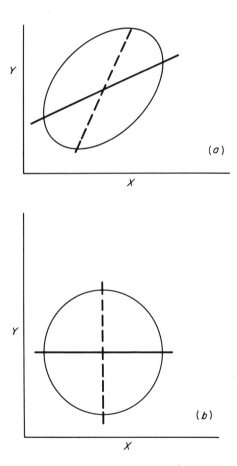

Figure 8-5. Regression Lines for Predicting Y from X (Solid Lines) and X from Y (Broken Lines) in Instances of Correlation (a) and No Correlation (b)

PREDICTING X FROM Y

The discussion in the present chapter to this point has been concerned with the prediction of scores scaled on the vertical (Y) axis from scores scaled on the horizontal (X) axis. Predictions can be made in the other direction as well; i.e., from Y to X. In order to determine the regression line for predicting X from Y, we wish to minimize the sum of the squares of the *horizontal* discrepancies about the line—i.e., $\sum (X - X')^2$. In Fig. 8-5, the regression lines for predicting X from Y (broken line) and Y from X (solid line) are represented schematically. It can be seen that the regression lines are different. This will be the case whenever r is less than $+1.00$ or -1.00. When there is no correlation between the two variables (i.e., if $r = 0$), the two regression lines are perpendicular to each other, as in Fig. 8-5(*b*). The formulas for predicting X from Y are the same as Forms. (8-1) through (8-6), with one modification. All X's, both scores and subscripts, should be rewritten as Y's, and all Y's as X's. The slope is now relative to the Y axis, and the intercept will be the point where the line crosses the X axis. The regression line for predicting X from Y is primarily of theoretical interest, because, in any practical problem, the predictor can always be scaled on the X axis and the criterion on the Y axis.

Exercises and Problems

1. On a piece of graph paper, draw the straight line for each of the following equations.
   a) $Y = -2X + 2$
   b) $Y = 3X - 1$
2. Consider the following set of scores for eight students on two tests.

Student	1	2	3	4	5	6	7	8
Score on X	2	5	3	4	5	7	8	6
Score on Y	1	2	4	3	6	5	7	4

   a) Compute directly from the raw scores the slope of the least-squares regression line for predicting Y from X.
   b) Compute the intercept, and write the regression equation in terms of raw scores.
   c) Using the equation from (*b*), compute the predicted Y-scores for Students 1, 3, and 5.

d) Compute the errors in prediction for Students 1, 3, and 5.
e) Construct a scattergram for the above data and draw the least-squares regression line.
f) Determine graphically the predicted scores and the errors in prediction for Students 1, 3, and 5.

3. The following data are for 300 students who have just completed their freshman year at a small liberal-arts college:

Aptitude scores (X)	Freshman grade-point averages (Y)
$\bar{X} = 62.0$	$\bar{Y} = 2.70$
$S_x = 8.0$	$S_y = .40$

$$r_{xy} = .60$$

a) Write the regression equation for predicting Y from X in terms of raw scores.
b) Two of this year's entering freshmen, John B. and Bill W., obtain scores of 58 and 70, respectively, on the aptitude test. What grade-point average do you predict for each?
c) What assumption or assumptions underly the predictions made in (b)?
d) Draw the regression line on a sheet of graph paper, and determine graphically the predicted scores of John B. and Bill W. Compare your answers with those in (b).
e) Write the regression equation in terms of deviation scores.
f) Write the regression equation in terms of standard scores.
g) Determine the standard error of prediction.
h) We can be 68 per cent confident that a freshman entering this year with an aptitude score of 58 will obtain a GPA somewhere between _____ and _____. We can be 95 per cent confident that such an individual will obtain a GPA between _____ and _____.
i) What assumption or assumptions underly the answers in (h)?

4. Give the appropriate symbol or, where possible, the numerical value for each of the following.

a) $\dfrac{\sum Y'}{N}$ b) $\dfrac{\sum (Y' - \bar{Y})^2}{N}$ c) $\dfrac{\sum (Y - Y')}{N}$

d) $\dfrac{\sum (Y - Y')^2}{N}$ e) $\dfrac{\sum (Y - \bar{Y})}{N}$ f) $\dfrac{\sum (Y - \bar{Y})^2}{N}$

5. The following are the data for 100 students on two personality tests, A and B:

$\bar{X}_A = 37.6$	$\bar{X}_B = 50.3$
$S_A = 4.2$	$S_B = 9.0$

$$r_{AB} = .60$$

Suppose, for each of the 100 students, a predicted score on B is obtained, using the least-squares regression equation. Suppose, furthermore, that an error score is obtained for each student by subtracting his predicted score from his actual score. Determine the value for each of the following.

a) The mean of the 100 predicted scores
b) The mean of the 100 error scores
c) The standard deviation of the 100 predicted scores
d) The standard deviation of the 100 error scores

6. The following are the data for a group of 105 children who were examined several times over a period of years.

IQ score at age 6 (X)	IQ score at age 15 (Y)
$\bar{X} = 102$	$\bar{Y} = 106$
$S_x = 16$	$S_y = 18$

$$r_{xy} = .65$$

a) Convert the following IQ scores at age 6 to standard scores: 102, 94, 126.
b) Use the standard score form of the regression equation to determine the predicted standard scores at age 15 for the standard scores obtained in (a).
c) Convert the predicted standard scores obtained in (b) to predicted IQ scores.

7. John Jones falls 1.5 standard deviations above the mean on variable X. His predicted score on Y, obtained using the least-squares regression equation, falls one standard deviation above $\bar{Y}$.
a)   What is the correlation between X and Y?
b) If b, the slope of the regression line in terms of raw scores, is equal to $+.67$, what do we know about S_X and S_Y?

8. In what sense would an r of .80 be interpreted as:
a) Twice an r of .40?
b) Four times an r of .40?
c) Approximately five times an r of .40?

9. The limits for r are -1.00 and $+1.00$. Would it ever be possible to obtain a slope, b, of greater than $+1.00$? Explain.

10. The least-squares regression equation for predicting scores on Y from scores on X is computed from the data for a sample of 500 students. Then, using the least-squares regression equation, a predicted score on Y is determined for each of the 500 students. The following are the summary statistics for the distribution of actual Y scores and for the distribution of predicted Y scores.

Actual Y-scores	Predicted Y-scores
Mean = 37.62	Mean = 37.62
Standard deviation = 4.00	Standard deviation = 3.00

a) What is the value of r_{XY}?
b) What is the value of the standard error of prediction?

11. Using the linear regression techniques described in this chapter, it is predicted that 68 per cent of those who obtain a score of 56 on a certain

arithmetic-aptitude test (X) will obtain a score between 32 and 40 on an arithmetic-achievement test (Y) administered at the end of the year.

a) What is the predicted achievement score for an aptitude score of 56?

b) What is the value of the standard error of prediction?

c) If the standard deviation of the actual achievement-test scores equals 8, what is the value of r_{XY}?

d) If $r_{XY} = .60$, what is the standard deviation of the actual achievement scores?

12. The correlation of test A with freshman GPA is .50 and the correlation of test B with freshman GPA is .71. Compare the two tests with regard to:

a) The proportion of GPA variance which can be predicted.

b) The standard error of prediction.

13. The use of the least-squares regression line for predicting Y from X:

a) Minimizes what standard deviation?

b) Maximizes what standard deviation?

14. Under what conditions will:

a) $S_y = S_{y'}$?

b) $S_y = S_{y \cdot x}$?

c) $S_{y'} = S_{y \cdot x}$?

Chapter 9

Statistical Inference and Probability

Statistical inference is the process of generalizing about an entire group from what is known about a sample of that group. This process, generalizing from samples to an entire group, is one in which everyone engages frequently, although usually without the help of statistical techniques. For instance, consider Mr. Jones, whose two friends own new Zeus automobiles. Both friends have had a good deal of engine trouble with their Zeuses and have discussed these troubles with Mr. Jones. Is Mr. Jones likely to buy a Zeus next time he needs a car? Possibly not; he may "conclude" from the experiences of his two friends that Zeuses are not very good automobiles. That is, he may infer from what he knows about a few Zeus automobiles that Zeus automobiles in general are subject to a great deal of engine trouble. Consider a second example. Suppose Mrs. Smith is taking a short cut through the park one day, on the way home from shopping. She notices a group of Boy Scouts playing football. One of the Boy Scouts unintentionally kicks the ball into Mrs. Smith, knocking her down and spilling her groceries all over the ground. Instead of helping Mrs. Smith to her feet and collecting her groceries for her, one of the boys rushes over, picks up the football and runs off to make a touchdown with the other boys hot on his heels. Mrs. Smith gets up, gathers her groceries in her arms and walks painfully on. If she has not had other contacts with Boy Scouts, Mrs. Smith is likely to infer from the actions of these few that Boy Scouts in general are a rude and thoughtless group. Is Mr. Jones justified in thinking that most Zeus automobiles are trouble-prone, or is Mrs. Smith justified in thinking that Boy Scouts as a

158

group are rude and thoughtless? Is it not possible that Mr. Jones's friends bought two of the very few lemons that the Zeus Motor Company has ever manufactured and that the few Boy Scouts Mrs. Smith saw are not representative of most Boy Scouts? The inferences of Mr. Jones and Mrs. Smith might be erroneous. The techniques of statistical inference help us to minimize the possibilities of such errors in our inferences and, in addition, provide us with some measure or indicator of how "good" our inferences are. That is, these techniques permit us to estimate how likely we are to be correct in our inferences from partial information. Before describing the techniques of statistical inference in more detail, it is necessary to clarify what is meant by two central terms: *population* and *sample*.

POPULATION

A population can be defined simply as the total group of elements (e.g., individuals) about which one wishes to generalize. The word *elements* can refer to more than humans or other living organisms. It may also refer to such things as automobiles, junior colleges, or lines of print from newspaper columns; to events such as tossing a coin or weighing an object; or even to intervals in time. In the examples given above, the populations were the group comprising all Zeus cars and that comprising all Boy Scouts. The particular population in which we are interested at any given time depends upon the research question we are asking. Consider the following examples.

1) *How well can the children in our state read?*   In this case, the population is "the children in our state." Now suppose we wanted to answer our research question. We would run into a difficulty immediately, for the population is not defined precisely enough. What is meant by "children"? Do we mean boys and girls who are twelve, thirteen, fourteen, and fifteen years old as well as those who are younger? What about those who are three years old or younger or those who are in institutions for the feeble-minded or who are blind or deaf? Before we can answer a research question, we must specify the population in as much detail as is necessary in order to exclude all of those in whom we are not interested and to include all of those in whom we are interested. In this case, for instance, we might specify as our population all of those who are in the fifth grade, who have no serious visual or hearing difficulties, who have attended regular classes (i.e., excluding special classes for abnormally slow learners) in the public schools since the age of five. Regardless of what the conditions for inclusion in the population might be, *they must be specified in sufficient detail*. Without such clarity, any conclusions we attempt to draw about the population will most certainly be ambiguous and misleading.

2) *How will the voters be split in the next schoolboard election in our city?* The population implied by this question is not all adults of voting age in our city, nor is it all registered voters, but it is that group of registered voters *who will vote* in the next schoolboard election. These are the people who are going to decide the election.

3) *What was the average yield of oranges per tree in southern California in 1960?* Here the population would be all the orange trees in southern California in 1960. Of course, we would have to be more specific than this in delimiting our population. For one thing, what do we mean by "southern California"? Where is the dividing line between southern California and northern California?

The foregoing questions involve single populations; however, some questions involve more than one population. Consider the following instances.

4) *Did last year's tenth-grade boys in our high school score higher than did the tenth-grade girls, on the mathematics part of the new aptitude test?*

5) *Did the seniors in our high school differ from the sophomores in the kinds of problems brought to their counselors last year?*

6) *Which of the five high schools in our city had the largest percentage of its 1960 graduates go on to college?* Here we have five populations, the class of 1960 from each of the five schools.

7) *How much did the present eighth-graders in our district gain in arithmetic skills from September of the seventh grade to September of the eighth grade?* Depending on how we look at this question, we may be dealing either with a single population (the present group of eighth-graders) or with two populations (the present group of eighth-graders in the September of their seventh grade and the present group of eighth-graders in the September of their eighth grade). That is, the same group of persons might be considered as two different populations if we are interested in their performances at two different times.

Thus far, all of the questions have involved what can be referred to as *real populations.* By a real population, we mean a population with well defined limits. Every element in the population exists now, existed at one time, or will exist in the future. Such a population includes a limited or finite number of elements. Barring practical considerations, we could, if we so desired, eventually locate and obtain a score for every member of the population; however, the populations implied in educational and psychological research often are what we will refer to as *hypothetical populations.* A hypothetical population does not have well defined limits. Such a population includes an infinite number of elements of which most do not exist now, have not existed in the past, and will not exist in the future. That is, most of the members are "hypothetical" elements. The following are questions which could be considered as implying hypothetical populations.

8) *Do tenth-grade boys like those in our high school tend to score higher than tenth-grade girls like those in our high school on the mathematics part of the new aptitude test?* Compare the wording of this question to that of Ques. 4. In that question we were concerned with real, limited populations, i.e., *the* tenth-grade boys and *the* tenth-grade girls *who attended* our high school last year. In Ques. 8, we are not concerned with real, limited groups, but with two hypothetical, unlimited groups of tenth-grade boys and girls *like* those in our high school. That is, we are concerned with tenth-grade boys and girls like those in our high school, "in general."

9) *Is method A better than method B for teaching the concept of multiplication to third-graders of average intelligence?* Here again we are not concerned with a particular, real, limited group of third-graders such as *the* third-graders who attended school in our district last year. Rather, we are concerned with two hypothetical groups of third-graders of average intelligence, a group which learned multiplication under teaching method *A* and another group which learned under method *B*. That is, we are concerned with third-graders of average intelligence, "in general."

10) *Is a certain gambler's die biased in that the number 6 comes up more often than it should?* The elements in the population implied by this question are events, throws of a single die. The population consists of an infinite number of such throws, most of which are hypothetical in the sense that they never have and never will occur. Essentially, the question deals with whether or not, in such a population, more than $1/6$ of the elements (throws) would have a score of 6 (i.e., come up 6).

11) *Are human adults able to react more quickly to a sound signal than to a light signal?* Here we are not interested in any real (finite) group of human adults, but human adults "in general."

SAMPLE

Conclusions about an entire population are often based on an examination of only a portion (sample) of the elements that make up the population. There are two general reasons for this. First, the time, expense, or inconvenience involved in examining every element in a real population can be prohibitive. Consider, for example, the task of predicting the results of an impending national election; it would be impractical to poll every eligible voter in the United States. Second, in the case of a hypothetical population, it is not possible to examine all members, because the majority are not identifiable. In the face of such difficulties we may select a sample from the entire group of elements comprising the population and infer from the characteristics of the sample what may be true for the population. Any such inferences, of course, will be correct only in the degree to which the sample is representative of the population.

There are numerous instances in which the method used to obtain a sample has precluded an accurate representation of the population. A widely quoted example of this is the *Literary Digest* fiasco of 1936. The *Literary Digest*, a national magazine, used mail ballots to poll a sample of 10 million eligible voters for the purpose of predicting the results of the 1936 presidential election. On the basis of the returns, it predicted a Landon victory; but Roosevelt won by a landslide. What went wrong? The enormous error in prediction can be partially attributed to the fact that the *Literary Digest* selected its sample largely from telephone directories and automobile-registration lists. As many second-guessers pointed out after the election, people who owned cars or who had telephones were economically better off than the rest of the voters and were primarily Republicans. The sample was not representative of the population of individuals who voted in that election.

Various specific procedures can be used to obtain an appropriate sample, but basic to statistical inference is the process of *random sampling*. In order that a sample may be truly random, two requirements must be met: First, *every element in the population must have an equal chance to be included in the sample*. It is easy to see that the *Literary Digest* sample was not random, for only those individuals in the voter population who owned automobiles or had telephone service could possibly have been included. Second, *whether or not any particular element is included in the sample must be completely independent of whether or not any other individual is included*. Suppose that one wants to obtain a random sample of the eligible voters in a small community, and every time a married person is selected for the sample his or her spouse is also selected. This might be done to save time by polling two people at one residence. But such a sample is not random because whether or not a married person is included in the sample is not independent of whether or not his or her spouse is included.

Sampling from a Real Population

Any of several techniques may be employed to draw a random sample. Comprehensive discussion of these will not be included here, but the interested student can consult one of the many available treatments of this subject. These techniques vary in complexity and practicality, but all are designed to meet or approximate the two criteria stated earlier. One might, for example, assign each element a number, write each number on a card, mix the cards thoroughly, and blindly draw enough cards to fill out the required sample size. Another technique involves the use of a table of random numbers to draw the sample.

It is frequently the case that techniques that rigorously meet the criteria of randomness are too time-consuming or expensive for the purposes at hand. In such instances, "*quasi*-random" techniques are used. One *quasi*-random technique applicable to human populations involves listing the individuals of the population alphabetically and drawing the sample by selecting every fifth, tenth, or *n*th one. Although this procedure does not precisely meet the criteria of randomness, it is often considered adequate. In educational research there are numbers of applications of statistical inference in which such techniques as those described above may be used appropriately.

For our purpose it will be sufficient to recognize that a representative sample is desired and that random selection is the basic way to approach representativeness. As will be evident later, all the principal techniques employed in statistical inference are predicated on the assumption of random selection of the sample. It should be apparent also that *random* does not mean *casual*. Randomness in sampling is achieved only by careful and systematic planning.

Sampling from a Hypothetical Population

The requirement that every element in the population must have had an equal chance of being included in the sample is, of course, impossible to achieve for a hypothetical population, since there is no chance at all for any of the non-existent "hypothetical" members of the population to be included. We can only select our sample from among those members of the population which do exist at the present time. Some might argue that, this being the case, it is impossible to obtain a truly random sample from a hypothetical population; however, the widespread use of statistical techniques which require random sampling for inferring about hypothetical populations suggests that there must be some sort of rationale behind such inferences.

Much of educational and psychological research dealing with hypothetical populations is concerned with differences between two populations. This is illustrated by Ques. 8 and 9. In Ques. 9, we are concerned with two hypothetical populations of third-graders of average intelligence, one of which learned multiplication under method *A* and one of which learned under method *B*. In answering this question, one would probably obtain a group of third-graders of average intelligence and divide them at random into two subgroups, *A* and *B*. Such a division could be accomplished by using the method of alphabetical listing suggested above or by using a table of random numbers. Group *A* would be subjected to teaching method *A* and group *B* to teaching method *B*; then, after a certain length of time, the groups could be compared with regard to their multiplication skills. In a situation like this, the usual practice is to assume that groups *A* and *B* are random samples from the hypothetical populations of third-graders which would have been obtained had an infinite number of third-graders been selected in exactly the same way, under the same conditions, and subjected to the same treatments (e.g., methods *A* and *B*). Any statistical inferences would be limited to these hypothetical populations. That is why it is important to specify *in sufficient detail*, the characteristics of the situation in which the sample groups were obtained, the way in which they were selected and assigned to groups, and the treatments to which they were subjected.

When one attempts to answer Research Ques. 8, he will have to proceed in slightly different fashion, but the principles involved in making an inference about a hypothetical population remain the same. In Ques. 8 we are concerned with a hypothetical population of tenth-grade boys and a hypothetical population of tenth-grade girls just like those in our school. In order to answer this question, we might compare the performances of all the tenth-grade boys in our school with the performances of all the tenth-grade girls. We would then assume that the tenth-grade boys in our school are a random sample of tenth-grade boys from a hypothetical population of an infinite number of tenth-grade boys selected in the same way. Very "unreal" considerations must be entertained in trying to arrive at a conception of the hypothetical population. For instance, the boys in the population could be considered to be from an infinite number of hypothetical schools identical to our school, in hypothetical communities with the same pattern of geographic, social, and economic characteristics, consisting of hypothetical families with the same pattern of background characteristics, and so on. The tenth-grade girls could be considered a random sample from a similar hypothetical population of girls. Any statistical inferences about differences in mathematics aptitude between boys and girls would be limited to such hypothetical populations.

To repeat the major point of the foregoing discussion, when dealing with hypothetical populations, any *statistical* inferences are limited to populations of elements selected in exactly the same way under exactly the same conditions. In practice, this means that statistical inferences involving hypothetical populations are usually severely limited. The researcher is often interested in generalizing his conclusions to groups of individuals in situations which have characteristics which differ in various degrees from the characteristics of the situation in which the sample was obtained.

For instance, a psychology professor, conducting research at a particular college on the effectiveness of teaching machines, may wish to make inferences about how effective the machines might be if they were used in other colleges as well. Such inferences would be beyond the hypothetical population defined by the situation in which his research was conducted and, consequently, would not be statistical inferences. The extent to which such non-statistical inferences are valid would depend upon the similarity between the relevant characteristics defining the original hypothetical population and the characteristics of the new group. This issue will be discussed further in subsequent chapters.

PROBABILITY AND PROBABILITY DISTRIBUTIONS

Let us assume that Mr. Adams received the following message from his stockbroker: "The probability is very great that there will be a radical upturn in the market very soon." If he had a good deal of confidence in his broker and some extra money in the bank, Mr. Adams would probably want to buy some stock as soon as possible. On the other hand, if the message had read, "The probability of any upturn in the market within the foreseeable future is very small," he might not be so eager to invest his money in the market. To use another example, suppose that a large and reputable research agency, under contract to a particular city, reported the following conclusion: "It is highly probable that the population of this community will be doubled in the next ten years." We would expect that the local schoolboard would begin thinking about possible sites for new schools. All these examples involve the popular usage of the term *probability*. Each describes a situation in which at least some uncertainty is implied and in which the term *probability* refers to the likelihood that a particular event of interest, such as a stock-market upturn, will occur.

In subsequent chapters on statistical inference, we shall be concerned with the probabilities of obtaining various results for elements selected at random from an entire group or population. The term *probability*, as it will be used in these chapters, requires a somewhat more technical definition: *Given a population of elements, the probability of randomly selecting a particular type of element is the relative frequency (i.e., proportion) with which that type of element occurs in the population.* For example, consider as the population of elements a group of 100 students, comprising 75 males and 25 females. The probability of randomly selecting *a male* from this population is .75 (i.e., 75/100), and the probability of selecting a female is .25 (i.e., 25/100). The requirement of randomness is basic to this definition; that is, the definition is applicable only in situations wherein

(1) each element has an equal chance of being selected and (2) the selection of any element is independent of the selection of any other element.

The meaning of a probability value can perhaps be better understood by considering the operation of repeated sampling *with replacement*. Suppose we randomly select an individual from our population of 100 students, record his sex, and then return him to the population. Suppose, further, that we repeat this process many times, each time replacing the individual who has been selected. Over the long run we would expect to select a male about .75 of the time and a female about .25 of the time. This illustrates an alternative way of looking at probability: *The probability of selecting a particular type of element (e.g., a male) is equal to the proportion of times we would expect to select that type of element randomly "in the long run."* Some additional examples may help clarify the foregoing.

Example 9-1. What is the probability of obtaining "heads" in a flip of a coin? Consider an infinitely large hypothetical population, each element of which is a flip of the coin. The relative frequency with which heads would occur in this population is .50; therefore, if a single flip is considered as an element selected at random, the probability of heads is .50. Or, alternately, suppose the coin were flipped many, many times—we would expect to obtain heads about .50 of the time, over the long run.

Example 9-2. Let us assume that the heights of a large group of women are normally distributed with a mean of 66.00 in. and a standard deviation of 2.00 in. If an individual is selected at random from this population, what is the probability that her height will be greater than 70 in.? In this example, the type of element in which we are interested is "a woman with a height of more than 70 in." The relative frequency with which this type of element occurs is easily determined through use of Appx. 2. A score of 70 corresponds to $z = +2.00$—i.e., $(70 - 66)/2$. In Col. 3 of Appx. 2 we find that, in a normal distribution, the relative frequency of scores with z's above $+2.00$ is .023. The probability that a randomly selected woman will be over 70 in. tall, therefore, is .023. The student should see at once that this is the theoretical proportion of times we would select such a woman if we sampled the population a large number of times, randomly and with replacement each time.

Example 9-3. Consider again the group of women in Ex. 9-2. If we selected an individual at random from this population, what is the probability that we would select one with a height greater than 70 in. *or* less than 62 in.? In this example, any woman with a height *either* greater than

70 in. *or* less than 62 in. would be of the type we are interested in. In Ex. 9-2, we determined that .023 of the women were over 70 in. tall. Since a height of 62 in. corresponds to $z = -2.00$, .023 is also the proportion of women in the group who are under 62 in. tall. Therefore, the relative frequency with which the type of woman we are interested in would occur in the population is .046 (i.e., .023 + .023 = .046), and the probability of selecting such a woman at random is .046.

The reader should be cautioned at this point lest he make an incorrect interpretation of the term *probability*, as defined. Suppose Mrs. Robert Jones were one of the group of women referred to in Ex. 9-2 above. Suppose the statement, "The probability that Mrs. Robert Jones is more than 70 in. tall is .023," were made. This statement makes no sense, because, regardless of whether we know her height or not, either Mrs. Jones is over 70 in. tall or she isn't. That is, the probability is either 1.00 or 0 for Mrs. Jones, even though we may not be sure which it is. A probability value does not refer to any particular element in the population. Rather, it refers to the proportion of times a particular type of element would be selected if the process of random sampling were repeated an infinite number of times. Thus, it is equal to the relative frequency with which this type of element occurs in the population.

Probability Distributions

When an entire group or population is divided into subgroups of different types, the relative frequency for each subgroup can be interpreted as the probability of obtaining an element from that subgroup if an element were selected at random from the population. Consider the relative-frequency distribution of height scores for the population of 200 men represented in Table 9-1. If one individual were to be selected at random from this population, the probability of obtaining a man with a height of less than 59.5 in. would be .01, that of obtaining a man with a height between 59.5 in. and 61.5 in. would be .03, and so on. Similarly, the probability of obtaining a man with a height between 61.5 and 67.5 in. would be .275 (i.e., .025 + .070 + .180 = .275). When a relative-frequency distribution is thus interpreted (i.e., in terms of probabilities) it is called a *probability distribution*. Table 9-1 illustrates an important property of all probability distributions: since the various subgroups (class intervals in Fig. 9-1) exhaust all of the individuals in the entire population, the probabilities associated with the subgroups total exactly 1.00.

The probability distribution represented in Table 9-1 was obtained by empirical procedures. That is, each of the 200 individuals in the population was weighed, the weights were organized into a frequency distribution,

Table 9-1

Empirical Relative-Frequency Distribution
of Heights of 200 Men

Height in Inches	f	Rel. f
78–79	4	.020
76–77	7	.035
74–75	18	.090
72–73	22	.110
70–71	39	.195
68–69	47	.235
66–67	36	.180
64–65	14	.070
62–63	5	.025
60–61	6	.030
58–59	2	.010
	200	1.00

and the relative frequencies (probabilities) were obtained by dividing each of the frequencies by 200. Most of the probability distributions utilized in statistical-inference procedures are not empirically determined. They are arrived at through deductive procedures utilizing mathematical techniques and the basic laws of the theory of probability. Probability distributions so derived will be referred to as *theoretical* (as opposed to *empirical*) probability distributions. An example of such a probability distribution is represented in Table 9-2. The relative frequencies (probabilities) are for a

Table 9-2

Theoretical Relative-Frequency Distribution
for Rolls of a Fair Die

Number on "Up" Side	Rel. f
6	.167
5	.167
4	.167
3	.167
2	.167
1	.167
	1.00

population of an infinite number of rolls of a "fair" die. One would expect each of the six sides to turn up 1/6 of the time. The relative frequencies obviously were not obtained by actually rolling a "fair" die an infinite number of times and recording the results.

One theoretical probability distribution of great importance to the theory and procedures of statistical inference has already been discussed in some detail. It was not referred to as a probability distribution at the time, although its relation to the laws of chance was briefly mentioned. This, of course, is the normal curve. If a relative-frequency distribution can be closely approximated by a normal curve, the relative frequencies and, thus, the probabilities can be obtained utilizing the procedures described in Chap. 5. As the reader will see in subsequent chapters, statistical-inference techniques lean heavily on the use of theoretical probability distributions.

Exercises and Problems

1. For one roll of a die, what is the probability of obtaining:
   a) A one?
   b) A six?
   c) Either a one or a two?
2. At a banquet for 300 people, one portable TV, three turkeys, and six symphonic records are to be given as door prizes. Ten slips of paper, each with the name of a prize on it, have been hidden under ten of the 300 dinner plates on a random basis, before the guests enter the banquet room. What is the probability that any one guest will win:
   a) The TV?
   b) A symphonic record?
   c) A door prize?
3. If you select a card from a well shuffled standard fifty-two-card deck, what is the probability you will select:
   a) A five of hearts?
   b) A five?
   c) A red card?
   d) A face card (aces not to be considered face cards)?
   e) A red face card?
   f) A red queen?
   g) A ten or less (aces high)?
4. The scores on a math-aptitude test for the fifth-grade boys in our school are normally distributed with a mean of 60 and a standard deviation of 8. If a boy is selected at random from this population, what is the probability that the boy's aptitude score will be:
   a) Above 60?
   b) Above 72?
   c) Either above 72 or below 48?
   d) Between 56 and 68?

5. If a boy is selected at random from the population specified in Prob. 4, the probability is .50 that his aptitude score will fall within ____ points of the mean of 60.

6. If a boy is selected at random from the population specified in Prob. 4, the probability is ____ that his aptitude score will fall within 10 points of the mean of 60.

7. What is the population implied in Prob. 1? What are the elements of the population?

8. Suppose the weather man says, "The probability of rain tomorrow is .75." How might the .75 be interpreted as a relative frequency?

9. Tommy Smith is one of the fifth-graders referred to in Prob. 4. What is the probability that his aptitude score is below 50? (Any comment concerning this question?)

Chapter 10

Sampling Distribution of a Statistic

In the previous chapter, the process of making inferences about unknown facts for an entire population from what is known about a sample was discussed in general terms. It is possible to make such inferences in fairly casual fashion, but one is more likely to arrive at accurate conclusions if appropriate statistical procedures are utilized. These procedures provide a systematic means of making inferences; and, in addition, they provide an objective basis for deciding how accurate the inferences might be. Although inference procedures are for use in situations in which the population facts are *unknown*, we shall concern ourselves in the present chapter with sampling from populations the characteristics of which are *known*. This will provide the necessary theoretical background for the specific techniques to be presented in subsequent chapters.

In the introductory discussion of probability presented earlier, the examples were concerned with the probabilities of obtaining various results when a *single element* is randomly selected from a population of known characteristics. In this chapter, we shall determine the probabilities of obtaining various results when a *sample of several elements* is selected. It should be pointed out that the rationale and techniques to be covered are appropriate only when the population is very large in relation to the sample. If the sample includes more than 5 per cent of the elements in the population, the techniques must be modified. (A number of more advanced texts discuss such modifications.) In most situations, however, involving real populations, the population will be very large relative to the sample, and the techniques presented here will apply. They will always be applica-

171

ble, of course, in situations involving hypothetical populations, for such populations contain an unlimited number of individuals.

Statistics and Parameters

We have referred to sample facts and population facts. In the terminology of statistical inference, these are known as *statistics* and *parameters*, respectively. For instance, the mean, median, standard deviation, and quartile deviation of the frequency distribution of heights for a *sample* of male college freshmen would be considered statistics. On the other hand, the mean, median, standard deviation and quartile deviation for the *entire population* of freshman boys from which the sample was selected would be considered parameters. Since it is necessary to make explicit distinctions between statistics and parameters in formulas, some new symbolization must be introduced. Thus far, we have used the symbols $\overline{X}$ and S to represent the mean and standard deviation respectively. From now on, $\overline{X}$ and S will designate the *sample* mean and *sample* standard deviation. For the population mean and standard deviation, the Greek letters μ (mu) and σ (sigma) will be used. To summarize:

$$\overline{X} = \text{sample mean}$$
$$\mu = \text{population mean}$$
$$S = \text{standard deviation of the sample}$$
$$\sigma = \text{standard deviation of the population}$$

SAMPLING DISTRIBUTIONS OF MEANS

A concept basic to all of statistical inference is that of *a sampling distribution*. In order to illustrate this concept, we shall refer to an artificially constructed population of 850 eleventh-grade boys from a large suburban school district. The frequency distribution of scores on a well known test of mathematics aptitude is approximately normal for this population and has the following mean and standard deviation.

$$\mu = 302.50, \qquad \sigma = 12.32$$

Now suppose we select a random sample of four individuals from this population and compute the sample mean. Would the sample mean be exactly equal to the population mean of 302.50? This is, of course, a possibility; however, it is also possible that a few individuals with very high scores and none with very low scores might be included in the sample. This would result in a sample mean somewhat greater than 302.50. Or, conversely, it is possible that more individuals with low IQs would be included, resulting in a mean less than 302.50.

That is, *although a sample mean may turn out to be exactly equal to the population mean, it will more probably turn out to be greater or less, because of the chance factors involved in random sampling.*

Suppose a second sample of four individuals is selected at random from the population. Again, it is unlikely that the mean of the sample will equal the mean of the population. Suppose we continue to select sample after sample, of four individuals each, from our artificial population of eleventh-graders, until thirty such samples have been selected. We then compute the mean of each sample and construct a relative-frequency distribution of the thirty sample means, as in Table 10-1. It should be pointed out that, once the aptitude scores are recorded for a sample, the individuals are returned to the population before another sample is selected. Thus, the population will not be depleted by taking many samples. The fact that the same individual can be included in several samples will cause us no problem. Now, we similarly select an additional thirty samples, this time of size 16, from the population and compute the means of these samples.

Table 10-1

Relative-Frequency Distribution of Sample Means for Groups of Thirty Samples Each, Randomly Selected from a Population in Which $\mu = 302.50$ and $\sigma = 12.32$

Value of Sample Mean $\overline{X}$	Means of 30 Samples of Size 4 f	Rel. f	Means of 30 Samples of Size 16 f	Rel. f
314–315	1	.03		
312–313	2	.07		
310–311	1	.03		
308–309	2	.07	2	.07
306–307	3	.10	6	.20
304–305	4	.13	9	.30
302–303	4	.13	4	.13
300–301	5	.17	6	.20
298–299	1	.03	2	.07
296–297	3	.10	1	.03
294–295	2	.07		
292–293	0	.00		
290–291	0	.00		
288–289	2	.07		
	30	1.00	30	1.00

Mean of sample means = 302.37. Standard deviation* of sample means = 6.31.

Mean of sample means = 303.43. Standard deviation* of sample means = 2.94.

* Corrected for grouping error

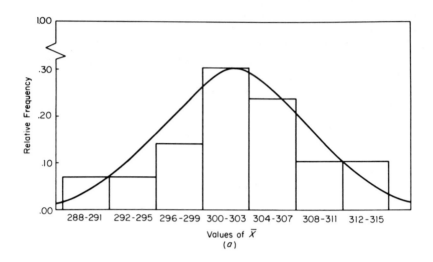

30 Samples of Size 4

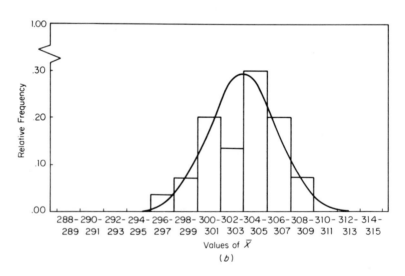

30 Samples of Size 16

Figure 10-1. Histograms for the Relative-Frequency Distributions of Means of Table 10-1 (Normal Curves Superimposed)

The relative-frequency distribution for this last set of thirty means is also presented in Table 10-1. The histograms for the two relative-frequency distributions of sample means are presented in Fig. 10-1. The histogram for the means of samples of size 4 has been constructed using larger class intervals than were used for the frequency distribution itself, in order to reduce chance irregularities.

The notion of a frequency distribution for thirty sample means may seem somewhat confusing at first, because all frequency distributions discussed previously have been based on groups of scores for individuals; however, this confusion should disappear if the reader will keep in mind the fact that the mean of a sample of several individuals is a *single number* and consequently can be treated as the "score" for that sample. A frequency distribution of the "scores" for thirty samples can be constructed, and the mean and standard deviation of the distribution of thirty "scores" can be computed, using the appropriate formulas from Chaps. 3 and 4.

The two relative-frequency distributions of sample means presented in Fig. 10-1 are empirical approximations of the theoretical distributions which would have been obtained had an infinite number of random samples been selected for each of the two sample sizes. The latter theoretical distributions would be known as *random-sampling distributions of means*. The relative-frequency distributions of Fig. 10-1 have been referred to as *empirical*, because each is based on the means of thirty samples actually selected from the population. A sampling distribution, on the other hand, is a *theoretical* notion. It could never be obtained by empirical procedures, because it would never be possible to select an infinite number of samples.

Properties of Sampling Distributions of Means

Most probably, the chance factors involved in random sampling would result in some differences between an empirical relative-frequency distribution of only thirty sample means and a theoretical distribution of an infinite number of sample means. Nonetheless, it will prove useful if several observations are made concerning Table 10-1 and Fig. 10-1: (1) The mean of the empirical distribution of thirty sample means is, in each case, close to the population mean of 302.50. (2) The variability of the distribution based on samples of size 16 is a good deal less than the variability of the distribution based on samples of size 4. (3) The histograms for both distributions can be fairly well approximated by normal curves. These observations reflect certain important properties of sampling distributions of means, properties which have been derived in the course of the development of statistical theory.

First of all, *the mean of a sampling distribution of means is equal to the mean, μ, of the population from which the samples were drawn.* In the examples discussed above, the mean mathematical-aptitude score for the population of eleventh-grade boys was 302.50; therefore, the mean of a random-sampling distribution of means for an infinite number of samples selected from this population would also equal 302.50. This should appear reasonable on an intuitive basis; for, if many random samples were selected, one would expect to obtain by chance about as many sample means above 302.50 as below 302.50, resulting in an average of about 302.50.

Second, *the value of the standard deviation of a sampling distribution of means is a function of both the population standard deviation, σ, and the sample size, N.* This theoretical value is called the *standard error of the mean* and is obtained by the formula:

$$\sigma_{\bar{X}} = \frac{\sigma}{\sqrt{N}} \qquad (10\text{-}1)$$

where $\sigma_{\bar{X}}$ is the symbol for standard error of the mean

For instance, the σ of the distribution of mathematics-aptitude scores for the population is 12.32; therefore, the standard error of the mean for samples of size 4 would be determined as follows.

$$\sigma_{\bar{X}} = \frac{\sigma}{\sqrt{N}} = \frac{12.32}{\sqrt{4}} = \frac{12.32}{2} = 6.16$$

The value of 6.31 obtained for the empirical distribution of Table 10-1 is a very close approximation of the theoretical value of 6.16. The standard error of the mean for samples of size 16 would equal:

$$\sigma_{\bar{X}} = \frac{\sigma}{\sqrt{N}} = \frac{12.32}{\sqrt{16}} = \frac{12.32}{4} = 3.08$$

Again, the value of 2.94 obtained for the distribution in Table 10-1 is close to the theoretical value.

The last paragraph illustrates a point that should be emphasized. There is not just one sampling distribution of means for any particular population. Rather, there are many, one for every possible sample size. All of these sampling distributions will have the same mean (i.e., the mean of the population) but different standard deviations; therefore, when referring to the standard error of a sample mean, one should always specify the sample size.

Third, *under certain conditions, sampling distributions of means can be closely approximated by normal curves.* That is, for any sample size, the relative-frequency distribution of means obtained from successive samples can be approximated by a normal curve, as illustrated in Fig. 10-1, if the population of raw scores is normally distributed. Furthermore, for samples which are fairly large, sampling distributions of means can be closely approximated by normal curves regardless of the shape of the population distribution of raw scores. The last statement involves what is known as the *Central Limit Theorem*.

Central Limit Theorem

The Central Limit Theorem is illustrated in Fig. 10-2. The top histogram represents the frequency distribution of scores from a particular population. Its shape is clearly not that of the normal curve. A total of 200 random samples of two cases each was drawn from the population, and the mean for each sample was computed. The middle histogram represents

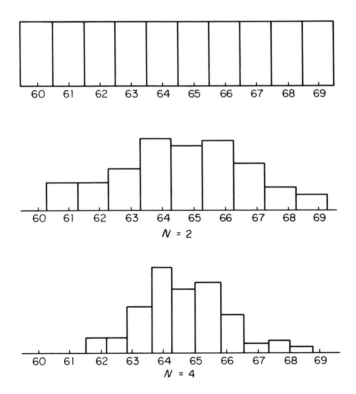

Figure 10-2. Distributions of 200 Random-Sample Means for N = 2 and N = 4, Each Set of Samples Drawn from a Non-normal Population

the frequency distribution of these 200 means. In addition, 200 random samples, of four cases each, were drawn from the population, producing the distribution of sample means shown by the bottom histogram. It can be seen that the distributions of sample means tend to appear more normal as the sample size is increased from two to four individuals. If the sample size were increased further, the trend toward normality would continue with the result that, for fairly large samples (i.e., those in which N is greater than 30), one could use the normal curve as an approximation of a sampling distribution of means, with a good deal of confidence, even though the population distribution of scores is far from normal.

Standard Error of the Mean

It is not difficult to understand why the standard deviation of a sampling distribution of the mean is referred to as a standard *error* of the mean. Suppose that the mean mathematics-aptitude score, μ, of our population of eleventh-grade boys were unknown. Which would most likely be a better estimate of its value, a sample mean based on four individuals, or a sample mean based on sixteen individuals? This question can be answered by referring to Fig. 10-1, where the sampling distributions of means for the two sample sizes are compared. It can be observed that the spread or dispersion of the sample means about the population mean, as represented by the standard *error*, is greater for the sampling distribution based on samples of size 4. That is, the *error* involved in using the sample mean with the larger standard error, as an estimate of the population mean, is likely to be greater than the error involved in using the sample mean with the smaller standard error. Furthermore, since the sample size, N, is in the denominator in the formula for the standard error ($\sigma_{\bar{X}} = \sigma/\sqrt{N}$), the standard error will always be greater for small samples and less for large samples.

A Random-Sampling Distribution of Means as a Probability Distribution

In the previous chapter, probability was explained in terms of the relative frequency with which elements of a particular type occur in the entire group or population of elements. Although the discussion was limited to the random selection of a single element, the same principles apply to the results of selecting a random sample of several elements. In order to understand this new application, the reader must be prepared to stretch the concept of "element" to include samples of several individuals. For instance, consider a group of an infinite number of random samples, of size 16, selected from the population of eleventh-grade boys we have been discussing. Now, try to conceive of this group of samples as a hypothetical population, each element of which is a sample of size 16. This is the population of all the possible samples of size 16 which might be selected. Associated with each element (sample), is a score—the sample mean, $\overline{X}$. In these terms, then, the random selection of a sample could be considered as the random selection of a single element from the hypothetical population of all possible samples.

Now, suppose we wished to determine the probability of obtaining a sample mean of greater than some specific value, say 306, if a single sample of size 16 were randomly selected from our population of eleventh-grade boys. The principles of the previous chapter can be applied. *The probability of selecting a random sample of a particular type* (e.g., one in which the mean mathematics-aptitude score falls above 306) *would equal the relative frequency with which that type of sample occurs in the hypothetical population of all possible samples.* The relative-frequency distribution of means for the hypothetical population of samples would be the random-sampling distribution of means; therefore, the desired probability can be determined if one has sufficient knowledge of the properties of the random-sampling distribution. These principles will be illustrated in detail in the next section.

Probability of Obtaining a Sample Mean Greater or Less than a Given Value

Example 10-1. For the population of eleventh-graders, the mean of the aptitude scores is 302.50, and the standard deviation is 12.32. Suppose a single sample of size 16 is to be randomly selected from this population. What is the probability that the sample mean, $\overline{X}$, will be greater than 306?

It is known that the sampling distribution of means for samples of size 16: (1) would have a mean equal to the population mean, μ, of 302.50, (2) would have a standard deviation equal to 3.08 (i.e., $\sigma_{\overline{X}} = \sigma/\sqrt{N} = 12.32/\sqrt{16} = 12.32/4 = 3.08$), and (3) could be approximated by a normal curve. This sampling distribution is illustrated again in Fig. 10-3. It should be emphasized that the sampling distribution is theoretical; only one sample of sixteen individuals is actually to be selected. The theoretical distribution represents the relative-frequency distribution of the means of all the many, many possible samples that *might* be selected (i.e., the hypothetical population of possible samples).

In order to determine the probability of obtaining a sample mean greater than 306, we must determine the proportion of sample means which would

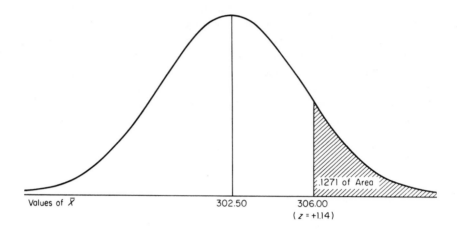

Figure 10-3. Sampling Distribution of Means of Samples of Size 16, Randomly Selected from a Normal Population, with μ Equal to 302.50 and σ equal to 12.32 ($\sigma_{\overline{X}}$ = 3.08)

fall above that value for the hypothetical population of all possible samples. A sample mean of 306 corresponds to a standard score of + 1.14.

$$z = \frac{306.00 - 302.50}{3.08} = +1.14$$

From Appx. 2 it is determined that only .1271 of the area under a normal curve falls above $z = +1.14$. We can conclude that only .1271 of all of the possible samples would have means above 306.00; therefore, if only one sample of sixteen individuals is to be selected, the probability that the mean, $\overline{X}$, will be above 306 is approximately .13. That is, if we selected 100 such samples, we would expect that, on the average, thirteen of them would have means above 306.

The reader should note that the z ratio used in Ex. 10-1 is of the following general form.

$$z = \frac{\overline{X} - \mu}{\sigma_{\overline{X}}} \qquad (10\text{-}2)$$

A ratio of this form will now be illustrated in a second example.

Example 10-2. Suppose the mean age of all graduating high-school seniors in a very populous county is 204.30 months and the standard deviation of the distribution of ages is 4.00 months. If a single random sample of 64 individuals is selected from this population, what is the probability

that the mean age at graduation for the sample will be either greater than
204.80 months or less than 203.80 months?

Here we must refer to the sampling distribution of means for samples
of size 64 selected from this population. The mean of the sampling distribution would equal μ or 204.30, and the standard error of the mean
would be:

$$\sigma_{\overline{X}} = \frac{\sigma}{\sqrt{N}} = \frac{4.00}{\sqrt{64}} = \frac{4.00}{8} = .50$$

A sample mean of 204.80 months corresponds to a standard score of 1.00.

$$z = \frac{\overline{X} - \mu}{\sigma_{\overline{X}}} = \frac{204.80 - 204.30}{.50} = \frac{.50}{.50} = +1.00$$

According to Appx. 2, .1587 of the hypothetical population of samples
have means which fall above a z of $+1.00$, or 204.80 months. A sample
mean of 203.80 months corresponds to a z of -1.00.

$$z = \frac{203.80 - 204.30}{.50} = \frac{-.50}{.50} = -1.00$$

Similarly, .1587 of the possible samples would have means of less than
203.80 months; therefore, for the type of sample we are interested in (i.e.,
with $\overline{X}$ either greater than 204.80 months or less than 203.80 months),
the relative frequency in the hypothetical population of possible samples is
approximately .32 (i.e., 1587 + .1587 = .3174). This is illustrated in Fig.
10-4. A probability of .32 suggests that it is quite possible for the mean

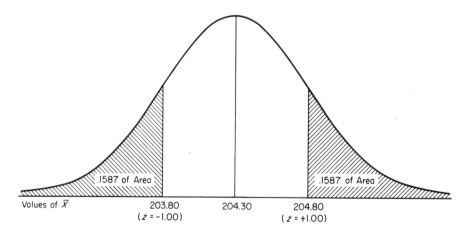

*Figure 10-4. Sampling Distribution of Means of Samples of Size
64, Randomly Selected from a Population, with μ Equal to
204.30 and σ Equal to 4.00 ($\sigma_{\overline{X}} = .50$; Total Shaded Area = .3174)*

age in a random sample of size 64 to be greater than 204.80 or less than 203.80.

One point should be emphasized concerning the foregoing example. Appendix 2 was used even though nothing was stated about the shape of the distribution of ages in the population of high-school seniors. This is quite legitimate, because for samples as large as this one (sixty-four individuals), the sampling distribution of the means will be approximately normal unless the shape of the population distribution is very odd indeed.

SAMPLING DISTRIBUTION OF DIFFERENCES BETWEEN MEANS

So far, we have been referring to an artificially constructed population of 850 eleventh-grade boys from which we have selected a number of samples. Let us now consider a situation which involves both this population and a second population of 850 eleventh-grade girls from the same school district. The frequency distribution of mathematics-aptitude scores is approximately normal for both populations. The means and standard deviations for the distributions of mathematics-aptitude scores are presented below.

$$\text{Males} \qquad \mu_M = 302.50, \qquad \sigma_M = 12.32$$
$$\text{Females} \qquad \mu_F = 298.03, \qquad \sigma_F = 10.78$$

Suppose the following series of operations is performed: (1) A pair of random samples is selected, a sample of sixteen individuals from the population of boys and a sample of nine individuals from the population of girls. (2) The mean mathematics-aptitude score is computed for each of the two samples. (3) The mean of the sample of girls is subtracted from the mean of the sample of boys (i.e., the difference $\overline{X}_M - \overline{X}_F$ is obtained). The individuals in the two samples are now returned to their respective populations, and a second pair of samples ($N_M = 16$ and $N_F = 9$) is selected. The sample means are computed; the difference, $\overline{X}_M - \overline{X}_F$, is determined; and the individuals are returned to the populations. This process is repeated until thirty pairs of samples in all have been selected and the difference between the means has been determined for each pair. The relative-frequency distribution for the thirty differences obtained is presented in Table 10-2. It is an empirical approximation of the theoretical relative-frequency distribution of differences between means which would have been obtained had an infinite number of pairs of samples of sizes 16 and 9 been randomly selected from the two populations. The theoretical distribution would be known as a *random-sampling distribution of differences between means*.

Examination of Table 10-2 may well raise a question in the minds of some readers, because the differences toward the bottom of the relative-

Table 10-2

Relative-Frequency Distribution of Differences between Sample Means ($\overline{X}_M - \overline{X}_F$) for Thirty Pairs of Samples Randomly Selected from Two Populations
($\mu_M = 302.50$ and $\sigma_M = 12.32$; $\mu_F = 298.03$ and $\sigma_F = 10.78$)

Value of Difference between Sample Means ($\overline{X}_M - \overline{X}_F$)	f	Rel. f
12 to 13	1	.03
10 to 11	3	.10
8 to 9	1	.03
6 to 7	3	.10
4 to 5	6	.20
2 to 3	5	.17
0 to 1	5	.17
−2 to −1	3	.10
−4 to −3	2	.07
−6 to −5	1	.03
	30	1.00

Mean of differences between means = 3.23
Standard deviation of differences between means = 4.39*

* Corrected for grouping error

frequency distribution are negative numbers. The presence of the negative numbers, if this is a source of confusion, can best be explained by reviewing the procedure used to obtain each of the differences. For each pair of samples, the mean of the female sample, $\overline{X}_F$, was always subtracted from the mean of the male sample, $\overline{X}_M$, to obtain the difference, $\overline{X}_M - \overline{X}_F$. When, for a particular pair, the mean of the female sample is smaller than the mean of the male sample, the difference between the means is positive. On the other hand, when the mean of the female sample is larger than the mean of the male sample, the difference between the means is negative. For example, if $\overline{X}_M = 303$ and $\overline{X}_F = 297$, then $\overline{X}_M - \overline{X}_F = 303 - 297 = +6$; or if $\overline{X}_M = 300$ and $\overline{X}_F = 301$, then $\overline{X}_M - \overline{X}_F = 300 - 301 = -1$. Since the mean of the female population, μ_F, is less than the mean of the male population, μ_M, one would expect that $\overline{X}_F$ would usually be less than $\overline{X}_M$ and the difference, $\overline{X}_M - \overline{X}_F$, would usually be positive. Because of the chance factors involved in random sampling, however, $\overline{X}_F$ will sometimes be greater than $\overline{X}_M$, and the resulting difference will be negative; therefore, when considering the difference between the means for a pair of samples selected from two different populations, it is important to specify which of the means was subtracted from the other as well as the algebraic sign of the difference. Of course, if the two sample means are equal, the difference between them will be zero.

Theoretical Characteristics of Sampling Distribution of the Differences between Means

The theory of mathematical statistics provides important information about the properties of a sampling distribution of differences between means. First of all, *the mean of the sampling distribution is equal to the difference between the means of the two populations*, (i.e., $\mu_1 - \mu_2$). In the present example, then, the theoretical mean of the sampling distribution would be 4.47 (i.e., $302.50 - 298.03 = +4.47$). The obtained value of 3.23 for the mean of the empirical distribution of thirty differences represented in Table 10-2 is close to the theoretical value.

Second, *the standard deviation of a sampling distribution of differences between means for pairs of samples selected in this way can be obtained by the formula:*

$$\sigma_{\overline{X}_1 - \overline{X}_2} = \sqrt{\sigma_{\overline{X}_1}^2 + \sigma_{\overline{X}_2}^2} \qquad (10\text{-}3)$$

The symbol $\sigma_{\overline{X}_1 - \overline{X}_2}$ represents the standard deviation of the sampling distribution (this is known as the *standard error of the difference between means*); $\sigma_{\overline{X}_1}$ is the standard error of the mean for the first population; and $\sigma_{\overline{X}_2}$ is the standard error of the mean for the second population. This formula can be used with the present data. We have already learned that the standard error of the mean aptitude score for samples of size 16, selected from the male population, may be obtained as follows.

$$\sigma_{\overline{X}_M} = \frac{\sigma_M}{\sqrt{N_M}} = \frac{12.32}{\sqrt{16}} = \frac{12.32}{4} = 3.08$$

The standard error of the mean for samples of size 9 selected from the female population would be obtained in similar fashion.

$$\sigma_{\overline{X}_F} = \frac{\sigma_F}{\sqrt{N_F}} = \frac{10.78}{\sqrt{9}} = \frac{10.78}{3} = 3.59$$

Substituting both of these results into Form. (10-3), we obtain the standard error of the difference between means.

$$\sigma_{\overline{X}_M - \overline{X}_F} = \sqrt{\sigma_{\overline{X}_M}^2 + \sigma_{\overline{X}_F}^2} = \sqrt{(3.08)^2 + (3.59)^2} = 4.73$$

Again, 4.73 is not far from the standard deviation obtained for the empirical distribution of Table 10-2. An alternate formula, which is somewhat more efficient for computing $\sigma_{\bar{X}_1 - \bar{X}_2}$, can be developed as follows.

$$\sigma_{\bar{X}_1 - \bar{X}_2} = \sigma_{\bar{X}_1}^2 + \sigma_{\bar{X}_2}^2 = \sqrt{\left(\frac{\sigma_1}{\sqrt{N_1}}\right)^2 + \left(\frac{\sigma_2}{\sqrt{N_2}}\right)^2}$$

$$= \sqrt{\frac{\sigma_1^2}{N_1} + \frac{\sigma_2^2}{N_2}} \qquad (10\text{-}4)$$

This will also be used with the present data.

$$\sigma_{\bar{X}_M - \bar{X}_F} = \sqrt{\frac{(12.32)^2}{16} + \frac{(10.78)^2}{9}} = 4.73$$

Finally, *a sampling distribution of differences between two means is approximately normal under the same conditions as those for sampling distributions of single means.* That is, it is approximately normal if either (1) the distributions of scores for the two populations are normal or (2) the two samples are relatively large (i.e., they have N's greater than 30).

Probability of Obtaining a Difference between Sample Means Which Is Greater or Less than a Certain Value

Example 10-3. Suppose a single sample of size 16 from the population of eleventh-grade boys and a single sample of size 9 from the population of eleventh-grade girls are to be selected. What is the probability of obtaining a difference between the two sample means $(\bar{X}_M - \bar{X}_F)$ of less than $+2$?

Three important facts are known about the sampling distribution of all the possible differences for such pairs of samples: (1) the mean of the sampling distribution is 4.47 (i.e., $\mu_M - \mu_F$); (2) the standard deviation of the sampling distribution, $\sigma_{\bar{X}_M - \bar{X}_F}$, equals 4.73; and (3) the sampling distribution is approximately normal. We are concerned with obtaining a difference between the sample means of less than $+2$. A sample difference of $+2.00$ corresponds to a z of $-.52$.

$$z = \frac{+2.00 - 4.47}{4.73} = \frac{-2.47}{4.73} = -.52$$

Using Appx. 2, it is determined that .3015 of the possible differences between sample means fall below a z of $-.52$, or $\bar{X}_M - \bar{X}_F = +2.00$ (see Fig. 10-5); therefore the probability of obtaining a difference, $\bar{X}_M - \bar{X}_F$, of less than $+2.00$ would be approximately .30.

Here again the reader should note the general form of the z ratio used.

$$z = \frac{(\bar{X}_1 - \bar{X}_2) - (\mu_1 - \mu_2)}{\sigma_{\bar{X}_1 - \bar{X}_2}} \qquad (10\text{-}5)$$

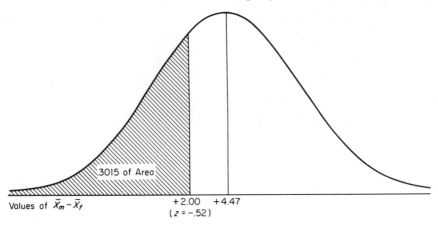

Values of the Difference $(\overline{X}_M - \overline{X}_F)$

Figure 10-5. Sampling Distribution of Differences between Means $(\overline{X}_M - \overline{X}_F)$ for Pairs of Samples Randomly Selected from Two Populations $(\mu_M - \mu_F = +4.47; \quad \sigma_{\overline{X}_M - \overline{X}_F} = 4.73)$

Example 10-4. For the same sample sizes as in Ex. 10-3, what is the probability that the mean mathematics-aptitude score of the female sample will be greater than that of the male sample?

If the mean of the female sample were greater than the mean of the male sample, the difference between the means $(\overline{X}_M - \overline{X}_F)$ would be negative; therefore, the probability of a difference between sample means which is less than zero (i.e., negative) must be determined. A sample difference of zero corresponds to a z of $-.95$.

$$z = \frac{(\overline{X}_M - \overline{X}_F) - (\mu_M - \mu_F)}{\sigma_{\overline{X}_M - \overline{X}_F}} = \frac{0.00 - 4.47}{4.73} = \frac{-4.47}{4.73} = -.95$$

Using Appx. 2, it is determined that .1711 of the possible differences fall below $z = -.95$, or $\overline{X}_M - \overline{X}_F = 0.00$; therefore, the probability that the mean of the sample of boys will be less than the mean of the sample of girls is approximately .17. This is illustrated in Fig. 10-6.

Thus far the discussion of sampling distributions has been limited to sample means and differences between the means for pairs of samples; however, the concept of a random-sampling distribution is a general one and applies to any statistic (e.g., medians, modes, standard deviations, quartile deviations) based on sample data. In order to illustrate its generality, the concept will be applied to sample standard deviations in the next section.

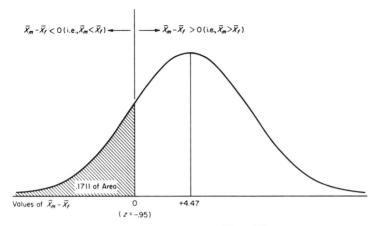

Values of the Difference $\overline{X}_M - \overline{X}_F$

Figure 10-6. Sampling Distribution of Differences between Means ($\overline{X}_M - \overline{X}_F$) for Pairs of Samples Selected from Two Populations ($\mu_M - \mu_F = +4.47$; $\sigma_{\overline{X}_M - \overline{X}_F} = 4.73$)

SAMPLING DISTRIBUTION OF STANDARD DEVIATIONS

Consider the distribution of IQ scores of a very large population of five-year-olds. Suppose, for this distribution, $\mu = 100.00$ and $\sigma = 15.00$. Suppose an infinite number of random samples of size 200 are selected from this population and the standard deviation, S, of IQ scores is determined for each of the samples. If the resulting sample S's are treated as scores, a relative-frequency distribution of standard deviations can be constructed. This theoretical relative-frequency distribution, represented in Fig. 10-7, would be known as a *random-sampling distribution of standard deviations*. If the sample size is very large, a sampling distribution of standard deviations has properties similar to those of a sampling distribution of means.

First of all, *the mean of a sampling distribution of standard deviations is approximately equal to the standard deviation of the population.* The word *approximately* is used because, for certain reasons which will not be covered here, the mean of a sampling distribution of standard deviations is slightly smaller than the population standard deviation. For samples of more than thirty or forty individuals, however, this difference is negligible.

Second, *if the population distribution is normal, the standard deviation of a sampling distribution of standard deviations (i.e., standard error of a standard deviation) can be obtained by the formula:*

$$\sigma_S = \frac{\sigma}{\sqrt{2N}} \qquad\qquad (10\text{-}6)$$

where σ_S is the standard error of the standard deviation, σ is the standard deviation for the entire population, and N is the sample size

For our example:

$$\sigma_S = \frac{15.00}{\sqrt{2\,(200)}} = .75$$

Third, *if the population distribution is normal, the shape of the sampling distribution is approximately normal for samples which are quite large* (N greater than 100). For smaller examples, another theoretical probability distribution, the χ^2 distribution, must be used. It will be discussed in Chap. 19.

Probability of Obtaining a Sample Standard Deviation Larger than or Smaller than a Certain Value

Example 10-5. Suppose a single sample of 200 individuals is to be selected from the population of five-year-olds whose distribution of IQ scores has a mean of 100.00 and a standard deviation of 15.00. What is the probability that the sample standard deviation, S, will be less than 14?

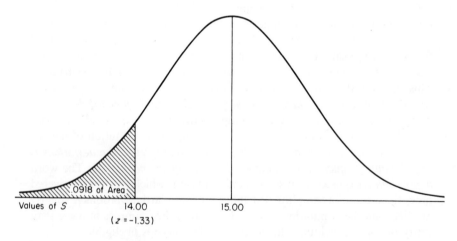

Values of S 14.00   15.00

.0918 of Area

($z = -1.33$)

Figure 10-7. Sampling Distribution of Standard Deviations of Samples of Size 200, Randomly Selected from a Normal Population, with μ Equal to 100.00 and σ Equal to 15.00 ($\sigma_S = .75$)

The principle involved here is the same as that used in the previous examples. The mean of the sampling distribution of standard deviations is approximately 15, and the standard deviation of the sampling distribution (standard error of the standard deviation) is easily obtained.

$$\sigma_S = \frac{\sigma}{\sqrt{2N}} = \frac{15.00}{\sqrt{400}} = .75$$

An S of 14, therefore, corresponds to a z of -1.33.

$$z = \frac{14.00 - 15.00}{.75} = \frac{-1.00}{.75} = -1.33$$

From Appx. 2 we find that .0918 of the area under a normal curve falls below a z of -1.33; therefore, the probability of obtaining a sample standard deviation of less than 14 is approximately .09. This is illustrated in Fig. 10-7.

RATIO STATISTICS: THE CRITICAL RATIO

We have been concerned with the general problem of determining the probabilities of obtaining various results for random samples selected from populations with known means and standard deviations. The sample results, thus far, have been expressed in terms of means $(\overline{X})$, differences between means $(\overline{X}_1 - \overline{X}_2)$ and standard deviations (S). In succeeding chapters, we shall often find it necessary to express sample results in somewhat more complicated terms. We shall frequently use a *ratio statistic*.

The notion of a ratio statistic can be illustrated with reference to the examples and discussion of the present chapter, in which z ratios of the following forms were utilized.

$$z = \frac{\overline{X} - \mu}{\sigma_{\overline{X}}}, \qquad z = \frac{(\overline{X}_1 - \overline{X}_2) - (\mu_1 - \mu_2)}{\sigma_{\overline{X}_1 - \overline{X}_2}}, \qquad \text{and } z = \frac{S - \sigma}{\sigma_S}$$

Each of these z ratios is a statistic, because each is based in part upon the results of a sample. Furthermore, each has a sampling distribution of which characteristics are known if certain conditions obtain. Consider again the sampling distribution of mean aptitude scores of Fig. 10-1, for samples of size 16, selected from our artificially constructed population of eleventh-grade boys. Suppose that each sample mean making up that theoretical distribution were transformed to a z ratio, using the appropriate formula $[z = (\overline{X} - \mu)/\sigma_{\overline{X}}]$ and the relative-frequency distribution of the sample z's were constructed. The theoretical distribution of z's would be a *random-sampling distribution of z ratios* [in which $z = (\overline{X} - \mu)/\sigma_{\overline{X}}$]. The sampling distribution of z ratios would have exactly the same shape as the sampling distribution of the means from which the z's were obtained; for, as was pointed out in Chap. 6, converting all of the scores in a frequency distribution to z- (standard) scores does not change the shape of the frequency distribution. If, therefore, a sampling distribution of means is normal, the corresponding sampling distribution of z ratios will also be normal.

Hereafter, we shall refer to a sample z ratio of which the sampling distribution is normal as a *critical ratio*, or *CR*. Not every z ratio can be considered a *CR*. For instance, suppose the distribution of raw scores in a population were extremely skewed. Then the sampling distribution of means of very, very small samples (e.g., $N = 3$) would also be skewed. Consequently, the sampling distribution of the ratio $z = (\overline{X} - \mu)/\sigma_{\overline{X}}$ would not be normal, and the ratio would not be a *CR*. If, on the other hand, very large samples (e.g., $N = 50$) had been selected, the sampling distribution would be approximately normal (Central Limit Theorem), and the ratio could be considered a critical ratio. Similarly, when the sampling distributions of differences between means and of standard deviations are approximately normal, the following can also be considered critical ratios.

$$CR = \frac{(\overline{X}_1 - \overline{X}_2) - (\mu_1 - \mu_2)}{\sigma_{\overline{X}_1 - \overline{X}_2}}, \qquad CR = \frac{S - \sigma}{\sigma_S}$$

The reader should be warned that the expression *critical ratio* (as well as its abbreviation, *CR*) is no longer widely used by psychologists and educators. It is presented here and will be used in subsequent chapters primarily for one reason: it is a convenient shorthand for designating a sample z ratio with a *normal* (or approximately normal) sampling distribution. Also, it does appear in older educational and psychological literature.

Appendix 2 as the Sampling Distribution of *CR*s

The reader will recall that whenever Appx. 2 was used to determine the probability of a sample mean greater or less than a certain value, it was first necessary to obtain the corresponding z ratio or *CR*. Appendix 2 was then entered with the value of the obtained z or *CR*, and the area or relative frequency was obtained. Thus, the normal probability distribution of Appx. 2 can be considered a table of the sampling distribution of *CR*s. It can be used directly to determine the probability of obtaining a sample *CR* as large as or larger than any specified value under conditions of random sampling. This point has been raised because in succeeding chapters we shall be concerned with determining the probabilities of obtaining various results for a variety of ratio statistics, some of which can be considered *CR*s. Several others, to be discussed later, have sampling distributions which follow another theoretical curve, Student's t distribution, which is tabled in Appx. 3. Consequently, they are referred to as t *ratios*.

Exercises and Problems

1. The frequency distribution of weights of a very large population of adult males is approximately normal and has a mean of 160.00 lb and a standard deviation of 18.00 lb. If 1,000 random samples of size 81 are to be selected (with replacement), what proportion of the samples would you expect to have means:
   a) Greater than 165.0 lb?
   b) Less than 157.0 lb?
   c) Between 158.0 and 162.0 lb?
   d) Within 12.0 lb of the population mean?
   e) At least 5.0 lb away from the population mean?
2. A normal distribution of the verbal-aptitude scores of a very large population of college freshmen has a mean of 520 and a standard deviation of 80. For a sample of size 4 selected from this population, the probability is:
   a) .25 that the sample mean will fall above a score of _____.
   b) .84 that the sample mean will fall above a score of _____.
   c) .50 that the sample mean will fall within _____ points of the population mean.
   d) .95 that the sample mean will fall within _____ points of the population mean.
3. For the population of Prob. 2, how large a sample size would be needed for the standard error of the mean to be equal to:
   a) 10?
   b) 20?
4. Suppose you randomly selected (with replacement) fifty samples of size 36 from a very large population, computed the mean for each sample, and constructed a frequency distribution of the fifty sample means. The mean of the distribution of sample means is 51.32, and the standard deviation is 1.03.
   a) What would you estimate the mean of the population to be?
   b) What would you estimate the standard deviation of the population to be?
5. The theory of statistics tells us that, if the distribution of scores for a population is normal, the standard error of the median can be obtained by the following formula.

$$\sigma_{\text{Mdn}} = \frac{1.235\sigma}{\sqrt{N}}$$

For a sample of size 81 selected from the population of Prob. 1, what is the probability that the sample median will be:
a) Greater than 165.0 lb?
b) Between 158.0 and 162.0 lb?
6. If a thousand samples of size 200 were selected from the population of Prob. 1, how many of the samples would you expect to have standard deviations (S)
a) More than 19.00?
b) Between 17.5 and 18.5?
7. Consider a large college population of engineering majors and another of liberal-arts majors. Suppose, for the distributions of scores on a particular attitude scale, the following are the parameters of the two populations.

Engineering majors	Liberal-arts majors
$\mu_E = 160.00$	$\mu_A = 155.00$
$\sigma_E = 30.00$	$\sigma_A = 32.00$

A sample of 100 engineering majors and a sample of sixty-four liberal-arts majors are to be randomly selected from the two populations.
a) What are the values of the mean and standard deviation of the sampling distribution of $\bar{X}_E - \bar{X}_A$?
b) What are the values of the mean and standard deviation of the sampling distribution of $\bar{X}_A - \bar{X}_E$?
What is the probability that:
c) The difference, $\bar{X}_E - \bar{X}_A$, between the two sample means will be greater than $+2.00$?
d) The difference, $\bar{X}_E - \bar{X}_A$, will be less than -2.00?
e) The difference, $\bar{X}_A - \bar{X}_E$, will be greater than $+5.00$?
f) The difference, $\bar{X}_A - \bar{X}_E$, will be greater than zero?
g) The difference, $\bar{X}_E - \bar{X}_A$, will be greater than zero?
h) The mean of the engineering sample will be greater than the mean of the "arts" sample?
i) The mean of the arts sample will be greater than the mean of the engineering sample?
j) The mean of the engineering sample will be at least five points larger than the mean of the arts sample?
k) The mean of the arts sample will be at least ten points less than the mean of the engineering sample?
8. Suppose two samples of size 64 are randomly selected from a very large population with a mean of 120.00 and a standard deviation of 16.00.
a) Is it very likely that a difference between the means of the two samples as large as or larger than six points would be observed? How likely?
b) What is the probability that the means of the two samples will be within two points of each other?
c) The probability is .50 that there will be a difference of at least _____ points between the means of the two samples.

9. For a population of which the distribution of scores is normal, the population median is equal to μ. Suppose the value of μ for a normal population is unknown and one random sample of size 50 is selected. Which would be a better estimate of μ, the sample mean or the sample median? Why? [Hint: compare the results of Prob. 5 with the results of Prob. 1(a) and (c).]

10. Suppose in Prob. 2 we had not been given the fact that the population distribution was normal. Could we nonetheless have obtained fairly precise answers to parts (a) through (d)? Why or why not?

11. Suppose the distribution of scores for the population of Prob. 1 were negatively skewed. Could the normal-curve table nonetheless be utilized in the solution of parts (a) through (e)? Why or why not?

12. Explain, on an intuitive basis, why the sampling distribution for $N = 2$ of Fig. 10-2 (p. 177) is "humped" toward the middle even though the population distribution of individual scores is perfectly rectangular. (Hint: compare the number of ways an extremely high or an extremely low mean could be obtained with the number of ways a mean toward the center could be obtained.)

13. The formula for σ_{Mdn} presented in Prob. 5 is applicable only if the population distribution is normal. Suppose you wished to obtain an empirical estimate of σ_{Mdn} for samples of size 5 selected from a given population of which the score distribution was rectangular (i.e., flat). If you had unlimited time and plenty of clerical and computational assistance, how would you go about doing this?

Chapter 11

Hypothesis Testing

If it is impossible, inconvenient, too expensive, or too time-consuming to examine an entire population, one can systematically select a few individuals (i.e., a sample) and examine them. On the basis of the discovered facts about the sample, inferences can be made concerning the properties of the entire population. The techniques of statistical inference provide a systematic means of making such inferences and, furthermore, provide some measure of the likelihood that one's conclusions are correct. Statistical-inference procedures can be divided into two broad classes: those concerned with *hypothesis testing* and those concerned with *estimation*. In this chapter, we shall deal with the basic concepts involved in testing hypotheses.

ESTIMATING VALUES OF σ, $\sigma_{\overline{X}}$, $\sigma_{\overline{X}_1 - \overline{X}_2}$

In each of the examples in the previous chapter, the value of the population standard deviation was known and was used to obtain the appropriate standard error (i.e., standard deviation of the sampling distribution), using one of the following formulas.

$$\sigma_{\overline{X}} = \frac{\sigma}{\sqrt{N}}, \qquad \sigma_S = \frac{\sigma}{\sqrt{2N}}, \qquad \sigma_{\overline{X}_1 - \overline{X}_2} = \sqrt{\frac{\sigma_1^2}{N_1} + \frac{\sigma_2^2}{N_2}}$$

When the techniques of statistical hypothesis testing are actually used, however, the value of σ (or σ_1 and σ_2) is unknown; it must be estimated from a sample selected at random from the population.

Since a sampling distribution of standard deviations theoretically centers on a value close to the population standard deviation, it might seem that a sample standard deviation, S, would be a good estimate of σ; however, another statistic, symbolized by s, is a more useful estimate than S. The only difference between s and S is that, in the former, $\sum x^2$ is divided by $N - 1$ as indicated in Form. (11-1).

$$s = \sqrt{\frac{\sum x^2}{N - 1}}, \qquad (11\text{-}1)$$

Thus, s will be slightly larger than S. This can be illustrated by an example. If, for the distribution of a random sample of six IQ scores

$$\sum (X - \bar{X})^2 = \sum x^2 = 1260$$

then:

$$s = \sqrt{\frac{\sum x^2}{N - 1}} = \sqrt{\frac{1260}{5}} = 15.9, \text{ and } S = \sqrt{\frac{\sum x^2}{N}} = \sqrt{\frac{1260}{6}} = 14.5$$

For a much larger sample, the difference between s and S will be negligible, since subtracting 1 from N will have very little effect. Nevertheless, to avoid confusion, s rather than S will always be used as the estimate of the population standard deviation, regardless of the sample size.

Once an estimate of the population standard deviation has been obtained, estimates of the standard errors can be obtained, using the formulas:

$$s_{\bar{X}} = \frac{s}{\sqrt{N}} \xrightarrow{\text{estimate}} \sigma_{\bar{X}} = \frac{\sigma}{\sqrt{N}} \qquad (11\text{-}2)$$

$$s_{\bar{X}_1 - \bar{X}_2} = \sqrt{\frac{s_1^2}{N_1} + \frac{s_2^2}{N_2}} \xrightarrow{\text{estimate}} \sigma_{\bar{X}_1 - \bar{X}_2} = \sqrt{\frac{\sigma_1^2}{N_1} + \frac{\sigma_2^2}{N_2}} \qquad (11\text{-}3)$$

For computational purposes, both formulas for the estimated standard errors can be written in slightly different form.

$$s_{\bar{X}} = \frac{s}{\sqrt{N}} = \frac{\sqrt{\dfrac{\sum x^2}{N - 1}}}{\sqrt{N}} = \sqrt{\frac{\sum x^2}{N(N - 1)}} \qquad (11\text{-}4)$$

and $\quad s_{\bar{X}_1 - \bar{X}_2} = \sqrt{s_{\bar{X}_1}^2 + s_{\bar{X}_2}^2} = \sqrt{\left(\dfrac{s_1}{\sqrt{N_1}}\right)^2 + \left(\dfrac{s_2}{\sqrt{N_2}}\right)^2}$

$$= \sqrt{\frac{\sum x^2}{N_1(N_1 - 1)} + \frac{\sum x_2^2}{N_2(N_2 - 1)}} \qquad (11\text{-}5)$$

In the present chapter, $s_{\bar{X}}$ and $s_{\bar{X}_1 - \bar{X}_2}$ will be used in place of $\sigma_{\bar{X}}$ and $\sigma_{\bar{X}_1 - \bar{X}_2}$ to compute the following ratio statistics.

$$CR = \frac{X - \mu}{s_{\overline{X}}} \qquad (11\text{-}6)$$

$$\text{and} \quad CR = \frac{(X_1 - X_2) - (\mu_1 - \mu_2)}{s_{\overline{X}_1 - \overline{X}_2}} \qquad (11\text{-}7)$$

As a consequence, the specific techniques described in this chapter provide probabilities which are only approximately correct. The approximations are quite good, however, when large samples are used and will certainly suffice to illustrate the overall approach of hypothesis testing. In the next chapter, exact techniques will be presented.

One final point should be mentioned before moving on to hypothesis testing. Many of the formulas to be presented throughout the remainder of the text will be expressed in terms of deviation-score sums (i.e., $\sum x^2$, $\sum y^2$, and $\sum xy$) rather than in terms of raw-score sums (i.e., $\sum X^2$, $\sum Y^2$, and $\sum XY$). The deviation formulas are simpler, and it is the writers' experience that they are a good deal more meaningful. The reader should bear in mind, however, that in a practical situation one would be ill-advised to determine the deviation-score sums directly by first computing a deviation score (i.e., $x = X - \overline{X}$ for each individual. Computational labor will be reduced and rounding errors minimized if the deviation-score sums are computed from raw scores. Formulas (4-4) and (7-4) would be appropriate for such computations. They are repeated below.

$$\sum x^2 = \sum (X - \overline{X})^2 = \frac{N \sum X^2 - (\sum X)^2}{N} \qquad (4\text{-}4)$$

$$\sum xy = \sum (X - \overline{X})(Y - \overline{Y}) = \frac{N \sum XY - (\sum X)(\sum Y)}{N} \qquad (7\text{-}4)$$

THE LOGIC OF HYPOTHESIS TESTING

Suppose Mr. Williams, the research director of a very large suburban school district, wishes to determine whether or not the third-graders in his district are reading at the norm level for this grade. He randomly selects a sample of sixty-four children from the population of interest (all the third-graders in the district) and administers a standardized reading test to each child in the sample at the end of the third grade. According to the manual accompanying this particular test, a score of 55 is the norm for the end of the third grade; therefore, Mr. Williams will attempt to infer from his sample whether or not the mean reading score, μ, for the district population of third-graders is equal to 55. Consider the conclusions he might draw for each of the following possible sets of results.

Case A. Suppose that, for his sample of sixty-four children, he finds that $\overline{X} = 56$. Mr. Williams is aware of the chance factors involved in random sampling; therefore, he would not expect to obtain a sample mean of exactly 55 even if μ were equal to 55. Since 56 is very close to 55, he concludes that the mean of the district population may well be equal to the published standard of 55. That is, he infers that 55 is a reasonable value for μ in the light of the sample mean of 56 he actually obtained.

Case B. Suppose, for his sample of sixty-four children, Mr. Williams finds that $\overline{X} = 76$. Again, he would not expect to obtain a sample mean of exactly 55 even if μ were equal to 55; however, it appears to him very unlikely that a random sample with a mean as "deviant" as 76 would be obtained if μ were equal to 55. He infers, therefore, that the mean reading-achievement score for the population of third-graders in his district does not equal the published standard of 55 and, furthermore, that it is above 55.

Let us examine in more detail the reasoning illustrated in each of the above cases. This reasoning can be divided into three explicit steps.

1) *A specific hypothesis about the population was formulated.* That is, in each case Mr. Williams started with the tentative assumption or hypothesis that the unknown mean of the entire population of third-graders in his district was equal to the published norm of 55.

2) *An attempt was made to answer the question: assuming the above hypothesis to be true, how likely is it that one would obtain sample results as "deviant" as those actually obtained?* That is, in each case Mr. Williams asked himself, "If the population mean is 55, how likely is it that I would obtain a sample mean as far from 55 as I actually obtained?" In the first case, he decided that a sample mean of 56 would not be at all unlikely if μ were 55. In the second case, however, he decided that a sample mean as far from 55 as 76 would be very unlikely.

3) *Finally, the original hypothesis concerning the parameter was accepted or rejected on the basis of the answer to the question posed in Step 2.* In the first case he accepted the hypothesis of a population mean of 55 as reasonable, because he had decided that a sample mean of 56 was not unlikely (if the hypothesis was true). In the second case, he rejected the hypothesis as unreasonable, because he had decided that a sample mean as deviant as 76 was quite unlikely (if the hypothesis was true).

These three steps constitute the basic logic behind all statistical hypothesis testing; however, there is an additional refinement which is essential, since the reasoning, as it stands, provides no objective basis upon which the question posed in Step 2 can be answered. Mr. Williams decided that if the population mean was 55, he might well obtain a sample mean of 56, whereas he probably wouldn't obtain a sample mean as deviant as 76. What would he decide for a sample mean of 57, 58, 59, 60, 61, 62, 63, or 64? The reader, at this point, should begin to see the importance of the previous chapter to hypothesis testing. The theory and techniques of that chapter provide an objective basis for determining the probability of obtaining sample results as deviant as those actually obtained, assuming a particular hypothesis to be true.

The Null Hypothesis

In statistical hypothesis testing, wide use is made of the term *null hypothesis*. For any statistical test, the *null hypothesis is the specific hypothesis which is formulated in Step 1 above and assumed to be true in Step 2 in the determination of the probability of obtaining results as deviant as those observed. That is, it is the specific statistical hypothesis which is to be tested.* Although the reader might be tempted, he should attach no additional meaning to the word *null*.

Unfortunately, there has been a good deal of confusion about what a null hypothesis is, because the term has also been used by some to denote a hypothesis of no difference between specified parameters of two populations. This latter usage will not be employed in the present text.

TESTING NULL HYPOTHESES
ABOUT POPULATION MEANS

Single Means

Example 11-1. Mr. Jones, the superintendent of schools in another very large school district, near Mr. Williams', wishes to find out whether or not the average reading achievement for the population of third-graders in his district differs from the published norm of 55. He randomly selects fifty children from his population and administers the same test used by Mr. Williams. The following are the data for the sample.

$$N = 50, \qquad \overline{X} = 59.10, \qquad \sum x^2 = 6592.21$$

In order to answer Mr. Jones's question, a null hypothesis about the unknown value of the population mean will be tested. The three steps described above are appropriate; but, in addition, the theory and techniques of the previous chapter will be utilized in Step 2.

1) *First the null hypothesis is formulated.* For this example the null hypothesis can be written symbolically as:

$$H_o : \mu = 55$$

where H_o stands for the null hypothesis and μ is the mean reading score for the population of third-graders in Mr. Jones's county

2) *Then, the probability of obtaining sample results as deviant as or more deviant than those actually obtained is determined under the assumption that the null hypothesis is true.* The sample mean of 59.10 deviates by 4.10 points from what would be expected "on the average" if $H_o : \mu = 55$ were true. A sample mean of 50.90 would be equally as deviant (i.e., 4.10 points from 55), although in the other direction; therefore, we shall determine the probability of obtaining a sample mean *either greater than 59.10 or less than 50.90* (assuming H_o to be true).

If the null hypothesis is true, the sampling distribution of means will have a mean of 55 as illustrated in Fig. 11-1; and, for samples as large as

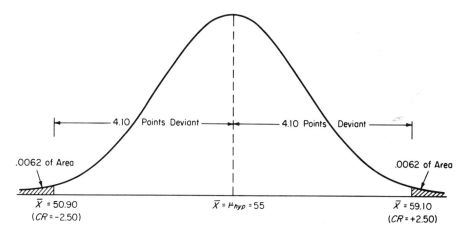

Figure 11-1. Sampling Distribution of Means, Assuming
$H_o : \mu = 55$ to Be True
(Total Shaded Area in Tails = .0124)

50, it will be approximately normal. The standard error of the mean can be estimated from the sample data using Form. (11-4).

$$s_{\overline{X}} = \sqrt{\frac{\sum x^2}{N(N-1)}} = \sqrt{\frac{6592.21}{(50)(49)}} = 1.64$$

Then, a critical ratio can be formed.

$$CR = \frac{\overline{X} - \mu_{HYP}}{s_{\overline{X}}} = \frac{59.10 - 55.00}{1.64} = \frac{4.10}{1.64} = +2.50$$

According to Appx. 2, the probability of obtaining a CR greater than $+2.50$, and thus a sample mean greater than 59.10, is .0062. Since a sample mean of 50.90 deviates an equal distance in the other direction, the probability of obtaining a sample mean of less than 50.90 would also equal .0062. Thus, if $H_o : \mu = 55$ is true, the probability of obtaining a sample mean as deviant as that obtained is .0124 (i.e., $2 \times .0062 = .0124$).

3) Finally, the null hypothesis is accepted or rejected on the basis of the probability determined in Step 2. Since .0124 is fairly small, Mr. Jones might well reject H_o as false. That is, since it is fairly unlikely that he would obtain a sample mean as deviant as 59.10 if the population mean were 55, Mr. Jones might decide that the null hypothesis is unreasonable in the light of his sample results. If he did draw this conclusion, he would probably conclude, further, that the mean for the population of third-graders is above 55, since the obtained sample mean of 59.10 is above 55.

This example illustrates two points which should be emphasized. First, even if a null hypothesis is true, the sample results will probably show some deviance. *The crucial question to be answered in deciding to accept or reject a null hypothesis is: is the degree of deviance more than that which could be accounted for by the chance factors involved in random sampling?* Second, the sample results are never in doubt, assuming random sampling and computational accuracy; it is the null hypothesis which is in doubt and is ultimately accepted as reasonable or rejected as unreasonable.

Differences between Means

The same approach can be used to test a hypothesis about the difference between the means of two populations.

Example 11-2. Professor White, a psychologist, is investigating the effects of a particular drug on human and animal learning. He wishes to answer the question: do rats who have been administered the drug differ from those who have not been administered the drug, with regard to the amount of practice required to learn a maze? He randomly divides a group of 120 laboratory rats into an experimental group of sixty animals and a control group of sixty animals. Each rat in the experimental group is administered a standard dose of the drug; those in the control group are not administered the drug. Then, each animal is allowed to run through the maze as many times as necessary to negotiate it with no errors (an error is defined as turning into a blind alley). The number of times (i.e., trials) required to learn the maze is recorded for each animal. The results for the two groups (in terms of the number of practice trials required) are as follows.

Experimental group (drug)   *Control group (no drug)*

$N_E = 60$ $N_C = 60$

$\overline{X}_E = 6.72$ $\overline{X}_C = 6.57$

$\sum x_E^2 = 259.40$ $\sum x_C^2 = 240.60$

In order to answer Professor White's question, a null hypothesis about the difference between the means of two hypothetical populations will be tested.

1) The relevant null hypothesis is that the true difference between the means of the two populations is zero. In other words, we assume that the drug has no effect. This can be expressed in symbols.

$$H_o : \mu_E - \mu_C = 0$$

where μ_E is the mean number of trials required to learn the maze for a hypothetical population of drugged rats, and μ_C is the mean number of trials for a hypothetical population of rats who have not been drugged

2) Assuming H_o to be true, the probability of obtaining sample results as deviant as or more deviant than those actually obtained must be determined. The difference of $+.15$ (i.e., $6.72 - 6.57 = +.15$) between the sample means deviates by .15 from what we would expect, on the average, if the hypothesized difference of 0 between the population means were correct; therefore, we shall determine the probability of obtaining a difference, $\overline{X}_E - \overline{X}_C$, either less than $-.15$ or greater than $+.15$.

If the null hypothesis is true, the sampling distribution of $\overline{X}_E - \overline{X}_C$ will center at zero, and for samples this large the distribution will be nearly normal. This is represented in Fig. 11-2. The standard error of the difference between means can be estimated, using Form. (11-5).

$$s_{\overline{X}_E - \overline{X}_C} = \sqrt{\frac{\sum x_E^2}{N_E (N_E - 1)} + \frac{\sum x_C^2}{N_C (N_C - 1)}} = \sqrt{\frac{259.40}{60\,(59)} + \frac{240.60}{60\,(59)}} = .376$$

A critical ratio can then be computed.

$$CR = \frac{(\overline{X}_E - \overline{X}_C) - (\mu_E - \mu_C)_{HYP}}{s_{\overline{X}_E - \overline{X}_C}} = \frac{.15 - 0}{.376} = +.40$$

The probability of obtaining a CR beyond .40 is .3446; therefore, if H_o

is true, the probability of obtaining sample results as deviant as or more deviant than those actually obtained will be .69 (i.e., twice .3446 = .6892).

3) The null hypothesis in this case would definitely not be rejected. If the null hypothesis were true (i.e., if $\mu_E - \mu_C = 0$), it is not at all unlikely that one would obtain sample results such as those actually obtained

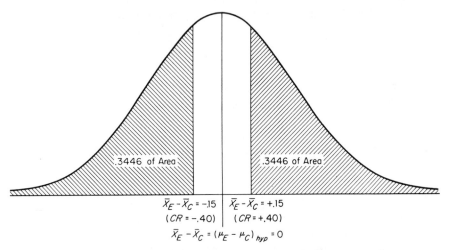

$$\bar{X}_E - \bar{X}_C = -.15 \quad \bar{X}_E - \bar{X}_C = +.15$$
$$(CR = -.40) \quad (CR = +.40)$$
$$\bar{X}_E - \bar{X}_C = (\mu_E - \mu_C)_{hyp} = 0$$

Figure 11-2. Sampling Distribution of Differences between Means, Assuming $H_o : \mu_1 - \mu_2 = 0$ to Be True (Total Shaded Area in Tails = .6892)

(i.e., $\bar{X}_E - \bar{X}_C = +.15$). Therefore, the null hypothesis that the drug has no effect on learning the maze would be accepted as reasonable in the light of the sample results actually obtained.

Level of Significance

The decision to accept or reject the null hypothesis depends upon the probability of obtaining sample results as deviant as or more deviant than those actually obtained if the null hypothesis is true. According to the reasoning used thus far, if the obtained probability is very small, as in Ex. 11-1, the null hypothesis is rejected as unreasonable. If the probability is large, as in Ex. 11-2, the null hypothesis is accepted as reasonable. *This implies that there is some specific value for the obtained probability which is the dividing line between accepting or rejecting the null hypothesis. If the obtained probability is greater than this value, the null hypothesis is accepted, whereas if it is less, the null hypothesis is rejected. This value is referred to as the level of significance.*

What level of significance should one use when performing a test of a null hypothesis? For the answer to this question, we must appeal to convention. In both education and psychology, the probability values .10, .05, and .01 seem to be the levels of significance most often used. If the obtained probability is less than .01, most researchers would reject the null hypothesis; whereas if the obtained probability is greater than .10, most would accept the null hypothesis. For values between .01 and .10, the decision is not so clear-cut. There is a group of more conservative researchers who believe that the null hypothesis should never be rejected unless the obtained probability is less than .01. On the other hand, there is a sizeable group who would reject the null hypothesis whenever the obtained probability is less than .05. The group who would reject the null hypothesis whenever the obtained probability is less than .10, is fairly small. Although the use of the particular values .10, .05, and .01 is based in great part on convention, there are also certain statistical considerations which are relevant. These considerations will be covered in Chap. 14.

The foregoing discussion suggests that the decision to accept or reject the null hypothesis is somewhat subjective after all. That is, if two different researchers tend to use two different levels of significance, one might reject the null hypothesis on the basis of a particular set of sample results, whereas the other might accept the null hypothesis on the basis of the same sample results. For instance, consider the first example. There, the probability of obtaining the sample results, assuming H_o to be true, was .0124. If Mr. Jones used .05 as his significance level, he would have rejected H_o and concluded that the average for his county was above the national standard of 55; another, more conservative researcher, using the .01 level, would have accepted H_o and drawn different conclusions. *Because of this, it is appropriate in reporting the results of any statistical test to report the obtained probability as well as the researcher's decision to accept or reject the null hypothesis.* Again referring to the first example, it would be appropriate for Mr. Jones to report that the obtained probability (P) was equal to .012 as well as to indicate his level of significance and whether he rejected the null hypothesis. Readers who prefer to use other levels of significance would be free to draw their own conclusions. It is common practice to use α (lower-case Greek *alpha*) as the symbol for level of significance. If, for his statistical test, Mr. Jones reports that $\alpha = .05$, he means that he used .05 as his level of significance.

Anyone who reads reports or discussions of educational or psychological research will come across such expressions as, "the results were not statistically significant," or "the difference between the means was highly significant." Any such references to statistical significance imply that hypothesis testing has been used. If results are referred to as *statistically significant*, the implication is that the obtained probability was less than the level of significance being used by the researcher and that the null hypothesis was rejected. A reference to a significant difference between means would imply that the null hypothesis $H_o : \mu_1 - \mu_2 = 0$ was tested and rejected. The degree of statistical significance of the results depends upon the obtained probability, P. If P is quite low, say .0001, the results would be considered a good deal more significant (in a statistical sense) than if the obtained probability were a much larger value, say .05 or .10.

RESEARCH HYPOTHESES

A null hypothesis is a statistical hypothesis which is tested directly. It is the hypothesis which we assume to be true when determining the probability of obtaining sample results as deviant as or more deviant than those actually obtained. It must be sufficiently specific to allow for the determination of that probability. For instance, when using the ratio

$$CR = \frac{(\overline{X}_1 - \overline{X}_2) - (\mu_1 - \mu_2)_{HYP}}{s_{\overline{X}_1 - \overline{X}_2}}$$

with a set of sample results, it is necessary to assume a *specific* value for the difference $\mu_1 - \mu_2$ (e.g., 0) in order to compute the CR and determine the probability. It is not necessary, however, to assume specific values for each of the two parameters, μ_1 and μ_2, involved in the difference.

A researcher who utilizes the techniques of statistical hypothesis testing is interested in testing some particular notion he has about the value of the parameter. The notion he wishes to test will be referred to as a *research hypothesis.** It is the research hypothesis that leads to the formulation of the null hypothesis. Occasionally the research hypothesis and the null hypothesis may be identical; usually they will not be. For instance, in the first example, Mr. Jones might have had good reason for believing that the mean reading score in the population *was not equal* to the published norm of 55, and he might have been interested in checking this. On the other hand, he might have been interested in checking the notion that the population mean *was equal* to the national standard of 55. Each of these two possible research hypotheses may be expressed symbolically.

$H_R : \mu \neq 55$ $H_R : \mu = 55$

The mean reading score for   The mean reading score for
the population does not equal   the population equals the pub-
the published standard of 55.   lished standard of 55.

* It should be noted that the term *research hypothesis** as used in this text is *not* synonymous with the term *alternative hypothesis* commonly used in discussions of hypothesis testing, although in most cases the research and alternative hypotheses will be the same.

It should be apparent that the research hypothesis $H_R : \mu \neq 55$ would be supported by rejection of the null hypothesis $H_o : \mu = 55$, whereas the research hypothesis $H_R : \mu = 55$ would be supported by acceptance of the null hypothesis $H_o : \mu = 55$.

Such relationships between research and null hypotheses allow us to test certain research hypotheses *indirectly* by testing a null hypothesis *directly*. Consider Ex. 11-2. Suppose that Professor White is primarily interested in testing the research hypothesis that drugged and undrugged rats *differ* with regard to trials required to learn the maze. In symbolic form, this research hypothesis is $H_R : \mu_E - \mu_C \neq 0$. The appropriate null or statistical hypothesis to be tested directly is $H_o : \mu_E - \mu_C = 0$. The conclusions drawn concerning the research hypothesis depend upon whether H_o is accepted or rejected. That is:

Acceptance of   <small>would lead to</small>   Conclusion—$H_R : \mu_E - \mu_C \neq 0$
$H_o : \mu_E - \mu_C = 0$ $\xrightarrow{}$ *not* supported by sample data

Rejection of   <small>would lead to</small>   Conclusion—$H_o : \mu_E - \mu_C \neq 0$
$H_o : \mu_E - \mu_C = 0$ $\xrightarrow{}$ supported by sample data

It should be pointed out that a number of statisticians consider hypothesis testing a useful approach for testing only those research hypotheses which are supported by rejection of a null hypothesis (e.g., $H_R : \mu \neq 55$ or $H_R : \mu_E - \mu_C \neq 0$). For those research hypotheses which are supported by acceptance of a null hypothesis (e.g., $H_R : \mu = 55$ or $H_R : \mu_E - \mu_C = 0$), they consider hypothesis testing a poor approach. This matter will be discussed in more detail in Chap. 14.

Directional Research Hypotheses

Assume that two different types of machines for the teaching of speed reading are to be compared. A group of 150 male freshmen who are referred to the reading clinic at a large university as slow readers are divided at random into two groups of seventy-five. Each member of Group I receives twenty hours of instruction on Type 1 machines and each member of Group II receives twenty hours of instruction on Type 2 machines. At the end of the instructional period, each participant is tested to determine how rapidly he is able to read certain standard materials. Speed of reading is measured in number of words read per minute. The mean speed score for each of the two groups, I and II, is then determined. Let us consider this example from three possible vantage points, each of which involves a different research hypothesis.

1) First, suppose that Dr. Brown, a professor of education who is a remedial-reading specialist, wishes to determine which of the two types of

machines is more effective. He has reason to believe that they are not equally effective, because their designs and the principles upon which they are based are quite different. Before conducting the research described, however, he has no firm basis for inferring *which* of the two types is better. Dr. Brown's research hypothesis would be

$$H_R : \mu_1 - \mu_2 \neq 0$$

where μ_1 is the mean reading speed for the hypothetical population of individuals selected in the same way and under the same conditions as those used in the research and who have been taught using Type 1 machines, and where μ_2 would represent the mean reading speed for the hypothetical population taught using Type 2 machines

This would be considered a *non-directional* research hypothesis, because it does not specify whether $\mu_1 - \mu_2$ is either greater than zero (Type 1 machines are better) or less than zero (Type 2 machines are better). It specifies only that $\mu_1 - \mu_2$ is *not equal* to zero.

2) Now let us consider a second vantage point, one which would lead to a *directional* research hypothesis. Suppose that the reading clinic already owns a number of Type 2 machines and that the Type 1 machines are on loan. Mr. Farrington, the director of the clinic, has been told by the salesman for the company which manufactures Type 1 machines that they are superior to Type 2 machines. Mr. Farrington, however, has a limited budget and does not wish to go to the expense of replacing his Type 2 machines with Type 1 machines unless Type 1 machines are, in fact, more effective; therefore, Mr. Farrington is interested primarily in the research hypothesis:

$$H_R : \mu_1 - \mu_2 > 0$$

Only if this hypothesis is supported will he consider changing from the machines he already has. Such a hypothesis would be considered a directional hypothesis, because it specifies that the population difference is *greater than* zero.

3) A third possible vantage point would lead to yet another research hypothesis, also directional. Dr. Smith, a psychology professor at the college, wishes to test certain theoretical notions about the psychological processes underlying reading. Thus far, the results of a fair amount of research have supported these notions. An analysis of the two types of machines in terms of these theoretical notions leads unambiguously to the prediction that Type 2 should be more effective; therefore, Dr. Smith's research hypothesis is:

$$H_R : \mu_1 - \mu_2 < 0$$

This is also a directional hypothesis because it specifies *less than.*

It was pointed out in the previous section that $H_o : \mu_1 - \mu_2 = 0$ is the appropriate null hypothesis to use with the research hypothesis $H_R : \mu_1 - \mu_2 \neq 0$. The same null hypothesis is also appropriate for the two directional research hypotheses $H_R : \mu_1 - \mu_2 > 0$ and $H_R : \mu_1 - \mu_2 < 0$. That is, for all three research hypotheses, $H_o : \mu_1 - \mu_2 = 0$ is tested directly, and:

Rejection of H_o $\xrightarrow{\text{would lead to}}$ Conclusion—H_R supported

Acceptance of H_o $\xrightarrow{\text{would lead to}}$ Conclusion—H_R not supported

The specific details of the procedures involved will be discussed in the next section.

ONE- AND TWO-TAILED TESTS OF THE NULL HYPOTHESIS

There is one essential difference between testing a null hypothesis for the purpose of checking a directional research hypothesis and testing a null hypothesis for the purpose of checking a non-directional research hypothesis. This difference will be discussed in the context of the previous example involving speed-reading machines.

Testing a Non-directional Research Hypothesis (Two-Tailed Test of a Null Hypothesis)

Example 11-3. In order to test Dr. Brown's non-directional research hypothesis $H_R : \mu_1 - \mu_2 \neq 0$, a direct test of the null hypothesis $H_o : \mu_1 - \mu_2 = 0$ is made. Suppose the following were the results, in terms of words per minute.

Group I (Type 1 machines)	Group II (Type 2 machines)
$N_1 = 75$	$N_2 = 75$
$\overline{X}_1 = 300.44$	$\overline{X}_2 = 298.62$
$\sum x_1^2 = 1847.62$	$\sum x_2^2 = 1554.31$

The standard error of the difference between means can be estimated with Form. (11-5):

$$s_{\overline{X}_1 - \overline{X}_2} = \sqrt{\frac{\sum x_1^2}{N_1 (N_1 - 1)} + \frac{\sum x_2^2}{N_2 (N_2 - 1)}} = \sqrt{\frac{1847.62}{(75)(74)} + \frac{1537.35}{(75)(74)}}$$

$$= \sqrt{.333 + .277} = .781$$

and a critical ratio computed.

$$CR = \frac{\overline{X}_1 - \overline{X}_2 - (\mu_1 - \mu_2)_{HYP}}{s_{\overline{X}_1 - \overline{X}_2}} = \frac{1.82 - 0}{.781} = +2.33$$

Since Dr. Brown's research hypothesis is non-directional, a large difference between sample means, either positive or negative, would be evidence in its support. The probability, therefore, of obtaining a difference between sample means that is as deviant as or more deviant than the 1.82 actually obtained, *in either direction*, must be determined, assuming H_o to be true. This would be the probability of obtaining a CR as deviant as 2.33 (*either* $+$ *or* $-$). The sum of the area in both tails of the normal curve beyond $CR = 2.33 \cdot$ is equal to .02. Consequently, if the .05 level of significance were used, H_o would be rejected, and the research hypothesis would be considered supported.

Such a statistical test, in which the probability used in determining whether or not to reject the null hypothesis is the probability obtained from both tails of the probability distribution, is known as a *non-directional* or *two-tailed test* of a null hypothesis. Usually, if H_o is rejected by using a two-tailed test, the conclusions drawn are not limited to a support of the non-directional research hypothesis. Most researchers would make a further conclusion which takes direction into account. That is, in Dr. Brown's case, the rejection of the null hypothesis on the basis of a two-tailed test would lead to the conclusion that the research hypothesis $H_R : \mu_1 - \mu_2 \neq 0$ had been supported; however, since the obtained difference between sample means is greater than zero, he would probably conclude more specifically that Type 1 machines are *more* effective than Type 2 machines.

Testing a Directional Research Hypothesis (One-Tailed Test of a Null Hypothesis)

Mr. Farrington is interested in determining whether or not Type 1 machines are, in fact, *more* effective than Type 2 machines for students referred to his clinic. In terms of mean reading speeds, his research hypothesis is $H_R : \mu_1 - \mu_2 > 0$. The possibilities alternative to the range of values for $\mu_1 - \mu_2$ specified in this research hypothesis are $\mu_1 - \mu_2 = 0$ and $\mu_1 - \mu_2 < 0$. These two alternative possibilities can be expressed in the single statement $\mu_1 - \mu_2 \leq 0$ (in which the symbol $\leq$ means *less than or equal to*). It might appear to the reader that the appropriate null hypothesis to test directly would therefore be $H_o : \mu_1 - \mu_2 \leq 0$, since its rejection would logically lead to the conclusion that the research hypothesis, $H_R : \mu_1 - \mu_2 > 0$, had been supported. A hypothesis such as $H_o : \mu_1 - \mu_2 \leq 0$, however, cannot be tested directly, because it includes a *range* of values for the difference between the two population means. That is, it would be impossible to obtain a value for the critical ratio

$$CR = \frac{X_1 - X_2 - (\mu_1 - \mu_2)_{HYP}}{s_{\overline{X}_1 - \overline{X}_2}}$$

unless a *specific* value (e.g., zero) were assigned to $(\mu_1 - \mu_2)_{HYP}$.

The null hypothesis appropriate for testing $H_R : \mu_1 - \mu_2 > 0$ would once again be $H_o : \mu_1 - \mu_2 = 0$. Rejection of this null hypothesis would constitute support for the directional research hypothesis; its acceptance, on the other hand, would lead to the conclusion that the research hypothesis was not supported by the sample results. One might wonder why rejection of $H_o : \mu_1 - \mu_2 = 0$ would necessarily imply support for $H_R : \mu_1 - \mu_2 > 0$, since there is yet another alternative, $\mu_1 - \mu_2 < 0$. The answer to this question lies in the procedure which would be used to determine the probability of obtaining deviant sample results. According to the data presented in Ex. 11-3, the difference between sample means $(\overline{X}_1 - \overline{X}_2 = +1.82)$ was in the direction specified in the research hypothesis $H_R : \mu_1 - \mu_2 > 0$. *Mr. Farrington is concerned with the extent to which the sample results deviate in this direction only, since deviation in the other direction would be evidence against rather than for the research hypothesis*; therefore, the probability upon which he will base his decision to accept or reject H_o will be the probability of obtaining a sample critical ratio *as large as or larger than* the $+2.33$ actually obtained, or .01. A statistical test such as this, in which the probability is that obtained from one tail of the probability distribution, is known as a *directional, or one-tailed, test of a null hypothesis.*

Decision Strategies for One- and Two-Tailed Tests

The basic nature of one- and two-tailed tests can perhaps be further clarified by reference to the different strategies involved in deciding whether or not to reject the null hypothesis. These strategies will be illustrated in the context of the previously described research on speed reading. Let us first review briefly the logic involved in testing a null hypothesis. The three steps previously discussed are as follows.

1) An assumption is made about the unknown population values or parameters. In this case the assumption is made that the difference between the mean reading speeds of the two hypothetical populations (one taught using Type 1 machines and the other using Type 2 machines) equals zero. Such an assumption is known as a *null hypothesis.*

2) Assuming the null hypothesis to be true, the probability of obtaining sample results as deviant as those *actually obtained* is determined. This probability is represented symbolically as *P*.

3) The null hypothesis is accepted as reasonable if *P* is large. On the other hand, it is rejected as unreasonable if *P* is small.

Let us assume that Dr. Brown, the remedial-reading specialist, Mr. Farrington, the clinic director, and Dr. Smith, the psychology professor, would consider a null hypothesis unreasonable in this case (would reject it) only if *P* were less than .01. That is, suppose all three use an α of .01 (i.e., the .01 level of significance). For the three research hypotheses, let us consider the strategy to be followed in deciding whether or not to reject the null hypothesis $H_o : \mu_1 - \mu_2 = 0$.

1. *Research hypothesis $\mu_1 - \mu_2 \neq 0$ (non-directional).* Dr. Brown would reject H_o and conclude that his research hypothesis was supported if the obtained difference between sample means were *far enough above* or *far enough below* 0 to suggest that H_o was unreasonable. How far above or how far below would be determined by the chosen level of significance, .01. Examination of Appx. 2 indicates that the value of *CR* above which

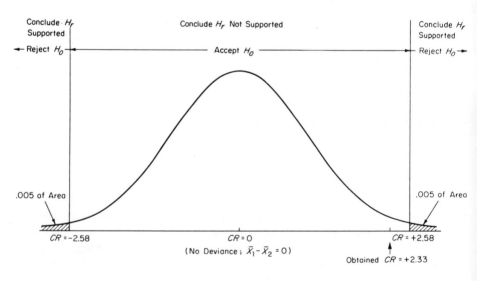

Figure 11-3. Dr. Brown's Strategy for Testing $H_R : \mu_1 - \mu_2 \neq 0$, Using $\alpha = .01$
(Total shaded area = .01. The strategy has been superimposed on the sampling distribution of CR—i.e., the normal curve—assuming $H_o : \mu_1 - \mu_2 = 0$ to be true.)

lies .005 of the total area under the normal curve is 2.58. The probability of obtaining a CR greater than $+2.58$ or less than -2.58 is .01 (i.e., $.005 + .005$); therefore, in order to reject $H_o : \mu_1 - \mu_2 = 0$ using the .01 level, Dr. Brown would need to obtain a difference between sample means far enough above or below 0 to yield a CR of at least 2.58, either positive or negative. The specific strategy he would use in deciding whether or not to reject H_o, using the .01 level, is presented below and in Fig. 11-3.

If $CR > +2.58$	reject H_o	Conclusion—Research hypothesis supported
If CR is between $+2.58$ and -2.58	accept H_o	Conclusion—Research hypothesis not supported
If $CR < -2.58$	reject H_o	Conclusion—Research hypothesis supported

The critical ratio actually obtained from the data presented in Ex. 11-3 ($CR = +2.33$) falls within the "acceptance" range; therefore, using this strategy, Dr. Brown would accept H_o and conclude that his research hypothesis was not supported.

2. *Research hypothesis* $\mu_1 - \mu_2 > 0$ *(directional)*.   Mr. Farrington would reject H_o and conclude that his research hypothesis had been supported if the obtained difference between sample means were far enough *above* 0 to suggest that H_o was unreasonable. Again, how far above would be determined by the α (level of significance) of .01. Using Appx. 2, we find that the probability of obtaining a CR ratio of $+2.33$ (approximately) is .01; therefore, Mr. Farrington would need a difference between sample means far enough above 0 to result in a sample CR of $+2.33$ or more, before he would reject H_o and conclude that H_R had been supported. The following is his specific strategy (see also Fig. 11-4).

If $CR > +2.33$	reject H_o	Conclusion—Research hypothesis supported
If $CR < +2.33$	accept H_o	Conclusion—Research hypothesis not supported

The obtained CR of $+2.33$ falls just on the edge of the *critical region* (i.e., the "rejection" range); therefore, using this strategy, Mr. Farrington would reject H_o and conclude that his research hypothesis was supported.

It should be apparent that in order to reject the null hypothesis at a particular level of significance (e.g., .01), a larger CR must be obtained for a two-tailed than for a one-tailed test. This explains why, for a level of

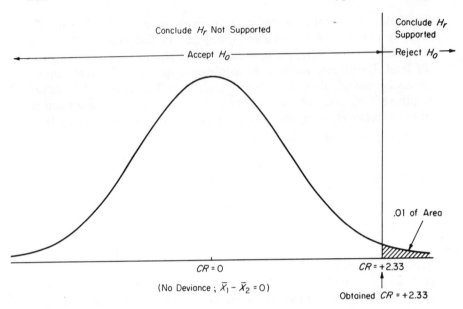

Figure 11-4. Mr. Farrington's Strategy for Testing $H_R : \mu_1 - \mu_2 > 0$, Using $\alpha = .01$

significance of .01, Dr. Brown would accept H_o for the two-tailed test but Mr. Farrington would reject H_o for the one-tailed test. It would seem, then, that one will be more likely to reject the null hypothesis and conclude that his research hypothesis is supported when he is using a one-tailed rather than a two-tailed test. The reader may reasonably inquire at this point why researchers don't always use one-tailed tests when they wish to demonstrate support for their research hypotheses. The answer to this question can most easily be illustrated by considering the third possible research hypothesis.

3. *Research hypothesis* $\mu_1 - \mu_2 < 0$ (*directional*). Dr. Smith would reject H_o and conclude that this research hypothesis was supported if the obtained difference between sample means were far enough below 0 to result in a CR of -2.33 or less. The following specific strategy is illustrated in Fig. 11-5.

    If $CR < -2.33$ reject H_o Conclusion—
                                         Research hypothesis supported

    If $CR > -2.33$ accept H_o Conclusion—
                                         Research hypothesis not supported

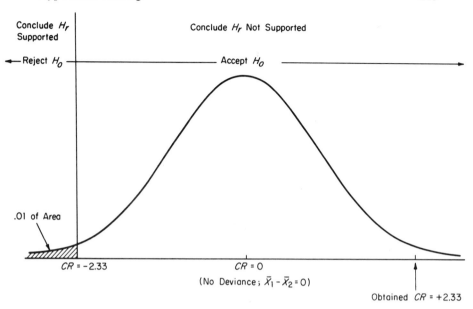

Figure 11-5. Dr. Smith's Strategy for Testing $H_R : \mu_1 - \mu_2 < 0$, Using $\alpha = .01$

The obtained CR of $+2.33$ is far from the critical region, since the critical region begins in the lower tail of the curve rather than in the upper tail; therefore, using this strategy, Dr. Smith would accept the null hypothesis that $\mu_1 - \mu_2 = 0$ and conclude that the research hypothesis was *not* supported. Thus, one is more likely to reject the null hypothesis at a given level of significance (e.g., .01) when using a directional or one-tailed test, *only if the direction specified in the research hypothesis is correct.* If it is incorrect, rejection of the null hypothesis is obviously very unlikely.

Some general implications for hypothesis testing can be drawn from this discussion. If a researcher has sufficient reason for hypothesizing direction, he is well advised to use a one-tailed test. He will, by doing so, be more likely to demonstrate support for his research hypothesis, if in fact it is correct. Although there is by no means consensus on what constitutes sufficient reason, many statisticians would probably agree to the utilization of one-tailed tests by Dr. Smith and Mr. Farrington. If, on the other hand, one has no basis for hypothesizing direction, his research hypothesis should be non-directional, and a two-tailed test should be used. Additional light should be shed on these matters by the discussion of Type I and Type II errors in Chap. 14.

Exercises and Problems

Use Form. (11-4) and Form. (11-5) where applicable.

1. Given the following scores from a sample of size 6:

$$6, 4, 6, 9, 3, 2$$

   a) Compute $\sum x^2$ using deviation scores.
   b) Compute $\sum x^2$ using raw scores.
   c) Compute an estimate of the population standard deviation.
   d) Compute an estimate of the standard error of the mean.
2. Compute $\sum x^2$ from the following sample data.

$$N = 100$$
$$\sum X = 5,302$$
$$\sum X^2 = 287,512$$

3. Suppose, for a sample of size 100, randomly selected from a particular population, the following are the sample results:

$$\overline{X} = 8.02$$
$$s = 2.71$$

   a) Is 10.00 a reasonable value for μ? Why or why not?
   b) Is 8.29 a reasonable value for μ? Why or why not?
   c) Is 7.48 a reasonable value for μ? Why or why not?
4. For each of the following research hypotheses, indicate the *critical value* of CR (i.e., the value or values dividing the acceptance region from the critical region) for the specified level of significance.
   a) $H_R : \mu > 55 \quad (\alpha = .05)$
   b) $H_R : \mu_A - \mu_B \neq 0 \quad (\alpha = .05)$
   c) $H_R : \mu \neq 100 \quad (\alpha = .01)$
   d) $H_R : \mu_A - \mu_B < 0 \quad (\alpha = .10)$
5. For the following data, test $H_R : \mu > 90$. Use $\alpha = .05$. State your final conclusions.

$$N = 60$$
$$\overline{X} = 90.85$$
$$\sum x^2 = 1239$$

6. For the following data, test $H_R : \mu_1 - \mu_2 \neq 0$. Use $\alpha = .01$. State your final conclusions.

Sample from Population 1	Sample from Population 2
$N_1 = 100$	$N_2 = 49$
$\overline{X}_1 = 116.46$	$\overline{X}_2 = 124.14$
$s_1 = 16.0$	$s_2 = 14.0$

For each of Probs. 7–10, specify H_R and H_o; determine the probability of obtaining sample results as deviant as those obtained (in the appropriate direction); and state your final conclusions. Indicate the level of significance used in arriving at your conclusions.

7. The research director of a very large school district wishes to determine whether or not the fifth-graders in his district are of about average intelligence as measured by a well known individual IQ test. According to the test manual, the test was constructed so that the average person of any age will obtain an IQ score of about 100. The following are the results (in terms of IQ points) for a random sample of fifth-graders from his district.

$$N = 50$$
$$\overline{X}_2 = 104.50$$
$$\sum x = 12,250$$

8. The directors of a charitable organization wish to determine whether or not a short series of special classes on how to solicit funds would improve the effectiveness of their volunteer door-to-door solicitors. Eighty experienced volunteer solicitors are divided at random into two groups. Those in one group are given the special training prior to this year's fund drive, and the others are not. The following are the results for the two samples for this year's fund drive (in terms of dollars solicited).

Trained	Untrained
$N_T = 40$	$N_U = 40$
$\overline{X}_T = 184.50$	$\overline{X}_U = 171.25$
$\sum x_T^2 = 93,600$	$\sum x_U^2 = 78,000$

9. A psychologist wishes to determine whether or not the severity with which boys are punished when they are very young has anything to do with their adjustment to the school situation in first grade. He administers a questionnaire on child-rearing practices to the parents of a sample of thirty-five first-grade boys who have been identified as poorly adjusted and to the parents of a sample of forty who have been identified as well adjusted. A severity-of-punishment score is derived from the questionnaire for each set of parents (a higher score indicates greater severity). The following are the results.

Poorly adjusted group	Well adjusted group
$N_P = 35$	$N_W = 40$
$\overline{X}_P = 17.68$	$\overline{X}_W = 15.25$
$\sum x_P^2 = 595$	$\sum x_W^2 = 468$

10. We wish to test the hypothesis that engineering majors at a large university tend to score lower on a certain attitude measure than liberal-arts majors. The following are the results for the two random samples of male students from the university.

Engineering majors	Liberal-arts majors
$N_E = 64$	$N_A = 81$
$\overline{X}_E = 92.36$	$\overline{X}_A = 96.78$
$s_E = 16.0$	$s_A = 27.9$

11. Suppose, in testing $H_R : \mu > 500$ you decide to use the following decision strategy.

If $\overline{X} > 509.50$, conclude H_R supported
If $\overline{X} < 509.50$, conclude H_R not supported

If, in fact, $\sigma = 84.0$, what is the level of significance associated with the above strategy for samples of size 144?

12. Why are the results obtained in the examples for this chapter not quite as accurate as those obtained in the examples for Chap. 10?

13. Suppose that in the report of a certain experiment you read that $\overline{X}_1 - \overline{X}_2 = +5.36$. Suppose, furthermore, you read that "the difference between means, although in the predicted direction, was not significant at the .05 level."
   a) What was H_o?
   b) What was H_R?
   c) What conclusions were drawn concerning H_R?
   d) The obtained CR must have been less than what value?

14. Why can't we use a null hypothesis $H_o : \mu > 12$?

15. Why must we assume H_o to be true in order to test it? Why can't we assume that it is false?

Chapter 12

Student's *t* Distribution

In the Chap. 10 discussion of sampling distributions, both μ and σ were known for each population. This allowed us to use a ratio of the following form in obtaining the probability of a sample mean as large as or larger than a specified value.

$$CR = \frac{\overline{X} - \mu}{\sigma_{\overline{X}}}, \quad \text{where } \sigma_{\overline{X}} = \frac{\sigma}{\sqrt{N}}$$

It was pointed out that the sampling distribution of this ratio statistic and sampling distributions of means are normal under the same conditions. Under these conditions, the statistic is called a *critical ratio*, or *CR*. Reference to the normal curve tabled in Appx. 2 will provide directly the probability of obtaining, under conditions of random sampling, a sample *CR* as large as or larger than any specified value.

In Chap. 11, the parameters μ and σ were both unknown, and a critical ratio like that above could not be computed; however, a similar ratio statistic was formed by utilizing an assumed (hypothetical) value for μ and estimates of σ and $\sigma_{\overline{X}}$ obtained from the sample data.

$$\frac{\overline{X} - \mu_{HYP}}{s_{\overline{X}}}, \quad \text{where } s_{\overline{X}} = \frac{s}{\sqrt{N}} = \sqrt{\frac{\sum x^2}{N(N-1)}}$$

Although the above ratio was used with Appx. 2 as if it were a critical ratio (i.e., a *z* ratio with a normal sampling distribution), strictly speaking it is not one because of the sampling "error" or variability in $s_{\overline{X}}$. Since $s_{\overline{X}}$ is only an estimate, it will vary from sample to sample; and, as a consequence, the sampling distribution of the ratio will depart somewhat from normality. If the sample size is large, however, the error in $s_{\bar{X}}$ will be negligible, and the normal curve will be a "close approximation" of the sampling distribution. This last statement is true regardless of the shape of the population distribution of scores (Central Limit Theorem). On the other hand, if the sample size is small, the sampling error in $s_{\bar{X}}$ is no longer negligible, and the sampling distribution of the ratio will depart noticeably from normality.

For samples of any size, *selected from a normal population*, the sampling distribution of the ratio

$$t = \frac{\bar{X} - \mu}{s_{\bar{X}}} \tag{12-1}$$

follows another theoretical probability distribution, the characteristics of which are well known to statisticians. This theoretical distribution is called *Student's t distribution*, and consequently the ratio is usually referred to as a t or t *ratio* rather than a critical ratio. The reader may wonder how, for large samples, the sampling distribution of a t ratio can follow the t distribution and, at the same time, be closely approximated by the normal curve. The answer is that the shape of the t distribution depends on the sample size and that, for large samples, it differs only slightly from the normal curve. This point will be discussed in greater detail in subsequent paragraphs.

There is not just one but an entire family of t distributions, one for each number of *degrees of freedom*. Although a technical discussion of degrees of freedom will not be attempted, a few brief comments of a general nature may be helpful. It was pointed out in Chap. 3 that the sum of the deviations about the mean [i.e., $\sum (X - \bar{X})$ or $\sum x$] will always equal zero. This is illustrated below for the deviation scores from a sample of four cases.

X	x
2	-2
4	0
3	-1
7	$+3$
$\sum X = 16$	$\sum x = 0$

$$\bar{X} = \frac{16}{4} = 4$$

Now consider another group of four deviation scores, three of which are -5, $+2$, and $+4$. If we know these three, we can find the fourth, because all four *must add up to zero*. Thus, the fourth must be -1, since $-5 + 2 + 4 - 1 = 0$. This illustrates the fact that only $N - 1$ of the deviation scores for a sample of size N are "free to vary"; the last one is determinate. Consequently, there are $N - 1$ degrees of freedom associated with the sum of squared deviations $(\sum x^2)$ for a sample of size N. Now consider again the estimated standard error, $s_{\bar{x}}$, for the t ratio we have been discussing.

$$ s_{\bar{x}} = \frac{s}{\sqrt{N}}, \quad \text{where } s = \sqrt{\frac{\sum x^2}{N - 1}} $$

It is obtained from the estimated population standard deviation (s) which is itself based on the sum of squared deviations $(\sum x^2)$ for the sample. Since there are $N - 1$ degrees of freedom associated with $\sum x^2$, there will also be $N - 1$ degrees of freedom associated with s and $s_{\bar{x}}$. Therefore, the t ratio

$$ t = \frac{\bar{X} - \mu}{s_{\bar{x}}} $$

will follow the theoretical t distribution for $N - 1$ degrees of freedom.

Two theoretical t distributions as well as the normal curve are illustrated in Fig. 12-1. Examination of the figure permits several interesting observa-

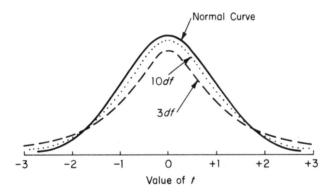

Figure 12-1. Two t Distributions Compared with the Normal Curve

tions. First, each t distribution is symmetric about a mean of zero, with the negative values of t in the left half of the distribution and positive t values in the right half; therefore, the area in the right tail of a t distribution curve that is above a particular positive value of t will always be equal to the area in the left tail below the corresponding negative value of t. For instance, in each of the t distributions illustrated, the area above $t = +1$ is equal to the area below $t = -1$, and the area above $t = +2$ is equal to the area below $t = -2$.

The second observation is that the t distributions are more "peaked" and have higher shoulders than the normal curve. That is, less of the area under a *t* distribution is in the center, and more of the area is in the tails. Notice that the proportion of area above $t = +2$ or below $t = -2$ is greater than the area under the normal curve above $z = +2$ or below $z = -2$. Third, the greater the degrees of freedom, the more the *t* distribution resembles a normal curve. Notice that the *t* distribution for $df = 10$ closely approximates the normal curve, whereas the *t* distribution for $df = 3$ is identifiably different. When the number of degrees of freedom is greater than 100 or 120, the theoretical sampling distribution of a *t* ratio is so close to normality that, for all practical purposes, Appx. 2 can be used. When the number of degrees of freedom is small, the difference between the normal curve and the *t* distribution is considerable, and the *t* table of Appx. 3 should be used with a *t* ratio.

The format of Appx. 3 is quite different from that of Appx. 2. The numbers across the top of the Appx. 3 table are areas in the tail of a *t* distribution, and the numbers in the left column are degrees of freedom. Each row of the table represents the *t* distribution for a different number of degrees of freedom. Each entry in a particular row is the value of *t* beyond which lies the tail area specified at the top of the table. For instance, consider the *t* distribution for $df = 19$ represented in Fig. 12-2. Notice that .01 of the area lies in the right tail beyond a *t* of $+2.539$, and

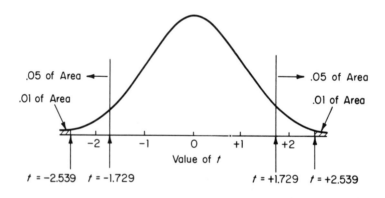

Figure 12-2. The t Distribution for df = 19

.01 of the area lies in the left tail beyond a *t* of -2.539. In Appx. 3 the *t* value which is in the row for $df = 19$ and in the column headed .01 is 2.539. Similarly, .05 of the area lies in the right tail beyond a *t* of $+1.729$, and .05 of the area lies in the left tail beyond a *t* of -1.729. The *t* value which is in the row for $df = 19$ and in the column headed .05 is 1.729.

The bottom row in Appx. 3 represents the *t* distribution for an infinite number of degrees of freedom. As has been pointed out, the shape of the *t* distribution approaches that of a normal curve as the number of degrees of freedom is increased. For an infinite number of degrees of freedom, the *t* distribution and the normal curve of Appx. 2 are identical; therefore, the *t* values in the bottom row in Appx. 3 may also be obtained from Appx. 2.

TESTING HYPOTHESES ABOUT A POPULATION MEAN

In testing hypotheses about single population means, sample results are considered to be "deviant" when the sample mean differs from what would be expected, on the average, *if the null hypothesis were true*. This "expected" value is μ_{HYP}. The greater the difference between $\overline{X}$ and μ_{HYP}, the more deviant are the results. Consequently, when the sample results are expressed in terms of a *t* ratio of the form

$$t = \frac{\overline{X} - \mu_{HYP}}{s_{\overline{X}}}$$

a very small value (either positive or negative) for *t* indicates only a slight degree of deviance, whereas a large value for *t* represents a relatively large degree of deviance. If the sample mean is greater than the hypothesized population mean, the sign of the *t* ratio will be positive; if it is less, the sign will be negative. Therefore, *assuming H_o to be true, the probability of obtaining sample results as deviant as those obtained is the probability of obtaining a sample t ratio as large or larger than that obtained* (in the direction hypothesized, for a one-tailed test). If the frequency distribution of scores for the population can be considered normal, the desired probability can be determined directly by entering Appx. 3 with the obtained value of *t*.

Example 12-1. We wish to test the research hypothesis that the average height for a certain population of adult males is greater than 69 in. The following are the results for a random sample of sixteen individuals selected from the population.

$$N = 16, \qquad \overline{X} = 70.05, \qquad \sum x^2 = 168.60$$

The research and null hypotheses are $H_R : \mu > 69$ and $H_o : \mu = 69$.

An estimated standard error can be obtained using the sample data:

$$s_{\overline{x}} = \sqrt{\frac{\sum x^2}{N(N-1)}} = \sqrt{\frac{168.60}{16(15)}} = .838$$

Then a *t* ratio can be computed:

$$t = \frac{\overline{X} - \mu_{HYP}}{s_{\overline{x}}} = \frac{70.05 - 69.00}{.838} = +1.25$$

Since the directional research hypothesis specifies "greater than," we obtain the probability from the right-hand tail of the *t* distribution only. The number of degrees of freedom can be determined as:

$$df = N - 1 = 16 - 1 = 15$$

We enter Appx. 3 with $df = 15$. The smallest entry in the row, 1.341, is the value of *t* for a tail area of .10. Since the obtained *t* value of +1.25 is less than 1.341, the probability of obtaining a sample *t* ratio of greater than +1.25 must be greater than .10. This is illustrated in Fig. 12-3. Using

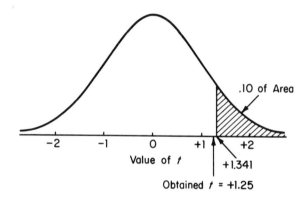

Figure 12-3. The t Distribution for df = 15

either the .01 or the .05 level of significance, we would accept H_o as reasonable and conclude that H_R was not supported.

Example 12-2. We wish to determine whether or not the mean score on a particular IQ test for the population of fifth-graders in a very large school district differs from the published "norm" of 100. The data for a random sample of 20 individuals are as follows.

$$N = 20, \qquad \overline{X} = 109.05, \qquad \sum x^2 = 4987.62$$

The research hypothesis is $H_R : \mu \neq 100$, since no direction has been specified. The null hypothesis is $H_o : \mu = 100$. An estimate of $\sigma_{\overline{x}}$ can be obtained:

$$s_{\overline{X}} = \sqrt{\frac{\sum x^2}{N(N-1)}} = \sqrt{\frac{4987.62}{20(19)}} = 3.62$$

and a t ratio computed.

$$t = \frac{\overline{X} - \mu_{HYP}}{s_{\overline{X}}} = \frac{109.05 - 100.00}{3.62} = \frac{9.05}{3.62} = +2.50$$

We determine from Appx. 3 that, for $df = 19$, 2.093 is the t value for a tail area of .025 and that 2.539 is the t value for a tail area of .01. Since $+2.50$ is between $+2.093$ and $+2.539$, the probability of obtaining a sample t of more than $+2.50$ is between .01 and .025. The probability, therefore, of obtaining results as deviant as those obtained, in either direction (i.e., a t ratio greater than $+2.50$ or less than -2.50) is between .02 and .05 (i.e., .01 + .01 = .02, .025 + .025 = .05). This is illustrated in Fig. 12-4. If we were to use the .05 level of significance, we would reject

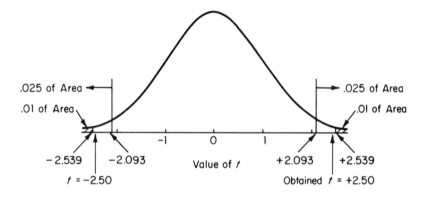

Figure 12-4. The t Distribution for df = 19

H_o and conclude that $H_R : \mu \neq 100$ was supported. Furthermore, we would conclude that the mean IQ for the population is above 100.

Two points should be mentioned concerning these examples. First, the use of the t distribution was based on the assumption that the samples were selected from populations with normal distributions of scores. Theoretically, the sampling distribution of the ratio

$$t = \frac{\overline{X} - \mu}{s_{\overline{X}}}$$

will follow one of the t distributions detailed in Appx. 3 only if this assumption of population normality is correct. However, it has been shown that the *t* distribution will be a good approximation even if the assumption is not met perfectly, provided the departure from normality is not great and the sample size is not extremely small. This point will be discussed in more detail later in the chapter. Second, note that the probabilities obtained in both examples were approximate. That is, each of the *t* distributions in Appx. 3 is presented in much less detail than is the normal curve in Appx. 2. The reason for this is that Appx. 3 contains many *t* distributions, one for each number of degrees of freedom. If each distribution were to be presented in greater detail, many pages would be required. It should be clear, however, that Appx. 3 is sufficiently detailed for testing hypotheses at the conventional levels of significance.

TESTING HYPOTHESES ABOUT THE DIFFERENCE BETWEEN THE MEANS

In the examples of Chap. 10 that involved the difference between the means of a pair of samples randomly selected from two populations, the parameters were known, and a ratio of the following form was used.

$$CR = \frac{\overline{X}_1 - \overline{X}_2 - (\mu_1 - \mu_2)}{\sigma_{\overline{X}_1 - \overline{X}_2}}$$

where $\sigma_{\overline{X}_1 - \overline{X}_2} = \sqrt{\sigma_{\overline{X}_1}^2 + \sigma_{\overline{X}_2}^2} = \sqrt{\frac{\sigma_1^2}{N_1} + \frac{\sigma_2^2}{N_2}}$

In the inference problems of Chap. 11, where the parameters σ_1, σ_2, μ_1, and μ_2 were unknown, $\sigma_{\overline{X}_1 - \overline{X}_2}$ was estimated from the sample data, and a hypothesized value was used for the difference, $\mu_1 - \mu_2$. A similar ratio was then computed.

$$\frac{\overline{X}_1 - \overline{X}_2 - (\mu_1 - \mu_2)_{HYP}}{s_{\overline{X}_1 - \overline{X}_2}}$$

where $s_{\overline{X}_1 - \overline{X}_2} = \sqrt{s_{\overline{X}_1}^2 + s_{\overline{X}_2}^2} = \sqrt{\frac{s_1^2}{N_1} + \frac{s_2^2}{N_2}}$

The sampling distribution of this ratio can be closely approximated by a normal curve when both samples are fairly large, but the approximation is poor for small samples. Fortunately, again, statistical theory provides a technique that can be used in certain circumstances with small samples. *If the distributions of scores for both populations are normal and if the two population standard deviations are equal (although their numerical values are unknown), the sampling distribution of the ratio*

$$t = \frac{(\overline{X}_1 - \overline{X}_2) - (\mu_1 - \mu_2)}{s_{\overline{X}_1 - \overline{X}_2}} \qquad (12\text{-}2)$$

where $\quad s_{\overline{X}_1 - \overline{X}_2} = \sqrt{\dfrac{s_c^2}{N_1} + \dfrac{s_c^2}{N_2}}$

and $\quad s_c^2 = \dfrac{\sum x_1^2 + \sum x_2^2}{N_1 + N_2 - 2}$

follows the t distribution, with df $= N_1 + N_2 - 2$.

In order to understand this particular *t* ratio, one should be aware of the nature of s_c^2. We have noted that one of the assumptions underlying the use of this *t* ratio is that the standard deviations of the two populations have the same value (i.e., $\sigma_1 = \sigma_2$). If the two population standard deviations are equal, the two population variances must also be equal (i.e., $\sigma_1^2 = \sigma_2^2$). Thus, the assumption is often referred to as *homogeneity of variance.* If the assumption is correct, it should seem reasonable to obtain a single estimate of σ_1^2 and σ_2^2 rather than two separate estimates. Furthermore, it should seem reasonable that the "best" single estimate would be a weighted average based on the squared deviations from both samples combined. The statistic s_c^2 is this single estimate. The subscript *c* is used because the estimate is of the variance *common* to both populations. Since there are $N_1 - 1$ degrees of freedom associated with $\sum x_1^2$ and $N_2 - 1$ degrees of freedom associated with $\sum x_2^2$, there are $N_1 - 1 + N_2 - 1 = N_1 + N_2 - 2$ degrees of freedom associated with the estimate s_c^2.

In testing hypotheses about the difference between the means of two populations, sample results are considered to be deviant when the difference between sample means, $\overline{X}_1 - \overline{X}_2$, differs from the value that would be expected, on the average, if H_o were true. Here, the expected value would be $(\mu_1 - \mu_2)_{HYP}$. The greater the difference between $(\overline{X}_1 - \overline{X}_2)$ and $(\mu_1 - \mu_2)_{HYP}$, the more deviant would be the results. Consequently, a large value (either positive or negative) for the *t* ratio

$$t = \frac{(X_1 - X_2) - (\mu_1 - \mu_2)_{HYP}}{s_{\overline{X}_1 - \overline{X}_2}}$$

would indicate a relatively large degree of deviance. The probability, therefore, if H_o is true, of obtaining sample results as deviant as those obtained would again be the probability of obtaining a sample *t* ratio as large as that obtained (in the direction hypothesized, for a one-tailed test).

Example 12-3. A psychologist wishes to test the hypothesis that people tend to forget *less* material while they are asleep than while they are awake. He randomly divides a class of thirty-five students into one group of eighteen and another group of seventeen. Each of the eighteen individuals in Group 1 memorizes certain verbal materials at 8:00 A.M. and is given a test eight hours later to determine how much he can remember. Each of the seventeen individuals in Group 2 memorizes the materials at 11:00 P.M., goes home to bed, and, eight hours after learning, is wakened and tested. The following are the sample results in terms of number correct on the recall test.

Group 1 (awake)	Group 2 (asleep)
$N_1 = 18$	$N_2 = 17$
$\overline{X}_1 = 24.28$	$\overline{X}_2 = 28.82$
$\sum x_1^2 = 376.51$	$\sum x_2^2 = 427.19$

For this example, the research hypothesis is $H_R : \mu_1 - \mu_2 < 0$, and the null hypothesis is $H_o : \mu_1 - \mu_2 = 0$. First, estimates of the common value of σ_1^2 and σ_2^2 and of $s_{\overline{X}_1 - \overline{X}_2}$ are obtained.

$$s_c^2 = \frac{\sum x_1^2 + \sum x_2^2}{N_1 + N_2 - 2} = \frac{376.51 + 427.19}{18 + 17 - 2} = 24.35$$

$$s_{\overline{X}_1 - \overline{X}_2} = \sqrt{\frac{s_c^2}{N_1} + \frac{s_c^2}{N_2}} = \sqrt{\frac{24.35}{18} + \frac{24.35}{17}} = 1.67$$

Then, the t ratio can be computed.

$$t = \frac{(\overline{X}_1 - \overline{X}_2) - (\mu_1 - \mu_2)_{HYP}}{s_{\overline{X}_1 - \overline{X}_2}} = \frac{(24.28 - 28.82) - 0}{1.67} = -2.72$$

The t distribution for exactly 33 degrees of freedom ($18 + 17 - 2 = 33$) is not included in Appx. 3; however, for all practical purposes, the use of the t distribution for $df = 30$ (the value in the table nearest 33 df) will give results of sufficient accuracy. For 30 degrees of freedom, 2.457 is the t value for a tail area of .01, and 2.750 is the t value for a tail area of .005. Since -2.72 is between -2.457 and -2.750, the probability of obtaining a sample t below (i.e., further in a negative direction than) -2.72 is between .01 and .005; therefore, if H_o is true, the probability of obtaining results as deviant as those obtained in the direction hypothesized is less than .01. Using the .01 level of significance, H_o is rejected, and it is concluded that the research hypothesis is supported by the sample data.

The use of the t distribution in Ex. 12-3 is based upon two assumptions: homogeneity of variance (i.e., $\sigma_1^2 = \sigma_2^2$) and normality of the two population distributions. How important it is that these assumptions be met in practice will be discussed in the final section of this chapter.

Example 12-4. A school psychologist believes that the standard order of administering items on the individual IQ test used in his school district involves certain frustrations for the child being examined, thus lowering his IQ score. He believes that children will tend to obtain slightly higher IQ scores if administered the items according to a revised order he has developed. He divides a group of eighteen third-graders into two samples. Each child in one sample is administered the test according to the revised order, and each child in the other sample is administered the test according to the standard order. The following statistics are obtained.

Revised order	Standard order
$N_R = 10$	$N_S = 8$
$\overline{X}_R = 103.60$	$\overline{X}_S = 101.62$
$\sum x_R^2 = 1863.71$	$\sum x_S^2 = 1415.52$

The research hypothesis is $H_R : \mu_R - \mu_S > 0$, and the null is $H_o : \mu_R - \mu_S = 0$. Estimates of the common variance and of $s_{\overline{X}_R - \overline{X}_S}$ are obtained:

$$s_c^2 = \frac{\sum x_R^2 + \sum x_S^2}{N_R + N_S - 2} = \frac{1863.71 + 1415.52}{10 + 8 - 2} = 204.95$$

$$s_{\overline{X}_R - \overline{X}_S} = \sqrt{\frac{s_c^2}{N_R} + \frac{s_c^2}{N_S}} = \sqrt{\frac{204.95}{10} + \frac{204.95}{8}} = 6.79$$

and a *t* ratio computed.

$$t = \frac{(\overline{X}_R - \overline{X}_S) - (\mu_R - \mu_S)_{HYP}}{s_{\overline{X}_R - \overline{X}_S}} = \frac{(103.60 - 101.62) - 0}{6.79} = +.29$$

For $df = 16$, 1.337 is the *t* value for a tail area of .10. Since $+.29$ is less than $+1.337$, the probability of obtaining sample results as deviant as those obtained in the direction hypothesized is greater than .10. Thus, using the .05 level of significance, we accept H_o as reasonable and conclude that the research hypothesis is not supported.

THE USE OF *t* RATIOS WITH LARGE SAMPLES

All the inference techniques to be discussed in this text assume random sampling. Theoretically, the sampling distributions of the ratios

$$t = \frac{\overline{X} - \mu}{s_{\overline{X}}} \quad \text{and} \quad t = \frac{\overline{X}_1 - \overline{X}_2 - (\mu_1 - \mu_2)}{s_{\overline{X}_1 - \overline{X}_2}}$$

$$\text{where} \quad s_{\overline{X}_1 - \overline{X}_2} = \sqrt{\frac{s_c^2}{N_1} + \frac{s_c^2}{N_2}}$$

follow Student's *t* distribution only if certain additional assumptions are tenable—assumptions which concern the population frequency distributions of scores on the variable in question. One assumption that applies to both ratios is that of normality for the population distributions. This might appear to limit radically the use of Student's t distribution with the two ratios, for normality is far from being a universal characteristic of score distributions; however, the assumption of normality for the populations becomes less and less important, the larger the size of the samples. Empirical evidence suggests that, for samples of approximately twenty individuals, the sampling distributions of these ratios are closely approximated by the t distribution, even for large departures from normality.

The second assumption applies only to the t ratio for the difference between sample means. This is the assumption of equal population variances (homogeneity of variance). Again, evidence suggests that for large samples this assumption is not important and, for practical purposes, need not be made. Consequently, for large samples (i.e., N greater than 30 or 40) there would seem to be no reason to obtain an estimate of common population variance, and the following ratio involving separate estimates of the population variances is appropriate.

$$t = \frac{(\overline{X}_1 - \overline{X}_2) - (\mu_1 - \mu_2)}{s_{\overline{X}_1 - \overline{X}_2}} \tag{12-3}$$

where $\quad s_{\overline{X}_1 - \overline{X}_2} = \sqrt{\dfrac{s_1^2}{N_1} + \dfrac{s_2^2}{N_2}} = \sqrt{\dfrac{\sum x_1^2}{N_1 (N_1 - 1)} + \dfrac{\sum x_2^2}{N_2 (N_2 - 1)}}$

It can be seen that this is the same ratio that was used in Chap. 11 as a critical ratio. Henceforth it will be referred to as an *approximate* or *large-sample t ratio*.

Example 12-5. Let us refer to the situation of Ex. 12-4. Suppose that the school psychologist had tested 105 children in all, forty-nine with the revised order and fifty-six with the standard order. The following are the results.

Revised order	*Standard order*
$N_R = 49$	$N_S = 56$
$\overline{X}_R = 105.88$	$\overline{X}_S = 99.30$
$\sum x_R^2 = 12{,}219.31$	$\sum x_S^2 = 16{,}827.94$

The research and null hypotheses are again $H_R : \mu_R - \mu_S > 0$ and $H_o : \mu_R - \mu_S = 0$. Using the foregoing data, $s_{\overline{X}_R - \overline{X}_S}$ may be determined and a large-sample t ratio computed.

$$s_{\overline{X}_R - \overline{X}_S} = \sqrt{\frac{\sum x_R^2}{N_R (N_R - 1)} + \frac{\sum x_S^2}{N_S (N_S - 1)}}$$

$$= \sqrt{\frac{12{,}219.31}{49 \,(48)} + \frac{16{,}827.94}{56 \,(55)}} = 3.26$$

$$t = \frac{(\overline{X}_R - \overline{X}_S) - (\mu_R - \mu_S)_{HYP}}{s_{\overline{X}_R - \overline{X}_S}} = \frac{(105.88 - 99.30) - 0}{3.26} = 2.02$$

From Appx. 2, it can be noted that the probability of obtaining a t greater than $+2.02$ is .0217; therefore, using the .05 level, H_o would be rejected as unreasonable and H_R would be considered tenable. If the .01 level were used, H_o would be accepted. The obtained t was referred to the normal-curve table of Appx. 2 because, for as many degrees of freedom as 103 (i.e., $df = 49 + 56 - 2 = 103$), Student's t distribution is closely approximated by the normal curve.

The large-sample t ratio presented above sometimes is used with small samples in situations in which the assumption of homogeneity of variance is not tenable; however, this use of the ratio with small samples requires that certain additional adjustments be made before the desired probability can be obtained. Approximate methods which involve such adjustments are described in more advanced texts.

Exercises and Problems

1. Suppose many samples of size 8 are randomly selected from a population which is normal and has a mean of 50. For each sample, a t ratio of the following form is computed:

$$t = \frac{\overline{X} - 50}{\sqrt{\dfrac{\sum x^2}{8(7)}}}$$

What proportion of the sample t ratios would you expect to be:
   a) Greater than $+2.365$?
   b) Less than $+1.415$?
   c) Less than -3.499?
   d) Between -2.365 and $+2.365$?
   e) Between -1.895 and $+3.499$?
   f) Between $+1.415$ and $+2.998$?
   g) Between -5.405 and -2.998?
2. The following scores are from a random sample of size 6 selected from a normal population.

$$2, 6, 3, 6, 5, 8$$

   a) Compute $\sum x^2$ using deviation scores.
   b) Compute $\sum x^2$ using raw scores.
   c) Compute an estimate of σ^2.

d) Compute an estimate of $\sigma_{\overline{X}}$.

e) Test $H_R : \mu > 4$; use $\alpha = .05$.

f) Test $H_R : \mu \neq 8$; use $\alpha = .05$.

3. The following are the scores from a random sample from population A and a random sample from population B.

Sample from A	Sample from B
3, 5, 7, 5	8, 9, 6, 5, 12

a) Compute $\sum x_A^2$ and $\sum x_B^2$ using deviation scores.

b) Compute $\sum x_A^2$ and $\sum x_B^2$ using raw scores.

c) Compute an estimate of the common population variance.

d) Test $H_R : \mu_A - \mu_B \neq 0$; use $\alpha = .05$.

For each of Probs. 4–6, specify H_R and H_o; determine the probability of obtaining sample results as deviant as those obtained (in the appropriate direction); and state your final conclusions. Indicate the level of significance used in arriving at your conclusions.

4. A psychologist wishes to determine whether two particular strains of laboratory rats differ with regard to maze-running ability. Samples from each strain are selected, and each sample rat is run through a test maze until he can negotiate it with no errors (i.e., turning into a blind alley) on two consecutive trials. The following are the results in terms of the number of practice trials required to learn the maze:

Sample from strain X	Sample from strain Y
$N_X = 12$	$N_Y = 14$
$\overline{X} = 20.42$	$\overline{Y} = 25.58$
$\sum x^2 = 192$	$\sum y^2 = 252$

5. An educational psychologist wishes to test the hypothesis that one can remember more of what he has learned if he is tested on the material immediately after learning. The students enrolled in his educational-psychology lecture course are divided at random into two groups. One group reads a short essay over and over again for thirty minutes. The second group reads the essay for twenty minutes. Then, immediately after the twenty-minute reading period, the second group is administered a ten-minute test on the essay. One month later, both groups are given a final test on the essay material. The following are the results from the final test in terms of the number of correct answers.

Group A (read all 30 min.)	Group B (read 20 min., tested 10 min.)
$N_A = 40$	$N_B = 40$
$\overline{X}_A = 15.60$	$\overline{X}_B = 17.40$
$\sum x_A^2 = 390$	$\sum x_B^2 = 780$

6. Mr. Smith, a high-school counselor, wants to know whether or not he can be effective in helping academically talented underachieving males improve their grades. He randomly divides a group of fifteen sophomore boys with

high aptitude scores and low grades into two groups. He counsels each boy in the experimental group once a week for an hour throughout the fall semester; the boys in the control group do not receive the special counselling. The following results are based on the grade-point averages received for the last third of the fall semester.

Experimental group	Control group
$N_E = 7$	$N_C = 8$
$\overline{X}_E = 2.624$	$\overline{X}_C = 2.399$
$\sum x_E^2 = .101$	$\sum x_C^2 = .180$

7. For a sample of size 6 selected from population A, $s_A = 7.00$; for a sample of size 8 selected from population B, $s_B = 9.50$. Assuming that populations A and B have equal variances, compute an estimate of the common variance.

8. Suppose, in testing $H_R : \mu \neq 100$ with data from a sample of size 4, Mr. Jones didn't know any better and used the normal-curve table to determine the probability of obtaining a sample t ratio as deviant as that which he obtained. Suppose he obtained a probability of .0190 using the normal-curve table. Would this value be too large or too small? What is the correct value? What assumption must be made in order to determine the correct value?

9. There is a slight difference between the procedures to be used in solving Probs. 5 and 6. What is the difference? Why is there a difference?

10. For each Prob. 3–6, specify the assumptions, if any, which underly the statistical test used.

Chapter 13

The Use of Dependent Samples

In the earlier examples dealing with differences between the means of two populations, the samples selected from the two populations were completely independent of each other. For instance, for the research on speed reading, individuals were assigned at random to the two sample groups. The selection of an individual for one of the groups was in no way related to the selection of any individual for the other group. The means of two samples selected independently in this way are known as *independent means.*

In educational and psychological research, however, the samples often are not independent. There are two types of situations in which this can occur: (*a*) those situations in which the same individuals are included in both samples and (*b*) those situations in which each individual in one of the samples has been paired on some basis with an individual in the other sample.

Suppose a psychologist wishes to test the hypothesis that people require more time to react to a light signal than to a sound signal. He uses the following experimental procedure: Each of ten volunteer subjects in his class in experimental psychology is given thirty practice trials with a light signal. For each trial, the subject is to press a button as soon as he sees a white signal light. After the thirty practice trials, the subject is given ten test trials. During each test trial, a special device measures the time between the onset of the light and the subject's pressing of the button. This is the subject's reaction time for that particular trial. The reaction times from the ten test trials are added together, and the total reaction time for the ten trials is recorded as the subject's *light reaction time.*

Then, each of the subjects is given thirty practice trials in which he is to press the button as soon as he hears a buzzer. After the thirty practice trials, he is given ten test trials, during each of which his reaction time is measured as before. The total reaction time for the ten test trials is recorded as his *sound reaction time*.

One way to view this study is in terms of two hypothetical populations consisting of experimental-psychology students who have been selected in the same way and under the same conditions as those used in the research. The elements of the first population would be students who, after thirty practice trials, react to the light signal for ten test trials, and the elements of the second population would be students who, after thirty practice trials, react to the sound signal for ten test trials. The research hypothesis would be that the mean light reaction time for the first population is greater than the mean sound reaction time for the second population. In symbolic form, this may be written as $H_R : \mu_1 > \mu_2$ or $H_R : \mu_1 - \mu_2 > 0$.

Now, let us consider the data for the ten subjects used in the experiment. The light reaction times are the scores for a sample of ten elements from the first population, and the sound reaction times are the scores for a sample of ten elements from the second population. It should be fairly evident that the selection of the sample from the first population was not independent of the selection of the sample from the second population, because the elements in the two samples are the *same* ten individuals. The means of samples which are dependent in this way are referred to as *dependent* or *correlated means*.

The values of two dependent (correlated) means tend to be related to each other. Suppose that most of the volunteers included in the group of ten happened by chance to be relatively slow individuals. If this were the case, their light reaction times and their sound reaction times would tend to be fairly high; therefore, the mean reaction times for both samples would be fairly high. On the other hand, if most of the volunteers included in the group of ten happened to be relatively quick, the means for both samples would tend to be fairly low. That is, if one of two dependent sample means is fairly high or fairly low, the other will tend to be correspondingly high or low. This is to be contrasted with the lack of relationship between the means of two independent samples. Suppose the psychologist had obtained twenty volunteers and had divided them at random into two groups of ten each. The value of the mean reaction time for one group would have no such relation to the mean reaction time for the second group. The specific statistical procedures to be used in making inferences from dependent means must be modified somewhat from those which are used with independent means. This modification can best be explained with reference to the appropriate sampling distributions.

Sampling Distribution of Differences between Dependent Means

The fact that the values of dependent means are related has definite implications for sampling distributions of differences between dependent means. If one reflects on the logic of the preceding paragraph, it should be possible to understand why differences between dependent means will tend to vary less than will the differences between independent means for successive pairs of samples. That is, the standard error (the standard deviation of the sampling distribution) of the difference between dependent sample means will be less than the standard error of the difference between independent sample means. This is reflected in a comparison of the following two standard-error formulas.

$$\sigma_{\overline{X}_1 - \overline{X}_2} \text{(independent)} = \sqrt{\sigma_{\overline{X}_1}^2 + \sigma_{\overline{X}_2}^2} \qquad \qquad (10\text{-}3)$$

$$\sigma_{\overline{X}_1 - \overline{X}_2} \text{(dependent)} = \sqrt{\sigma_{\overline{X}_1}^2 + \sigma_{\overline{X}_2}^2 - 2r_{12}\, \sigma_{\overline{X}_1}\, \sigma_{\overline{X}_2}} \qquad (13\text{-}1)$$

where $\sigma_{\overline{X}_1} = \dfrac{\sigma_1}{\sqrt{N}}$, $\sigma_{\overline{X}_2} = \dfrac{\sigma_2}{\sqrt{N}}$, and r_{12} is the correlation between scores from Population 1 and scores from Population 2

It can be seen that the two formulas are the same except for the term $2r_{12}\, \sigma_{\overline{X}_1}\, \sigma_{\overline{X}_2}$, which, when subtracted from $\sigma_{\overline{X}_1}^2 + \sigma_{\overline{X}_2}^2$, results in $\sigma_{\overline{X}_1 - \overline{X}_2}$ (dep.) being less than $\sigma_{\overline{X}_1 - \overline{X}_2}$ (indep.).

Although the correlation coefficient, r, has been discussed earlier, a brief review might be helpful at this point. If each score in one group of scores can be paired with a score in a second group of scores (for example, when they are based on the same individuals), r is a measure of the extent to which a high score from one group tends to go with a high score from the second group, a medium score with a medium score, and a low score with a low score. That is, it is a measure of the extent to which the values of two groups of paired scores are related. If the relationship is perfect, $r = 1$ or -1; whereas if there is no relationship, $r = 0$. When we are concerned with determining $\sigma_{\overline{X}_1 - \overline{X}_2}$ (dep.), the relationship between the two groups of scores usually will be positive but less than perfect. We would expect reaction time to a light signal and reaction time to a sound signal to be positively correlated. In other words, this r will usually be somewhere between 0 and $+1$. In the case of samples selected independently, there is no basis for pairing scores, and there is no relationship between the two groups of scores. That is why the term $2r_{12}\, \sigma_{\overline{X}_1}\, \sigma_{\overline{X}_2}$ does not appear in the formula for the standard error of the difference between independent means.

Aside from the standard error, the characteristics of a sampling distribution of differences between dependent means are the same as the characteristics of a sampling distribution of differences between independent means.

1) The mean of the sampling distribution is equal to the difference between the means for the two populations.

2) The sampling distribution will be normal if the distributions of scores for the two populations are normal.

3) The sampling distribution will tend to be normal for large sample sizes regardless of the shapes of the distributions of scores for the two populations (Central Limit Theorem).

TESTING HYPOTHESES USING DEPENDENT MEANS ($\overline{X}_1 - \overline{X}_2$ APPROACH)

When one desires to test a null hypothesis about the difference between two population means, the population standard deviations usually will be unknown, and Form. (13-1) cannot be used. An estimated standard error for dependent means must then be obtained as follows.

$$s_{\overline{X}_1-\overline{X}_2}(\text{dep.}) = \sqrt{s_{\overline{X}_1}^2 + s_{\overline{X}_2}^2 - 2r_{12}s_{\overline{X}_1}s_{\overline{X}_2}} \qquad (13\text{-}2)$$

where $\quad s_{\overline{X}_1}^2 = \dfrac{\sum x_1^2}{N(N-1)}, \quad s_{\overline{X}_2}^2 = \dfrac{\sum x_2^2}{N(N-1)}$

$$s_{\overline{X}_1}s_{\overline{X}_2} = \left(\sqrt{\frac{\sum x_1^2}{N(N-1)}}\right)\left(\sqrt{\frac{\sum x_2^2}{N(N-1)}}\right) = \frac{\sqrt{(\sum x_1^2)(\sum x_2^2)}}{N(N-1)}$$

and $\quad r_{12} = \dfrac{\sum x_1 x_2}{\sqrt{(\sum x_1^2)(\sum x_2^2)}}$

The term $2r_{12}s_{\overline{X}_1}s_{\overline{X}_2}$ can be simplified somewhat:

$$2r_{12}s_{\overline{X}_1}s_{\overline{X}_2} = \left(\frac{2\sum x_1 x_2}{\sqrt{(\sum x_1^2)(\sum x_2^2)}}\right)\left(\frac{\sqrt{(\sum x_1^2)(\sum x_2^2)}}{N(N-1)}\right) = \frac{2\sum x_1 x_2}{N(N-1)}$$

and a more convenient computational form for the estimated standard error can be developed.

$$s_{\overline{X}_1-\overline{X}_2}(\text{dep.}) = \sqrt{s_{\overline{X}_1}^2 + s_{\overline{X}_2}^2 - 2r_{12}s_{\overline{X}_1}s_{\overline{X}_2}}$$

$$= \sqrt{\frac{\sum x_1^2}{N(N-1)} + \frac{\sum x_2^2}{N(N-1)} - \frac{2\sum x_1 x_2}{N(N-1)}}$$

$$= \sqrt{\frac{\sum x_1^2 + \sum x_2^2 - 2\sum x_1 x_2}{N(N-1)}} \qquad (13\text{-}3)$$

Using the estimated standard error, the following sample ratio can be determined.

$$t = \frac{\overline{X}_1 - \overline{X}_2 - (\mu_1 - \mu_2)_{HYP}}{s_{\overline{X}_1 - \overline{X}_2}\,(\text{dep.})} \tag{13-4}$$

The sampling distribution of the foregoing ratio follows Student's t distribution with $N - 1$ degrees of freedom, if an assumption of normality is tenable. The exact nature of this assumption will not be discussed here, for it is more easily explained in the context of a later section of the present chapter; however, it can be said that the normality assumption has practical importance only when the above t ratio is used with relatively small samples. It should be noted that the N used in computing the degrees of freedom is the number of *pairs*, not the total number of scores in both samples. No assumption of homogeneity of population variance is involved when dependent samples are used.

The reader should perhaps be reminded that both a sum of squared

Table 13-1

Computation of $\overline{X}_1$, $\overline{X}_2$, $\sum x_1^2$, $\sum x_2^2$, and $\sum x_1 x_2$ from Original Scores

Subject	Total Reaction Time to Light (Seconds) X_1	Total Reaction Time to Sound (Seconds) X_2	X_1^2	X_2^2	$X_1 X_2$
1	1.62	1.35	2.6244	1.8225	2.1870
2	1.84	1.84	3.3856	3.3856	3.3856
3	1.27	.83	1.6129	.6889	1.0541
4	.92	1.18	.8464	1.3924	1.0856
5	1.34	1.42	1.7956	2.0164	1.9028
6	1.93	.69	3.7249	.4761	1.3317
7	2.25	1.65	5.0625	2.7225	3.7125
8	2.17	2.06	4.7089	4.2436	4.4702
9	2.03	1.65	4.1209	2.7225	3.3495
10	2.68	1.97	7.1824	3.8809	5.2796
	18.05	14.64	35.0645	23.3514	27.7586

$$\overline{X}_1 = \frac{\sum X_1}{N} = \frac{18.05}{10} = 1.805, \qquad \overline{X}_2 = \frac{\sum X_2}{N} = \frac{14.64}{10} = 1.464$$

$$\sum x_1^2 = \sum (X_1 - \overline{X}_1)^2 = \frac{N\sum X_1^2 - (\sum X_1)^2}{N} = \frac{10\,(35.0645) - (18.05)^2}{10} = 2.484$$

$$\sum x_2^2 = \sum (X_2 - \overline{X}_2)^2 = \frac{N\sum X_2^2 - (\sum X_2)^2}{N} = \frac{10\,(23.3514) - (14.64)^2}{10} = 1.918$$

$$\sum x_1 x_2 = \sum (X_1 - \overline{X}_1)(X_2 - \overline{X}_2) = \frac{N\sum X_1 X_2 - (\sum X_1)(\sum X_2)}{N}$$

$$= \frac{10\,(27.7586) - (18.05)(14.64)}{10} = 1.333$$

deviations and a sum of cross-products can be obtained using raw-score Forms. (4-4) and (7-4).

$$\sum x_1^2 = \sum (X_1 - \bar{X}_1)^2 = \frac{N \sum X_1^2 - (\sum X_1)^2}{N} \tag{4-4}$$

$$\sum x_1 x_2 = \sum (X_1 - \bar{X}_1)(X_2 - \bar{X}_2) = \frac{N \sum X_1 X_2 - (\sum X_1)(\sum X_2)}{N} \tag{7-4}$$

Since the data for text samples are usually given in deviation-score form, a further demonstration of how to apply the above formulas might be helpful. Such a demonstration, using the reaction times for the ten students used in the experiment described earlier, is presented in Table 13-1. The results obtained in Table 13-1 are then utilized in Ex. 13-1. The reader is reminded that the reaction time given for each student is the total time for the ten test trials.

Example 13-1. Given the following data for the ten volunteers used in the reaction-time experiment, the research hypothesis $H_R : \mu_1 - \mu_2 > 0$ will be tested indirectly by testing the null hypothesis $H_o : \mu_1 - \mu_2 = 0$ directly.

Reaction to signal light	*Reaction to buzzer*
$N = 10$	$N = 10$
$\bar{X}_1 = 1.805$ seconds	$\bar{X}_2 = 1.464$ seconds
$\sum x_1^2 = 2.484$	$\sum x_2^2 = 1.918$

$$\sum x_1 x_2 = 1.333$$

An estimated standard error for dependent samples can be computed, using Form. (13-3):

$$s_{\bar{X}_1 - \bar{X}_2}(\text{dep.}) = \sqrt{\frac{\sum x_1^2 + \sum x_2^2 - 2 \sum x_1 x_2}{N(N-1)}}$$

$$= \sqrt{\frac{2.484 + 1.918 - 2(1.333)}{10(9)}} = \sqrt{\frac{1.736}{(10)(9)}} = .139$$

and a sample t ratio can be formed.

$$t = \frac{\bar{X}_1 - \bar{X}_2 - (\mu_1 - \mu_2)_{HYP}}{s_{\bar{X}_1 - \bar{X}_2}(\text{dep.})} = \frac{.341 - 0}{.139} = +2.45$$

Since the research hypothesis is directional, a one-tailed test of the null hypothesis would be in order. That is, we are interested in differences between sample means in the direction specified in the research hypothesis; therefore, we must determine the probability of obtaining a sample t ratio as large as or larger than (in a positive direction only) the $+2.45$ actually obtained. According to Appx. 3, the probability is .025 for a t

of $+2.262$ for $10 - 1 = 9$ df, and .01 for a t of $+2.821$; therefore, using the .05 level of significance, H_o would be rejected, and it would be concluded that reaction time tends to be greater to the signal light than to the buzzer.

AN ALTERNATE APPROACH (USING $\overline{X}_D$)

As originally stated, the psychologist's research hypothesis was that reaction time would be greater to a light signal than to a sound signal. In Ex. 13-1, this research hypothesis was formulated more specifically in terms of the *difference between the mean reaction times for two hypothetical populations of students*, one population being defined by the white-signal-light condition and the other by the buzzer condition. In this section, we shall formulate the original research hypothesis more specifically in terms of the *mean of the difference scores for a single population*.

Suppose that every volunteer's total reaction time to the buzzer were subtracted from his total reaction time to the white signal light, to obtain a difference score, or D. This is illustrated in Table 13-2 for the same ten pairs of reaction times used in Table 13-1. If an individual obtained the same total reaction time to both types of signal, as did Individual 2,

Table 13-2

Computation of $\overline{X}_D$ and $\sum x_D^2$ from Original Scores

Subject	Total Reaction Time to Light (Seconds) X_1	Total Reaction Time to Sound (Seconds) X_2	$D = X_1 - X_2$	D^2
1	1.62	1.35	.27	.0729
2	1.84	1.84	0.00	0.0000
3	1.27	.83	.44	.1936
4	.92	1.18	$-.26$	.0676
5	1.34	1.42	$-.08$	.0064
6	1.93	.69	1.24	1.5376
7	2.25	1.65	.60	.3600
8	2.17	2.06	.11	.0121
9	2.03	1.65	.38	.1444
10	2.68	1.97	.71	.5041
			3.41	2.8987

$$\overline{X}_D = \frac{\sum D}{N} = \frac{3.41}{10} = .341$$

$$\sum x_D^2 = \sum (D - \overline{X}_D)^2 = \frac{N \sum D^2 - (\sum D)^2}{N} = \frac{10\,(2.8987) - (3.41)^2}{10} = 1.736$$

his D-score will be zero. On the other hand, if his reaction time to the white signal light was greater, his D-score will be positive or greater than zero. If his reaction time to the light was less, his D-score would be negative or less than zero. Thus, if reaction time tends to be greater to a light signal than to a sound signal, it would be expected that the average D-score would be greater than zero. The original research hypothesis thus may be formulated more specifically in terms of the mean-difference score for a single hypothetical population of experimental-psychology students.

$$H_R : \mu_D > 0$$

where μ_D is the mean difference-score for the population.

A null hypothesis may also be formulated in these terms.

$$H_o : \mu_D = 0$$

Example 13-2. The research hypothesis stated above will be tested, starting with the same ten pairs of reaction times used for Ex. 13-1. The following are the summary results based on the ten D-scores (see Table 13-2 for details).

$$\overline{X}_D = .341 \text{ seconds}, \qquad x_D^2 = 1.736$$

where $\overline{X}_D$ is the mean of the ten D-scores $[\overline{X}_D = (\sum D)/10]$, and x_D is the deviation of an individual's D-score from the mean of the sample of ten D-scores (i.e., $x_D = D - \overline{X}_D$)

In case it is not already apparent, it should be pointed out that the D-scores are, for purposes of statistical computations, the same as scores obtained from a single measure or test. The only reason for labelling them D instead of X is to emphasize the general nature of the situation in which they were obtained. Thus, all the previously discussed techniques and formulas involving X are applicable to D-scores, and the techniques of the previous chapter would apply to a test of a null hypothesis about a mean of a single population of D-scores. First, the following can be computed.

$$s_{\overline{X}_D} = \frac{s_D}{\sqrt{N}} = \sqrt{\frac{\sum x_D^2}{N(N-1)}} = \sqrt{\frac{1.736}{10\,(9)}} = .139$$

where s_D is an estimate of the standard deviation of the population of difference scores and $s_{\overline{X}_D}$ is an estimate of the standard error of the mean difference

A t ratio can then be formed.

$$t = \frac{\overline{X}_D - (\mu_D)_{HYP}}{s_{\overline{X}_D}} = \frac{.341 - 0}{.139} = +2.45$$

For a t of $+2.45$ and 9 df, P is between .01 and .025 (one-tailed). Again, using the .05 level, H_o would be rejected, and it would be concluded that the research hypothesis had been supported.

The reader may have noticed that exactly the same results were obtained in both Ex. 13-1 and Ex. 13-2. This is no coincidence; it could be shown algebraically that for pairs of scores based on the same group of individuals, the following relationships always hold.

$$\overline{X}_1 - \overline{X}_2 \text{(dep.)} = \overline{X}_D \qquad \sum x_1^2 + \sum x_2^2 - 2\sum x_1 x_2 = \sum x_D^2$$
$$1.805 - 2.484 = .341 \qquad\qquad\qquad 1.736 = 1.736$$

$$s_{\overline{X}_1 - \overline{X}_2} \text{(dep.)} = s_{\overline{X}_D}$$
$$.139 = .139$$

The research hypothesis of Ex. 13-1 ($H_R : \mu_1 - \mu_2 > 0$) is, therefore, equivalent to the research hypothesis of Ex. 13-2 ($H_R : \mu_D > 0$). Similarly, the two null hypotheses are equivalent ($H_o : \mu_1 - \mu_2 = 0$, and $H_o : \mu_D = 0$). Thus, the two t ratios also would be equal. Furthermore, the assumption of normality involved in both approaches is the same. The assumption is more clearly understood with reference to the $\overline{X}_D$ approach; for, in this context, it is the same as the assumption of normality which underlies any t test of a null hypothesis about a single population mean. That is, it would be assumed that the distribution of difference scores for the entire population is normal. As has been mentioned before, this assumption is of practical importance only when the sample is relatively small.

If the two approaches illustrated above are equivalent, does it make any difference which one is used? The answer to this question is two-fold. It has been pointed out that there is no difference in the obtained results; however, if one is concerned about the labor involved in the computations necessary for each of the approaches, there may be a difference. Using any one of several electric desk calculators commonly available, it is possible to obtain $\sum X_1^2$, $2\sum X_1 X_2$, and $\sum X_2^2$ all in one operation. In such circumstances, the $\overline{X}_1 - \overline{X}_2$ approach is more efficient.

SAMPLES BASED ON DIFFERENT BUT MATCHED INDIVIDUALS

In both examples above, each pair of scores was based on a single individual. In this section, we shall discuss the situation in which each pair of scores is based on two different but matched individuals.

Suppose a testing company has published two equivalent forms of an arithmetic-achievement test for seventh-graders, Forms A and B. By "equivalent forms" we mean that an individual's score on Form A can be compared directly with his own or another individual's score on Form B. Several conditions must obtain before two forms can be considered equivalent, an obvious one of which is that the forms be equally difficult. Certainly, if Form *A* were more difficult than Form *B*, it would make no sense to compare a score from Form *A* directly with one from Form *B*; we would expect a person's score on Form *A* to be lower because of its greater difficulty.

Suppose Mr. Smith, the testing director for a large city school district, wishes to test the research hypothesis that the two forms are *not* equally difficult, using different people for the two samples. He administers the two forms to two different groups of individuals because he suspects that if the same individual is given both forms of the test fairly close together in time, the individual's score on the second form might be higher because he has learned a little through his experience with the first form. He selects 100 seventh-graders, fifty of whom are to take Form *A*, and the other fifty of whom are to take Form *B*. Mr. Smith wants to make sure that the two groups are comparable in intelligence, for he knows that general intelligence is a factor in how well an individual performs on an arithmetic test; therefore, he uses the following procedure: First, he administers each of the 100 seventh-graders an IQ test. Then, he attempts to group the 100 as well as he can into fifty pairs, with the two individuals in each pair having approximately the same IQ score. For each of the fifty pairs, he randomly assigns one individual to group *A* and the other to group *B*. Finally, he administers Form *A* to group *A* and Form *B* to group *B*.

By this procedure, every one of the sample of fifty scores from Form *A* has been paired with a score from Form *B*. For purposes of statistical analysis, this situation (pairs of scores based on matched individuals) is considered to be identical with that of pairs of scores based on the same individuals. The means of the two samples are dependent, and both the $\overline{X}_1 - \overline{X}_2$ method and the $\overline{X}_D$ method are applicable.

Advantages of Matching

There are two possible advantages of Mr. Smith's procedure of matching individuals in the sample groups. The first deals with the interpretation of the results. Since the two groups were matched on intelligence, any difference between the mean math-achievement scores cannot be attributed to differences in intelligence. If, on the other hand, the groups had not been matched, and, by chance, the individuals selected to take Form *A* turned out to be more or less intelligent than those selected to take Form *B*, interpretation of the sample results would be difficult. It should be pointed out, however, that completely random assignment (no matching) to two groups will rarely result in groups which differ widely on some relevant variable (intelligence, in this case) if large samples are used.

A second and perhaps more important advantage concerns the standard-error term. The standard error of the difference between the means of dependent samples will usually be less than the standard error for independent samples. This decrease in the standard error is represented by the term $-2r_{12} \, s_{\overline{X}_1} \, s_{\overline{X}_2}$ in Form. (13-2).

$$s_{\overline{X}_1 - \overline{X}_2} \, (\text{dep.}) = \sqrt{s_{\overline{X}_1}^2 + s_{\overline{X}_2}^2 - 2r_{12} \, s_{\overline{X}_1} \, s_{\overline{X}_2}}$$

It can be seen that the decrease in the standard error depends upon the size of the obtained correlation coefficient, r_{12}, between the scores for Sample 1 and the scores for Sample 2. The larger r_{12}, the larger will be the term $2r_{12} \, s_{\overline{X}_1} \, s_{\overline{X}_2}$ and the smaller will be the standard error. This tells us that a difference between the means of two matched groups will often more accurately represent the population difference than a difference between the means of two independent groups. When this is the case, we would be more likely to draw correct conclusions concerning our null and research hypotheses from the matched groups.

Using matched groups will, however, reduce the standard error only in the degree in which the variable used as a basis for matching is related to the variable under investigation. For the above example, we would expect a substantial relationship between the matching variable of measured intelligence and arithmetic achievement score, and, consequently, we would expect matching to result in a substantial decrease in the size of the standard error. Had the students taking Forms *A* and *B* been matched, however, on some irrelevant basis, such as body height, no decrease in the standard error would have been expected. The higher the relationship between the pairing or matching variable and the variable under investigation, the higher will be r_{12}, the correlation between the scores for Sample 1 and the scores for Sample 2, and, thus, the greater will be the advantage from matching.

It should be emphasized that the matched-groups procedure is not always best. If the relationship between the matching variable and the variable under investigation is quite low, and, if the sample size is small, more might be lost than gained by matching. (This point will be commented upon briefly in the next chapter.) Furthermore, there are certain situations in which matching can lead to difficulties because of what are known as *regression effects*. Finally, for groups which have not been matched, there are statistical procedures, known as *covariance techniques*, which will accomplish some of the same things as matching but do not involve some of its limitations. Although regression effects and covariance techniques are beyond the scope of this text, they are mentioned here in order to encourage caution in the use of matching as an experimental procedure.

Summary

In this chapter and the previous one, the procedures for testing hypotheses about (1) the mean of a single population, (2) the difference between means of two populations, using independent samples, and (3) the difference between means of two populations, using dependent samples, were discussed. In this chapter, Item 3 was shown to be equivalent to Item 1; for when the scores are based on the same or on matched individuals, a hypothesis about the difference between the means of two populations of scores is equivalent to a hypothesis about the mean of a single population of difference scores.

The basic logic of hypothesis testing is the same for all three cases. Only the details differ. These details are summarized in Table 13-3.

Exercises and Problems

1. Suppose the data from two samples of four each are to be used in testing $H_R : \mu_1 - \mu_2 > 0$. How large a t would be required for rejecting H_0 at the .05 level:
   a) If the two samples were independent?
   b) If the two samples were matched?
2. The following are the scores for the same five individuals obtained under both experimental and control conditions.

Subject	Experimental	Control
1	12	9
2	6	8
3	8	6
4	5	1
5	9	6

   a) Compute $\sum x_E^2$, $\sum x_C^2$ and $\sum x_E x_C$ using deviation scores.
   b) Compute $\sum x_E^2$, $\sum x_C^2$ and $\sum x_E x_C$ using raw scores.
   c) How large is the correlation between the scores obtained under the two conditions?
   d) Compute an estimate of $\sigma_{\bar{X}_E - \bar{X}_C}$.
   e) Test $H_R : \mu_E - \mu_C > 0$; use $\alpha = .01$.
   f) What assumption or assumptions underlly the test performed in (e)?
3. Analyze the data of Prob. 2 using difference scores.
   a) Compute $\sum x_D^2$ using deviation scores.
   b) Compute $\sum x_D^2$ using raw scores.

Table 13-3

Summary of Techniques for Testing Hypothesis about Single Means and Differences between Two Means

	Small Samples	Large Samples
Single Population Means	$H_o: \mu = \mu_{HYP}$ $t = \dfrac{\bar{X} - \mu_{HYP}}{s_{\bar{X}}}$ where $s_{\bar{X}} = \dfrac{s}{\sqrt{N}} = \sqrt{\dfrac{\sum x^2}{N(N-1)}}$ Degrees of Freedom: $N - 1$ Assumptions: Normality of population score distribution	$H_o: \mu = \mu_{HYP}$ Same Assumptions: None
Differences between Two Population Means (Independent Samples)	$H_o: \mu_1 - \mu_2 = 0$ $t = \dfrac{\bar{X}_1 - \bar{X}_2 - 0}{s_{\bar{X}_1 - \bar{X}_2}}$ where $s_{\bar{X}_1 - \bar{X}_2} = \sqrt{s_{\bar{X}_1}^2 + s_{\bar{X}_2}^2} = \sqrt{\dfrac{s_c^2}{N_1} + \dfrac{s_c^2}{N_2}}$ and $s_c^2 = \dfrac{\sum x_1^2 + \sum x_2^2}{N_1 + N_2 - 2}$ Degrees of Freedom: $N_1 + N_2 - 2$ Assumptions: a) Normality of population score distributions b) Homogeneity of variance; $\sigma_1^2 = \sigma_2^2$	$H_o: \mu_1 - \mu_2 = 0$ $t = \dfrac{\bar{X}_1 - \bar{X}_2 - 0}{s_{\bar{X}_1 - \bar{X}_2}}$ where $s_{\bar{X}_1 - \bar{X}_2} = \sqrt{s_{\bar{X}_1}^2 + s_{\bar{X}_2}^2} = \sqrt{\dfrac{\sum x_1^2}{N_1(N_1 - 1)} + \dfrac{\sum x_2^2}{N_2(N_2 - 1)}}$ Degrees of Freedom: $N_1 + N_2 - 2$ Assumptions: None

Differences between Two Population Means (Dependent Samples: $\overline{X}_1 - \overline{X}_2$ Approach)

$H_o : \mu_1 - \mu_2 = 0$

$$t = \frac{\overline{X}_1 - \overline{X}_2 - 0}{s_{\overline{X}_1 - \overline{X}_2}}$$

where $s_{\overline{X}_1 - \overline{X}_2} = \sqrt{s_{\overline{X}_1}^2 + s_{\overline{X}_2}^2 - 2r_{12}\, s_{\overline{X}_1}\, s_{\overline{X}_2}}$

$$= \sqrt{\frac{\sum x_1^2 + \sum x_2^2 - 2\sum x_1 x_2}{N(N-1)}}$$

Degrees of Freedom: $N - 1$, where N is the number of pairs

Assumptions: Normality of population distribution of difference scores

$H_o : \mu_1 - \mu_2 = 0$

Same

Assumptions: None

Differences between Two Population Means (Dependent Samples: $\overline{X}_D$ Approach)

$H_o : \mu_D = 0$

$$t = \frac{\overline{X}_D - 0}{s_{\overline{X}_D}}$$

where $s_{\overline{X}_D} = \frac{s_D}{\sqrt{N}} = \sqrt{\frac{\sum X_D^2}{N(N-1)}}$

Degrees of Freedom: $N - 1$, where N is the number of pairs

Assumptions: Normality of population distribution of difference scores.

$H_o : \mu_D = 0$

Same

Assumptions: None

   c) Compute an estimate of $\sigma_{\bar{X}_D}$.

   d) Test $H_R : \mu_D > 0$; use $\alpha = .01$.

4. The same nine people are administered an attitude inventory before and after seeing a movie designed to change their attitudes. Test the hypothesis $H_R : \mu_2 - \mu_1 < 0$, using the following sample results.

Before	After
$\bar{X}_1 = 27.56$	$\bar{X}_2 = 23.00$
$s_1 = 3.00$	$s_2 = 6.00$

$$r_{12} = .25$$

5. Sixty pairs of fourth-graders, each pair matched as well as possible on IQ scores, are formed. One member of each pair is assigned randomly to group *A* and the other to group *B*. Each child in both groups is presented with twenty puzzle problems; however, those in group *A* have had special instruction in general problem-solving skills before they are presented with the problems, whereas those in group *B* have not. The following are the results for the two groups (in terms of the number of problems solved correctly).

Group A	Group B	
$\bar{X}_A = 11.26$	$\bar{X}_B = 10.76$	$\sum x_A x_B = 302$
$\sum x_A^2 = 542$	$\sum x_B^2 = 965$	

   a) Compute an estimate of σ_A.

   b) Compute an estimate of $\sigma_{\bar{X}_A - \bar{X}_B}$.

   c) Test the hypothesis that the kind of instruction given to group *A* is effective.

6. Twenty-five overweight women who have been trying, unsuccessfully, to reduce, volunteer to take a special weight-reducing pill for two weeks. Each woman's weight loss over the period is obtained by subtracting her weight at the end from her weight at the beginning (i.e., $D = X_1 - X_2$). The following are the sample results in terms of pounds lost.

$$\sum D = 75 \qquad \sum D^2 = 625$$

   a) Compute $\bar{X}_D$ and $\sum x_D^2$.

   b) Test the hypothesis that the pill is effective.

7. If, for the data of Prob. 6, $s_{\bar{X}_1} = 2.00$ and $s_{\bar{X}_2} = 2.00$, what is the correlation between the initial weights and the final weights?

8. If original scores obtained in Prob. 4 had been analyzed using the difference score approach (i.e., using $D = X_2 - X_1$):

   a) What would be the value of $\bar{D}$?

   b) What would be the value of $s_{\bar{D}}$?

   c) Compute an estimate of the variance of the population of difference scores.

   d) What would be the value of $\sum x_D^2$?

9. To what extent did the matching performed in the experiment of Prob. 5 actually prove to be advantageous? Perform the computations necessary to show the effects of the matching.

10. Suppose in an experiment to test the hypothesis $H_R : \mu_1 - \mu_2 \neq 0$, matched groups were used. Suppose the following are the sample results.

$$\overline{X}_1 = 21.3 \qquad\qquad \overline{X}_2 = 18.5$$
$$\sum x_1^2 = 7600 \qquad\qquad \sum x_2^2 = 5800$$
$$\sum x_1 x_2 = 570$$

Was the matching worth the trouble? Why or why not?

Chapter 14

Hypothesis Testing: Factors to Be Considered in Forming Conclusions

INCORRECT INFERENCES ABOUT POPULATION VALUES

Statistical hypothesis testing is a systematic means of making inferences about a population from what is known about a sample randomly selected from that population. For instance, we may wish to test a research hypothesis about an unknown population mean. It may be, however, too expensive, too inconvenient, too time-consuming, or simply impossible to examine each individual in the population in order to obtain the actual value of the parameter; therefore, an appropriate null hypothesis that the unknown mean equals a specific value is formulated, a random sample is selected from the population, and a direct test of the null hypothesis is performed. If the null hypothesis is accepted, we make one inference (i.e., that the value specified in the null hypothesis is a reasonable one for the population mean). If it is rejected, we make another inference (i.e., that the population mean differs from the value specified in the null hypothesis in the direction specified in the research hypothesis). Whether the research hypothesis can be considered as supported depends on which of these two inferences is made.

Can we ever be certain that the inference is correct? The answer is negative; for the inference, although arrived at through systematic statistical procedures, is nonetheless based on only a small part of the entire population. Although random sampling is likely to result in a sample which is representative of the population, it is still possible for a sample value to differ considerably from the population value because of chance factors. Hence, there is always the possibility that an inference based on a sample is incorrect. A test of a null hypothesis may lead to one of two types of incorrect inferences. These are known as Type I and Type II errors. Although we can never know when we have made a Type I or Type II error, statistical theory does provide us with certain information concerning the likelihood that we may have done so.

Incorrectly Rejecting the Null Hypothesis: Type I Error

A Type I error can occur only if the null hypothesis is actually true; if it is false, it cannot be *incorrectly* rejected. In other words, if we reject H_o when it is false, we do so correctly, not incorrectly; therefore, we can speak of making a Type I error only if we assume H_o *is in fact true*. Of course, in practice we never know whether it is true or false.

Suppose Dr. Black, a psychologist, wishes to test the one-tailed research hypothesis that the mean population score on a certain personality variable is greater than 100 (i.e., $H_R : \mu > 100$). He plans to obtain scores for a random sample of size 144 and perform a one-tailed test of the null hypothesis $H_o : \mu = 100$. Furthermore, he intends to use the .05 level of significance. That is, he plans to reject $H_o : \mu = 100$ if the probability (assuming H_o to be true) of obtaining at t as large as or larger than that which he actually obtains is less than .05. According to Appx. 3, .05 is the probability (if $H_o : \mu = 100$ is true) of obtaining a sample t ratio $[t = (\overline{X} - 100)/s_{\overline{X}}]$ of approximately $+1.64$ or more. (For as many as 143 df, we can use either the t distribution of Appx. 3 or the normal-curve table of Appx. 2.) Therefore, the strategy for deciding whether to reject H_o and conclude that the research hypothesis has been supported is:

    a) If a t greater than $+1.64$ is obtained, reject H_o.
    b) If a t smaller than $+1.64$ is obtained, accept H_o.

Consider the situation which would obtain if $H_o : \mu = 100$ *were in fact true*. Then, the probability of obtaining a t greater than $+1.64$ would be .05. Since Dr. Black intends to reject H_o if $t > +1.64$, the probability of obtaining sample results which will lead him to reject H_o is .05. If H_o is in fact true, rejecting H_o amounts to making a Type I error; therefore, if H_o is true, the probability of obtaining sample results which will lead to a Type I error is .05. This is represented in Fig. 14-1. The shaded area in that figure is both the level of significance and the probability of a Type I error.

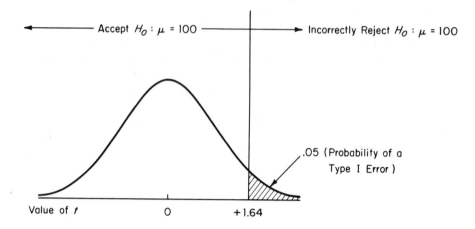

Figure 14-1. Sampling Distribution of t for df = 143 if $H_o : \mu = 100$ Were True
(The decision strategy for testing $H_R : \mu > 100$ using $\alpha = .05$ is superimposed.)

The foregoing discussion can be summed up as follows.

1)   When testing a null hypothesis, we never *know for sure* whether it is true or false. If we did know, there would be no sense in performing a statistical test.

2)   Even if H_o is true, our sample results may lead us to reject it incorrectly (i.e., make a Type I error).

3)   In practice, if we reject H_o, we cannot know for sure whether we have made a Type I error, because we do not know whether H_o is true or false; however, we do know something about the probability of making such an error.

4)   If H_o is true, the probability of obtaining sample results which would lead us to make a Type I error is equal to the level of significance we plan to use in deciding whether to accept or to reject; therefore, if we use .10 as our standard, we are more likely to make a Type I error in those situations in which H_o might in fact be true than if we use .05 or .01.

Incorrectly Accepting the Null Hypothesis: Type II Error

A Type II error can occur only if the null hypothesis is actually false; for, if it is true, it cannot be *incorrectly* accepted. That is, if we accept H_o

when it is true, we do so correctly, not incorrectly. We can, therefore, speak of making a Type II error only if *we assume H_o is false.*

Let us continue with the example begun in the previous section. Suppose Dr. Black obtained the following results from his sample of 144.

$$\overline{X} = 103.00$$

$$s_{\overline{X}} = \sqrt{\frac{\sum x^2}{N(N-1)}} = 3.00$$

$$t = \frac{103.00 - 100.00}{3.00} = +1.00$$

The probability of obtaining a t of $+1.00$ or more is approximately .16 (Appx. 2). Therefore, he would accept the null hypothesis that $\mu = 100$. Does this *prove* the null hypothesis that $\mu = 100$? Certainly not. All it indicates is that a sample mean as large as the 103 actually obtained would not be too unlikely if the population mean were equal to 100. In other words, *100 is not an unreasonable value for μ in the light of the sample mean of 103 actually obtained.* This is far from proving that the population mean is 100, for there are many other possible values for μ which would not be unreasonable in the light of the same sample results. Consider the value of 102. For the null hypothesis $H_o : \mu = 102$, the following t ratio would be obtained.

$$t = \frac{103.00 - 102.00}{3.00} = .33$$

According to Appx. 2, the probability is .37; therefore, 102 is not an "unreasonable value" for the unknown population mean. In fact, since .37 is greater than .16, one might be tempted to feel that 102 is even more reasonable than 100. Now consider the value of 103. For the null hypothesis $H_o : \mu = 103$, the t ratio would be equal to zero.

$$t = \frac{103.00 - 103.00}{3.00} = .00$$

Here again, since the probability of .50 is greater than .05, 103 would not be an "unreasonable" value for the unknown population mean. Obviously, there are many other values which would also not be unreasonable (e.g., 101.5, 101.6, 101.61) in the light of *the same sample results.*

Which one of the many possible values for the population mean is the one "true" value? This we never know, for if we did there would be no need for statistical inference; therefore, when Dr. Black accepts the null hypothesis $H_o : \mu = 100$, he may well be accepting it incorrectly. That is, μ may in fact be some other value, such as 101, 102, or 101.5. If it is some other value, acceptance of $H_o : \mu = 100$ amounts to making a Type II error.

Advantage of Rejecting H_o

In any test of a null hypothesis, the sample results will lead to one of two possible courses of action: we shall either reject H_o or accept H_o. Let us consider for a moment the extent to which we could rely on our conclusions if the results of a piece of research lead us to reject H_o. There are two possible explanations for obtaining such results. First, it is quite possible that the null hypothesis is in fact false and that the sample results are merely reflecting this. If this is so, then we have rejected H_o correctly, and our resulting conclusions would be sound. On the other hand, there is always the possibility that H_o is in fact true and that chance factors led to our rejection of it. If this is so, we have rejected H_o incorrectly (that is, made a Type I error), and our resulting conclusions would be false. We can never be absolutely sure which of these two is the real explanation; however, we do know the probability of obtaining sample results which would lead us to reject H_o incorrectly, if it is in fact true (that is, to make a Type I error). This probability has been shown to be the level of significance used in deciding whether to reject H_o; therefore, if our sample results do lead to a rejection of the null hypothesis, we have some notion of how much confidence we can place in our conclusions.

Now, let us consider the extent to which we could rely on our conclusions if the results of research led us to *accept* H_o. Again, there are two possible explanations for such results. First, it is possible that H_o is in fact true and that the sample results are merely reflecting this. Under such a condition, our acceptance of H_o would be correct, and our resulting conclusions would be sound; however, it is quite possible that H_o is in fact false and that chance factors led to our acceptance of it (that is, to a Type II error). We can never know which of these two possible explanations is the real one. Furthermore, we do not know the probability of incorrectly accepting H_o when it is in fact false (that is, the probability of making a Type II error). It is impossible to determine this probability without knowing the "true" value of the parameter with which the hypothesis is concerned. In an inference problem, of course, this value is unknown; therefore, if our results do lead to the acceptance of the null hypothesis, the basis for deciding how much confidence to place in our conclusions is less clear. These are among the reasons why many contend that statistical hypothesis testing should not be used in situations in which the research hypothesis would be supported by *acceptance* of the null hypothesis (e.g., $H_R : \mu = 100$, $H_o : \mu = 100$).

It should be mentioned that the issues involved in deciding when hypothesis testing is appropriate are somewhat more complex than the foregoing discussion would indicate. Those who do advocate its use when H_R and H_o are the same, point out that one would only rarely be interested in demonstrating that an unknown parameter is equal to the "exact" value specified in the null hypothesis. They point out that the use of what is known as an *operating characteristic curve* allows one to be fairly confident that the value of the unknown parameter falls within a certain range of the value specified in the null hypothesis, if H_o is accepted. For further discussion of this issue, as well as a discussion of *operating characteristic curves*, the reader is referred to a more advanced text.

Reducing the Probability of Making a Type II Error

Although we can never determine the probability of obtaining sample results which would lead to accepting H_o incorrectly (when in fact it is false), there are several means at our disposal for reducing this probability.

a) Increase the level of significance used as the standard for rejecting the null hypothesis. A researcher is in complete control of the probability of making a Type I error. He decides on the level of significance to be used as a standard for rejecting the null hypothesis. If he decides to use the .01 level of significance as his standard, he is much less likely to reject H_o incorrectly (when in fact H_o is true) than if he decides to work at the .05 or the .10 level. Should he use the .001, .0001 or .00001 level in order to decrease even further the likelihood of a Type I error? The answer to this is that *the smaller the level of significance he decides upon, the greater will be the likelihood of his making a Type II error.*

Consider once again the example in which Dr. Black performed a one-tailed test of the null hypothesis $H_o : \mu = 100$. Suppose, for purposes of this discussion, that $H_o : \mu = 100$ was false and that the "true" value for the unknown parameter μ was 102. Accepting H_o would amount to making a Type II error. Let us compare the likelihood of his making a Type II error under two conditions: when using a very low level of significance, say .001, and when using a level of significance of .05.

It will be recalled that Dr. Black's research hypothesis was one-tailed ($H_R : \mu > 100$). If he were to use the .05 level of significance, he would reject $H_o : \mu = 100$ for a t of $+1.64$ or larger. Using an obtained $s_{\bar{x}}$ of 3, a t of $+1.64$ corresponds to a sample mean of 104.92.

$$t = \frac{\overline{X} - \mu_{HYP}}{s_{\overline{X}}}, \qquad +1.64 = \frac{104.92 - 100}{3}$$

He would, therefore, reject H_o for a sample mean of 104.92 or more (if $s_{\bar{x}} = 3$). If he were to use the .001 level of significance, he would reject H_o for a t of $+3.09$ or larger (Appx. 2). Using the same obtained $s_{\bar{x}}$ of 3, a t of $+3.09$ corresponds to a sample mean of 109.28.

$$+3.09 = \frac{109.28 - 100}{3}$$

Now, if the true mean is in fact 102 rather than 100 as hypothesized, which of the two decision strategies under consideration would be more likely to lead Dr. Black to accept $H_o : \mu = 100$ and thus to make a Type II error? It should be apparent that, if the true mean were 102, Dr. Black would be less likely to obtain a sample mean as large as 109.28 than one as large as 104.92. Consequently, he would be more likely to accept $H_o : \mu = 100$, and thus make a Type II error, if the .001 level of significance were used rather than the .05 level.

This comparison is represented in Fig. 14-2. The two decision strategies have been superimposed upon the theoretical distribution of sample means (assuming $\sigma_{\bar{x}} = 3$) that would obtain if the population mean were in fact 102 rather than the 100 specified in the null hypothesis. The shaded area in each case represents the probability of obtaining a sample mean and thus a t (if $s_{\bar{x}} = 3$) within the acceptance region set up on the basis of the null hypothesis $H_o : \mu = 100$; therefore, it represents the probability of making a Type II error. It can be seen that the shaded area is less for the decision strategy for the .05 level of significance than it is for the decision strategy for the .001 level.

The inverse relationship between the level of significance used and the probability of making a Type II error would hold for any other "true" value of μ as well. Hence, one usually does not work at levels of significance as small as .001 or .0001, because the risk of making a Type II error becomes too great. On the other hand, one usually does not attempt to decrease the risk of making a Type II error by working at a high level of significance such as .20 or .30, because the risk of making a Type I error would be too great. The compromise values that most research workers in psychology and education seem to have settled on are .05 and .01.

b)   Use a one-tailed test rather than a two-tailed test.   A researcher can reduce the likelihood of making a Type II error in some instances by using a one-tailed rather than a two-tailed test.

Continuing with the previous example, let us again suppose that the null hypothesis $H_o : \mu = 100$ is false and that the true value for μ is 102. Accepting $H_o : \mu = 100$ would amount to making a Type II error. Let us suppose, furthermore, that Dr. Black had decided to work at the .05 level of significance. There are two possible one-tailed tests of $H_o : \mu = 100$

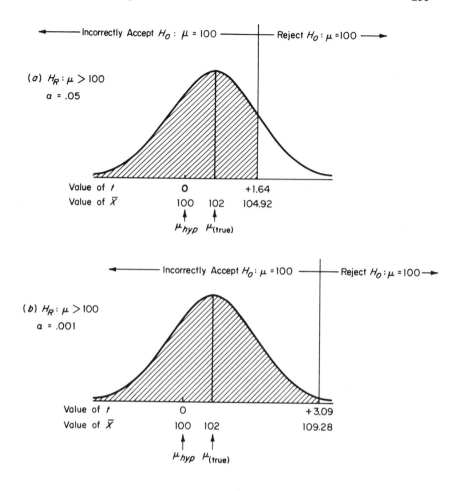

*Figure 14-2. Sampling Distribution of Means if $H_o : \mu = 100$
Were False and μ Were in Fact Equal to 102*
(*Decision strategies for testing $H_R : \mu > 100$ using $\alpha = .05$ and
$\alpha = .001$ are superimposed. The shaded areas equal the probabilities of making a Type II error. The df $= 143$.*)

which he could have performed, that for $H_R : \mu > 100$ and that for
$H_R : \mu < 100$. For the research hypothesis $H_R : \mu > 100$, he would have
rejected $H_o : \mu = 100$ only had he obtained a t of $+1.64$ or more. For
$s_{\bar{X}} = 3$, obtaining a t of $+1.64$ or more is equivalent to obtaining a sample
mean of 104.92 or more as demonstrated on p. 253. On the other hand,
for the research hypothesis $H_R : \mu < 100$, he would have rejected $H_o : \mu =$

100 only had he obtained a t of -1.64 or less. For $s_{\overline{X}} = 3$, a t of -1.64 is equivalent to a sample mean of 95.08.

$$t = \frac{\overline{X} - \mu_{HYP}}{s_{\overline{X}}}, \qquad -1.64 = \frac{95.08 - 100}{3}$$

In Fig. 14-3(a) and (b) these two one-tailed strategies have been super-imposed upon the theoretical distribution of sample means (assuming $\sigma_{\overline{X}} = 3$) that would obtain if the population mean were in fact 102 rather

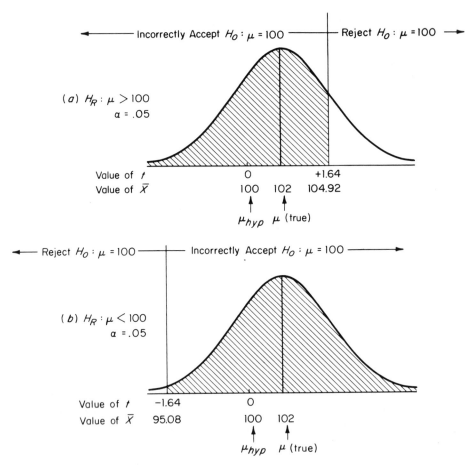

Figure 14-3. Sampling Distribution of Means if $H_o : \mu = 100$ Were False and μ in Fact Were Equal to 102
(*The decision strategies for testing $H_R : \mu > 100$, $H_R : \mu < 100$, and $H_R : \mu \neq 100$ are superimposed ($\alpha = .05$). The shaded areas equal the probabilities of making a Type II error. The df = 143.*)

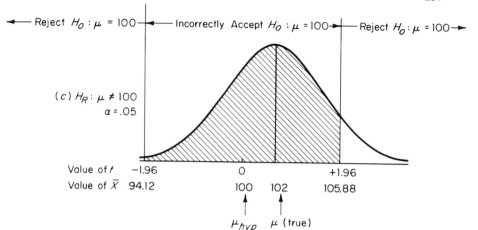

Figure 14-3. (*continued*)

than the 100 specified in the null hypothesis. If Dr. Black had decided to use a two-tailed test ($H_R : \mu \neq 100$), he would have rejected $H_o : \mu = 100$ only had he obtained a t of more than $+1.96$ or less than -1.96. For $s_{\bar{x}} = 3$, t ratios of $+1.96$ and -1.96 are equivalent to sample means of 105.88 and 94.12.

$$+1.96 = \frac{105.88 - 100}{3}, \qquad -1.96 = \frac{94.12 - 100}{3}$$

The strategy for this two-tailed test is represented in Fig. 14-3(*c*). The shaded area in each case represents the probability of obtaining a sample mean and thus a sample t ratio (if $s_{\bar{x}} = 3$) within the acceptance region; therefore, it represents the probability of making a Type II error. It can be seen that the shaded area is somewhat larger for the two-tailed test $H_R : \mu \neq 100$ than it is for the one-tailed test $H_R : \mu > 100$; however, the shaded area is much larger for the one-tailed test in the wrong direction, $H_R : \mu < 100$, than it is for either of the other two tests.

This example illustrates the generalization which can be drawn concerning the effect of using a one-tailed test on the probability of making a Type II error.

1) If the null hypothesis is in fact false and if the direction of the one-tailed research hypothesis is correct, one would be somewhat less likely to make a Type II error if the one-tailed rather than the two-tailed test were used.

2) On the other hand, if the direction of the one-tailed research hypothesis is incorrect, as in Fig. 14-3(*b*), one would be much more likely to make a Type II error if the one-tailed rather than the two-tailed test were used.

The moral to this was first drawn in the last chapter, where one-tailed tests were introduced. *If an experimenter has a sound basis for a directional research hypothesis, he should use a one-tailed test. If, however, he has little or no basis for a directional research hypothesis, he should use a two-tailed test.*

c) Decrease the standard error. Because of the chance factors involved in random sampling, a sample may not be representative of the population from which it was selected. In such cases, the sample results may lead to acceptance of the null hypothesis when it is in fact false and thus to a Type II error. The more likely it is that the sample results are representative of the population, the less likely it is that those results will lead to a Type II error (if in fact H_o is false).

A measure of the extent to which a statistic based on sample results is likely to be representative of the population is the standard error of that statistic. The smaller the standard error, the more likely it is that the sample value is representative; therefore, for any given level of significance that one might decide to use, it is often possible to decrease the probability of making a Type II error by decreasing the standard error of the sample value used in testing the null hypothesis. The discussion in this and the last few chapters should suggest two ways in which the standard error of sample values can be reduced.

First, the use of a larger sample will result in a smaller standard error. In each of the standard-error formulas discussed thus far, the sample size has been a factor in the denominator. Thus, the larger the sample, the smaller the standard error.

$$\sigma_{\overline{X}} = \frac{\sigma}{\sqrt{N}}, \qquad \sigma_S = \frac{\sigma}{\sqrt{2N}}, \qquad \sigma_{\overline{X}_1 - \overline{X}_2} = \sqrt{\sigma_{\overline{X}_1}^2 + \sigma_{\overline{X}_2}^2} = \sqrt{\frac{\sigma_1^2}{N_1} + \frac{\sigma_2^2}{N_2}}$$

Second, when testing a null hypothesis about the difference between the means of two populations, the use of the same or matched individuals in the two samples may result in a smaller standard error. The decrease in the standard error of the difference between dependent means is represented in the standard-error formula by the term $-2r\,\sigma_{\overline{X}_1}\,\sigma_{\overline{X}_2}$.

$$\sigma_{\overline{X}_1 - \overline{X}_2} = \sqrt{\sigma_{\overline{X}_1}^2 + \sigma_{\overline{X}_2}^2 - 2r\,\sigma\overline{X}_1\,\sigma\overline{X}_2} \qquad (13\text{-}1)$$

The larger the obtained correlation coefficient, r, the larger will be the term $2r\,\sigma_{x_1}\,\sigma_{x_2}$, and the smaller will be the standard error. It was pointed out in Chap. 13 that the use of matched groups will be effective in reducing the size of the standard error only to the extent to which the variable used as the basis for matching is related to the variable under investigation.

If the relationship between the two variables is low, the decrease in the standard error as a result of matching may well be negligible. In such a circumstance, the use of matched groups can actually *increase* slightly the probability of making a Type II error over and above what it would be for independent groups. This can come about with small samples as a result of the fact that the degrees of freedom to be used with matched groups is half the degrees of freedom for independent groups of the same size. For instance, suppose that by forming five matched pairs from a group of ten individuals the standard error is reduced only negligibly beyond what it would have been had the ten been divided at random into two independent groups. In such a situation, the obtained t would be about the same regardless of whether the groups were matched or not; however, if the groups were matched, the degrees of freedom would be 4 (i.e., $5 - 1$), whereas if they were not, the degrees of freedom would be 8 (i.e., $5 + 5 - 2$). If the .01 level and a one-tailed test were used, the critical values of t for the dependent and the independent groups would be 3.747 and 2.896, respectively. Thus, one would be more likely to accept H_o (and thus to make a Type II error if H_o is not true), using the matched groups, because a larger t value is needed for rejection.

Increasing the Power or Sensitivity of a Statistical Test

In most applications of statistical hypothesis testing in education and psychology, the research hypothesis is in opposition to the null hypothesis. That is, support of the research hypothesis follows from *rejection* of the null hypothesis. When this is the case, the researcher naturally wants to use a hypothesis-testing procedure which has a good chance of leading to the rejection of H_o (if in fact it is false) in order to demonstrate support for the H_R (if in fact it is true). *The power or sensitivity of a statistical test is the probability that the test will lead to the rejection of H_o (when it is false) and thus to the conclusion that the research hypothesis is supported.* Since Type II error is accepting H_o when it is false, the less the probability of a Type II error, the greater is the power or sensitivity of the test.

An experimenter, therefore, can increase the power or sensitivity of his test by using one or more of the ways discussed for decreasing the probability of a Type II error. Once he has decided on the level of significance he will use, these means are:

1) Use a one-tailed test if there is a basis for a directional research hypothesis.
2) Use samples which are as large as possible.
3) Use scores based on the same or matched individuals where appropriate.

INFERENCES FROM EXPERIMENTAL RESULTS

Many of the complexities involved in designing experiments and analyzing the data from them require a much greater understanding of statistical theory than could be obtained from an elementary text. It is appropriate and possible, however, to consider here a few broad notions that are basic to the drawing of inferences from experimental results. An understanding of these few notions will provide the reader with a better basis for sensing the nature of experiments and for anticipating some of the complexities involved.

Real versus Hypothetical Populations

In the chapters concerned with sampling distributions and statistical inference, the examples dealt with both real and hypothetical populations —a distinction made in Chap. 9. A real population was defined as a population each of whose members exists now, existed at one time, or will exist in the future. Barring certain practical considerations, we could, if we so desired, locate and obtain a score for each member of the population. Hypothetical populations, on the other hand, were described as populations which include an infinite number of members, most of whom have never and will never really exist. It was pointed out that many, if not most, educational and psychological research questions involve hypothetical populations. This is particularly true of research questions which lead to experiments.

Educational and Psychological Experiments

The purpose of an experiment is to compare the effects of certain "treatments" on populations of individuals. Several examples of research questions which would lead to experiments should help to clarify this point.

a) Is special individual counselling on a regular weekly basis effective in helping academically talented high-school males with poor academic records improve their academic performances over what they would be with no special counselling? The "treatments" would be special individual counselling and no special counselling.

b) Is the new experimental approach to teaching grammar in the fifth grade, as developed by a local university, more effective than the conventional method which has been used in our district for years? The treatments would be teaching grammar by the new method and teaching grammar by the conventional method.

c)   Can reading the book, *How to Get Along with Others*, advertised by a management relations firm, really help an adult increase his income? The treatments would be reading the book and not reading the book.

For each of these research questions, we would probably be interested in the effects of the treatments on more than an immediately available group of existing individuals. For instance, with regard to research question (*a*), we would probably be interested in the effectiveness of individual counselling for more than just those academically talented underachieving males presently enrolled in our high school. Most probably, we would also be interested in its effectiveness for next year's talented male underachievers, for those the year after that, and so on. Furthermore, counselors in other high schools might be interested in its effectiveness with their talented male underachievers this year and in the future. That is, we would probably want to draw some *general* conclusions about the effectiveness of the new method in helping talented male underachievers, *conclusions which are not limited to any specific group of existing individuals.*

Treatment Populations

In order to answer research question (*a*), an experiment may be performed. We proceed by selecting fifty academically talented male underachievers from our high school and dividing them at random into two samples of twenty-five each. The individuals in one sample receive special individual counselling on a weekly basis for one semester (counselled group). Those in the other do not (non-counselled group). At the end of the semester we may compare the semester grade-point averages of the two groups. The research hypothesis implied in the research question could be formulated in terms of a comparison between the mean semester grade-point averages for two hypothetical populations.

$$H_R : \mu_C > \mu_{NC} \quad \text{or} \quad \mu_C - \mu_{NC} > 0$$

where μ_C and μ_{NC} are the mean grade-point averages for the counselled and non-counselled populations, respectively

This research hypothesis could be tested indirectly by testing directly the null hypothesis

$$H_o : \mu_C - \mu_{NC} = 0$$

using techniques discussed in previous chapters.

In order to draw sound conclusions from the experiment, it is essential to understand the nature of the populations referred to in the hypotheses. It must be assumed that the talented male underachievers in the counselled group are a random sample from a hypothetical population of talented male underachievers, selected the same way, under the same conditions, and who have been subjected to the treatment of intensive individual counselling. It must also be assumed that the talented male underachievers in the non-counselled group are a random sample from another hypothetical population of talented underachievers, selected the same way, who have been subjected to the same treatment of no individual counselling. These two populations are the *hypothetical treatment populations* implied by the experiment. Any *statistical* inferences made on the basis of the sample results would be limited to these hypothetical treatment populations. For instance, suppose that the majority of the talented underachievers in our experiment were from families of the lower socio-economic level, that very few of their parents have even completed high school, and that the area in which they were brought up and now live has a warm, dry climate. Suppose further that Mr. Thompson, a highly skilled counselor who has been at the high school for many years, was the only counselor involved in the experiment. Any *statistical inferences* based on the experiment would be limited to talented male underachievers who come from families of the lower socio-economic level in which very few of the parents have finished high school, who were raised and now live in a warm, dry climate, and so on. Furthermore, the statistical inferences would be limited to situations in which Mr. Thompson, or someone *exactly* like Mr. Thompson, was the counselor and counselled *exactly* the way he did for the experiment.

Of course, we might be able to show that the climate had no real effect on the results of the experiment. In such a case, we would be justified in extending our inferences about the effectiveness of this method to talented male underachievers who live in a different climate. On the other hand, we would probably not assume that coming from a lower socio-economic background and having parents with little formal education had no effect on the results of the experiment. It is quite possible that counselling with underachievers from a different type of family background would have led to different results. In any case, our experiment gives no evidence for or against either assumption; therefore, at least as far as our experiment is concerned, any inference to a group not included in the hypothetical treatment populations is made on other than a statistical basis and is *not a statistical inference*.

The implications of this discussion are fairly simple. It is safe to generalize about the treatment effects to individuals and situations which differ from those of the hypothetical treatment populations only if one can reasonably assume that the characteristics by which they differ would have a negligible influence on those effects. Any such non-statistical inferences beyond the hypothetical treatment populations stand or fall on the validity of that assumption.

Real Effects and Chance Effects

In statistics texts, as well as in the research literature of education and psychology, one often finds such expressions as "the effects were real" or "the effects were due to chance." Both of these expressions are used to describe the results of experiments; therefore, it is important to understand what they mean in terms of the concepts discussed thus far. Referring to the experiment of the previous section, let us consider the possible results which might have been obtained, if, in reality, counselling of the type used has absolutely no effect on an underachiever's grade-point average. If counselling has no effect, the mean semester grade-point averages of the two hypothetical treatment populations should be equal. Assuming that this is the case, would we expect the mean grade-point averages of the two samples to be exactly equal? Of course not. Even if the means of the hypothetical treatment populations were equal, the mean grade-point averages of the two samples would probably be unequal because of the chance factors involved in random sampling. That is, it is possible that the mean GPA of the counselled sample group would turn out to be larger than that of the non-counselled sample group because of sampling error alone. In such a case, the *observed difference* between the mean GPAs of the two sample groups would be considered a *chance difference*. In other words, the *observed effects* (i.e., the observed difference between means) would be attributed to the non-representativeness of the sample rather than to any real effects of the counselling.

On the other hand, suppose the type of counselling used really does have a beneficial effect on the GPAs of counselled students (i.e., $\mu_C > \mu_{NC}$). If the observed mean GPA of the counselled sample turns out to be greater than that of the non-counselled sample, the *observed difference* between the two sample means would be considered to be a *real difference* (i.e., at least partly due to counselling). In other words, the *observed effects* would be considered *real effects*.

To summarize, whether or not it is concluded that the observed sample differences or effects are real or merely due to chance depends upon the inferences made about the hypothetical treatment populations. If the results of the experiment under discussion lead to the rejection of the null hypothesis $H_o : \mu_C - \mu_{NC} = 0$ and thus to the conclusion that the research hypothesis $H_R : \mu_C - \mu_{NC} > 0$ has been supported, then the observed difference between the mean GPAs of the two sample groups would be considered a real difference; the observed effects would be considered real effects. On the other hand, if the results of the experiment lead to the acceptance of the null hypothesis, then any observed difference between the sample means would be considered a chance difference; the observed effects would be attributed to sampling error.

The One-Teacher Experiment

The foregoing counselling experiment is an example of what might be called a *one-teacher experiment*. This is an experiment which involves only one, or at the most a very few, teachers or counselors, although it may involve a large number of students or counselees. Since such experiments are often conducted, it would be well to examine them in terms of the extent to which they provide useful information.

In the counselling experiment only one counselor, Mr. Thompson, was involved. Therefore, the hypothetical treatment population about which statistical inferences can be made is limited to similar individuals counselled in the same way *by Mr. Thompson or someone exactly like Mr. Thompson.* Can any inference be made, based on our experiment, about the effectiveness of individual counselling in situations in which other counselors might be used? In order to do so, we would have to assume that any differences between the way Mr. Thompson counselled and the way the other people would counsel would not be related to the effectiveness of the counselling. Anyone who is at all familiar with individual counselling is aware of the possible errors in this assumption. Often, there are large differences among counselors in the techniques they use, the kinds of interactions that usually obtain between them and their counselees, their general effectiveness with different types of counselees, and so on; therefore, this assumption as well as any non-statistical inference (based on our experiment) about the effectiveness of individual counselling in situations in which counselors other than Mr. Thompson are used would be quite debatable. Even if several counselors had been involved, a statistical test using *students* as the basic unit of analysis (i.e., a test of the null hypothesis that the means of the two hypothetical populations of *students* are equal) would involve the same problem, since any statistical inferences would be limited to populations of students treated in the same way (i.e., counselled by those particular individuals or by other personnel whose counselling would have exactly the same effects).

This experiment has its analogy in many experiments on the effectiveness of different teaching methods. Such experiments typically involve only a few classes of students and thus, at the most, only a few teachers. Teaching method *A* is used in several of the classrooms, and teaching method *B* is used in the remaining few classrooms. A mean score on some appropriate achievement test is obtained for the sample group of students taught with method *A* and for the sample group taught with method *B*. The null hypothesis that the average scores for the two hypothetical populations of *students* are equal is tested using a *t* ratio with *students* as the basic unit of analysis, and conclusions concerning the relative effectiveness of the two methods are drawn. Here, again, any statistical inferences would be limited to hypothetical populations of similar students taught in exactly the same way. Any conclusions concerning the relative effectiveness of the methods when used by other teachers would be based on the assumption that the relative effectiveness of the two methods does not depend to any important extent on which teacher uses them. Whether or not this assumption is a good one cannot be determined from this particular experiment.

Additional comment should be made concerning experiments like those described above, in which several teachers or several counselors are involved, yet which are analyzed with simple *t* tests and with students as the basic units of analysis. A further complication arises because, within each sample of students, there are subgroups which usually receive systematically different treatments. Suppose, for instance, that the sample taught with method *A* was composed of two different classes taught by two different teachers. The students in one of the classes would probably undergo a learning experience systematically different in various respects from the experience of the students in the other class. In these circumstances, the use of a simple *t* test of the hypothesis $H_o : \mu_A - \mu_B = 0$ is questionable. For reasons which will not be discussed here, the accuracy of the probability obtained from such a test would be in doubt.

The implication of this discussion is that the conclusions which can be safely drawn concerning treatment effects are often severely limited and often not very useful when one or at most only a few counselors or teachers are involved in an experiment. Fortunately, however, it is sometimes possible to set up an experiment in such a way that the conclusions drawn are not so severely limited. Such an experiment will be discussed in the following section.

The Class as the Basic Unit of Analysis

Let us now consider the second of the initial research questions mentioned. This involves a comparison of the effectiveness of two methods of teaching grammar to fifth-graders, a new experimental method and a conventional method presently in use. Suppose our school district is fairly large and that there are forty fifth-grade classes, each taught by a different teacher. The classes are divided at random into two groups, *O* and *N*. In each class in group *O*, the *old* method of teaching grammar is used, whereas in each class of group *N*, the *new* method is used. Then, at the end of the unit on grammar, an achievement test on the use of principles of English grammar is administered to the students in all forty classes. The mean score for each class is determined, resulting in one sample of twenty scores for the classes in group N and another sample of twenty scores for the classes in group O. Then the research hypothesis

$$H_R : \mu_N - \mu_O > 0$$

is tested indirectly by testing directly the null hypothesis

$$H_o : \mu_N - \mu_O = 0$$

The individuals making up the two hypothetical treatment populations with which the hypotheses are concerned are individual classes rather than individual students. The mean achievement scores for the two populations, μ_N and μ_O, are means of the scores of all the classes (one score for each class) in each population. Since the two samples of classes are fairly small ($N = 20$ for each), a t ratio for the difference between independent means would be used.

By considering each *class*, rather than each student, as an individual in the experiment, the hypothetical treatment populations would consist of fifth-grade *classes* of students and teachers similar to those classes used in the experiment and in which the new method or the old method of teaching grammar was used. Consequently, our statistical inferences would not be limited to any particular teacher or teachers as in the case in which only one or a few teachers were used and the hypothetical treatment populations were populations of students.

Exercises and Problems

1. A researcher plans to test the hypothesis $H_R : \mu \neq 50$. Complete the following sentences.
   a) A Type I error is possible only if the population mean is _____.
   b) A Type II error is possible only if the population mean is _____.
2. A researcher plans to test $H_R : \mu \neq 50$, using the data from a sample of size 10. For each of the following decision strategies, indicate the probability of making a Type I error (assuming H_o to be true).
   a) Reject H_o if $t > +1.833$ or < -1.833
   b) Reject H_o if $t > +3.250$ or < -3.250
   c) Reject H_o if $t > +1.833$ or < -2.821
   d) Reject H_o if $t > +3.250$ or < -1.383
3. Mr. Jones tends to worry about drawing incorrect conclusions. He plans to use the .01 level of significance in testing $H_R : \mu_1 - \mu_2 > 0$. His samples are of size $N_1 = 6$ and $N_2 = 10$.

a) If he obtains a $t = -.83$, which type of error would he be worried about? Why?

b) If he obtains a $t = +3.85$, which type of error would he be worried about? Why?

4. For a sample of size 400, Mr. Smith obtains $s_{\bar{X}} = 2$. If he plans to test $H_R : \mu \neq 200$, and wishes to limit the probability of making a Type I error to .05, what are the critical values of $\bar{X}$ (i.e., the values which border the critical regions)?

5. Suppose a researcher wishes to test $H_R : \mu > 100$ using the .05 level of significance; however, if he obtains a sample mean sufficiently below 100 so as to suggest that H_o is unreasonable, he will "forget" his directional hypothesis and switch to a test of $H_R : \mu \neq 100$ $(\alpha = .05)$ with that same sample data. What is the probability that the researcher's decision strategy will lead him to make a Type I error (assuming H_o to be true)?

6. An educational psychologist wishes to determine, for fourth-graders, which of two modes of presentation will result in the most rapid learning of a certain mathematical concept. He examines the IQ-test scores of all the fourth-graders in a local school district and selects for his experiment those children who have IQ scores between 100 and 110 (inclusive). He divides this group, randomly, into two subgroups and presents the concept to subgroup A, using mode A, and to subgroup B, using mode B. Following the presentation of the concept, he administers a quiz on the concept to both groups, and, using the results of the quiz, he tests $H_R : \mu_A - \mu_B \neq 0$ $(\alpha = .01)$. Consider his use of only those children with IQs between 100 and 110 rather than a representative sample of fourth-graders. What would be the effect of this:

a) On the probability of making a Type I error?

b) On the probability of making a Type II error?

c) On the nature of the hypothetical treatment populations?

d) On the nature of the inferences which could legitimately be made from the results of the experiment?

7. Suppose in each of the following two situations you had your choice of using a level of significance of either .10 or .001. In each case, which of these two levels would you prefer to use? Discuss your reasons?

a) You are the director of a large reading clinic. You wish to determine whether or not the clinic should spend a very large sum of money to replace the type B machines it already owns with type A machines. A group of slow readers is divided at random into two groups, one of which practices on type A machines and the other of which practices on type B machines. The mean reading speed is obtained for each group after the practice period, and the hypothesis $H_R : \mu_A - \mu_B > 0$ is tested.

b) You are the director of a large reading clinic which presently has no speed-reading machines. You plan to invest a very large amount of money in either type A machines or type B machines depending upon which type is more effective. The two types of machines are equal with regard to all other factors such as cost, convenience, durability, date of delivery, and so forth. An experiment of the sort described in (a) is run and the data are used to test the hypothesis $H_R : \mu_A - \mu_B \neq 0$.

8. In an experiment on reaction times, each of 50 individuals is tested under two conditions, A and B. In performing a t test of the hypothesis $H_R : \mu_A - \mu_B > 0$, you mistakenly use the procedure for testing the significance of the difference between *independent* means. What effect will your mistake have on:

   a) The probability of making a Type I error? Why?
   b) The probability of making a Type II error? Why?

9. A student runs an experiment in which scores for a sample of five people are obtained under condition C and scores for a sample of four people are obtained under condition D. A t test ($\alpha = .01$) leads to the acceptance of the null hypothesis $H_o : \mu_C - \mu_D = 0$. The student concludes, "The data prove that the two conditions have exactly the same effect." Any comment?

10. Compute the probability of making a Type II error for the situation illustrated in:

    a) Fig. 14-3(a)
    b) Fig. 14-3(c)

11. You plan to select a random sample of size 100 and to use the following decision strategy for testing $H_R : \mu > 50$:

$$\text{Reject } H_o \text{ if } \overline{X} > 65$$

Suppose that H_o is, in fact, false and that for the "true" value of μ the probability is .50 that you will make a Type II error. What is the "true" value of μ?

Chapter 15

Statistical Inference: Estimation

The previous several chapters have dealt with an extremely important and widely used approach to making inferences about unknown parameters—statistical hypothesis testing. These techniques appeared to be quite useful in that they offer systematic, objective procedures for answering a variety of research questions. In each case, the research question led to an assumption that an unknown population mean, or the difference between two unknown population means, equalled some value. This assumption, called the *null hypothesis*, was accepted as reasonable or rejected as unreasonable in the light of sample results actually obtained; then conclusions were drawn concerning the research hypothesis. In essence, then, the hypothesis testing discussed thus far involves determining whether *one particular value*, the value specified in the null hypothesis, is reasonable in the light of the sample results.

Often, however, a researcher is not concerned with whether one particular value is reasonable. He might be interested in such questions as the following.

1) What is the average level of reading achievement of third-graders in Mr. Jones's county?

2) How large is the difference between Mr. Jones's county and Mr. Brown's county with regard to the average reading achievement of third-graders?

3) In terms of the average score obtained on an achievement test, how much more effective is the proposed method of teaching arithmetic than the old, conventional method presently in use?

Each of these research questions asks: what is the value of the unknown parameter or of the difference between the two unknown parameters? In answering such a question, there is no basis for assuming that the unknown parameter, or that the difference between the unknown parameters, is any *particular* value. That is, there is no basis for formulating a null hypothesis. Hypothesis testing would not be used; another approach to statistical inference—estimation—is more appropriate.

POINT ESTIMATION

A very common technique for making an inference about an unknown parameter is to use, as an estimate of that parameter, a single statistic based on a random sample. For instance, the mean, median, and standard deviation for a random sample tend to reflect the mean, median, and standard deviation, respectively, of the population and may be used as estimates of those parameters. Similarly, if one were interested in the difference between the means of two populations, he could use, as an estimate of that difference, the difference between the means of two samples selected randomly from those populations. All such estimates, in which *single sample values* are used, are known as *point estimates*.

Biased and Unbiased Estimates

The statement that a statistic "reflects" a parameter means, in more precise terms, that the sampling distribution of the statistic tends to center upon the value of the parameter. When this is so, it makes sense to use the statistic as an estimate of the parameter. For example, a distribution of means from a large number of random samples will center on the value of the population mean. In fact, as we learned earlier, the mean of a sampling distribution of means is exactly equal to the population mean. Thus, although a single sample mean used as an estimate of the population mean may be too large or too small, the average of many such estimates would equal the population value. Because of this, a sample mean is considered to be an *unbiased estimate* of the population mean. That is, *a statistic is considered to be an unbiased estimate of a parameter if the mean of the sampling distribution of the statistic equals the value of the parameter.*

Not all estimates are unbiased. The standard deviation of a sample is an example. Although the sampling distribution of the statistic

$$S = \sqrt{\frac{\sum x^2}{N}}$$

tends to center on the value of σ, the mean of the sampling distribution is slightly smaller than σ. On the average, then, a sample standard deviation, S, will be a slight underestimate of σ. Thus, S is a biased estimate of σ.

Estimation of the Population Variance

Throughout the book thus far, the standard deviation, σ, has been used more often than the variance, σ^2, as a measure of the variability of a population of scores. This has been done because the concepts of standard error and critical ratios and t ratios are easier to understand if σ is used rather than σ^2; however, in terms of probability theory and mathematical statistics as a whole, the population variance, σ^2, is the more basic and useful of the two parameters. For this reason, it is important to be able to obtain an unbiased estimate of σ^2 from a random sample.

One possible estimate of σ^2 would be the statistic:

$$S^2 = \frac{\sum x^2}{N}$$

Just as S is a biased estimate of σ, however, so is S^2 a biased estimate of σ^2. The theoretical sampling distribution of S^2 based on samples of size 6

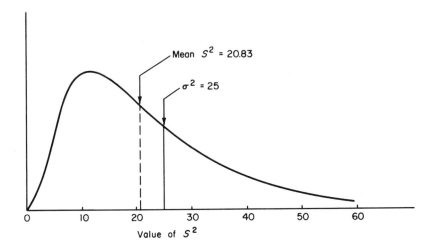

Figure 15-1. Theoretical Sampling Distribution of Sample Variances (S^2) for Samples of Size 6 Selected from a Normally Distributed Population with $\sigma^2 = 25$

selected from a normal population is represented in Fig. 15-1. It can be seen that the mean of the sampling distribution is 4.17 (i.e., $25 - 20.83$) less than the population variance. Consequently, S^2 will, on the average, be slightly too small as an estimate of σ^2.

Using techniques beyond the scope of this book, a statistic has been derived that is an unbiased estimate of σ^2.

$$s^2 = \frac{\sum x^2}{N - 1} \qquad (15\text{-}1)$$

It should be apparent upon comparison of the formulas for s^2 and S^2 that the bias in the latter is quite small for large samples. Although s^2 is an unbiased estimate of σ^2, it can be shown that s is not an unbiased estimate of σ. This may not seem logical to the beginning student, but it is a fact. Nevertheless, s is used as an estimate of σ, because the square of s is an unbiased estimate of the more basic parameter, σ^2.

Efficiency of a Point Estimate

For a normally distributed population of scores, the mean and the median have the same value; therefore, either the mean or the median of a random sample could be used as an estimate of the parameter μ. If the relative ease with which these two statistics can be computed were not a consideration, the mean rather than the median would always be used as an estimate of μ. The reason is that, for a normal population, the standard error of a sample mean is less than the standard error of a sample median for samples of the same size. The following are the two standard error formulas.

$$\sigma_{\bar{x}} = \frac{\sigma}{\sqrt{N}}, \qquad \sigma_{\text{Mdn}} = \frac{1.53\sigma}{\sqrt{N}}$$

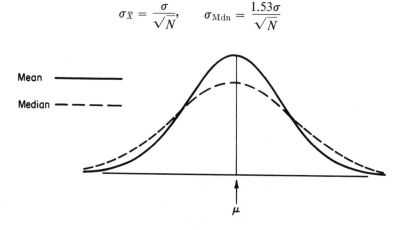

Figure 15-2. Theoretical Sampling Distributions of Means and Medians of Samples of Size 100 Selected from a Population with $\mu = 50$ and $\sigma = 5$

The means of many random samples of a particular size would, therefore, tend to cluster more closely around μ than the medians of many random samples of the same size; and, as a consequence, a sample mean would be the better estimate of μ. This is illustrated by a comparison of the two theoretical sampling distributions in Fig. 15-2.

When several statistics can be used as point estimates of the same parameter, the one with the smaller standard error is said to be a more *efficient* estimate.

Limitations of Point Estimates

Point estimation by itself is a simple and easily understood technique for making an inference about a parameter; however, it provides no basis for determining how "good" the inference is. For instance, suppose the research director of a school district wishes to estimate the mean score of all eighth-graders in the county on a reading-achievement test he plans to adopt. A random sample of eighth-graders is administered the test, and a mean of 62.61 is obtained. It is then inferred that the mean for the population is 62.61. Because of the chance factors involved in random sampling, it is very unlikely that the mean of a sample will be exactly equal to the mean of the population; therefore, the inference is probably incorrect. How incorrect is it?

Without some information other than the estimate itself, it is impossible to answer this question. If, in addition, we knew that the estimate was based on a sample of size 100, we would be fairly sure that it is a better estimate than if the sample size had been less—say 50 or 25. If we knew further that $s = 11.3$, and thus that $s_{\bar{x}} = 11.3/\sqrt{100} = 1.13$, we would have an even better basis for judging how "good" the estimate might be (i.e., how close it might be to the actual population mean). However, an alternative approach, *interval estimation*, provides a more systematic means of taking the degree of error into account.

INTERVAL ESTIMATION

Sampling Distribution of an Interval

Let us suppose that μ and σ, for the distribution of scores of the entire population of eighth-graders in the county on the reading-achievement test referred to in the previous section, are equal to 61.00 and 10.8, respectively. If many, many samples of size 100 are randomly selected from the population and the mean is computed for each sample, the sample means would form a distribution which is approximately normal. This distribution would be the random-sampling distribution of means for samples of size 100. The mean of the sampling distribution would equal the population mean of 61, and its standard deviation (i.e., standard error of the mean) would equal:

$$\sigma_{\overline{X}} = \frac{\sigma}{\sqrt{N}} = \frac{10.8}{\sqrt{100}} = 1.08$$

According to Appx. 2, the normal distribution, the values of -1.96 and $+1.96$ include the middle .95 (i.e., $.4750 + .4750 = .95$) of the area under a normal curve. Suppose that a sample of size 100 is randomly selected, and an interval running from $1.96\sigma_{\overline{X}}$ below the sample mean to $1.96\sigma_{\overline{X}}$ above the sample mean is determined. If the mean of the sample were 61.50, the interval would be:

$$\overline{X} \pm 1.96\sigma_{\overline{X}} = 61.50 \pm (1.96)(1.08) = 61.50 \pm 2.12$$

It would run from $61.50 - 2.12 = 59.38$ to $61.50 + 2.12 = 63.62$. Let us consider the intervals which would result for several other possible values of $\overline{X}$. If a sample mean of 63.12 were obtained, the interval would run from 61.00 to 65.24.

$$63.12 \pm (1.96)(1.08) = 63.12 \pm 2.12$$
$$63.12 - 2.12 = 61.00 \text{ and } 63.12 + 2.12 = 65.24$$

If a sample mean of 58.88 were obtained, the interval would run from 56.76 to 61.00.

$$58.88 \pm (1.96)(1.08) = 58.88 \pm 2.12$$
$$58.88 - 2.12 = 56.76 \text{ and } 58.88 + 2.12 = 61.00$$

Finally, if a sample mean of 64.00 were obtained, the interval would run from 61.88 to 66.12.

$$64.00 \pm (1.96)(1.08) = 64.00 \pm 2.12$$
$$64.00 - 2.12 = 61.88 \text{ and } 64.00 + 2.12 = 66.12$$

In each case, $1.96\sigma_{\overline{X}} = 1.96(1.08) = 2.12$ was added to and subtracted from the sample mean in order to obtain the interval. The sampling distribution of means and the foregoing intervals are illustrated in Fig. 15-3.

Notice that three of the intervals overlap the population mean of 61.00. If a sample mean above 63.12 or below 58.88 were obtained, the resulting interval (e.g., interval for $\overline{X} = 64$) would not overlap 61.00 (i.e., μ). On the other hand, if a sample mean between 58.88 and 63.12 were obtained, the resulting interval would overlap the population mean of 61.00. The probability of obtaining a sample mean between 58.88 and 63.12 is easily determined.

$$CR = \frac{\overline{X} - \mu}{\sigma_{\overline{X}}} = \frac{58.88 - 61.00}{1.08} = -1.96, \quad \frac{63.12 - 61.00}{1.08} = +1.96$$

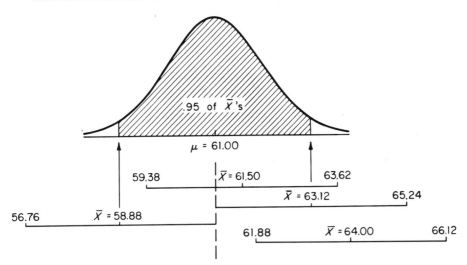

Figure 15-3. Sampling Distribution of Means when $\mu = 61.00$
and $\sigma_{\overline{X}} = 1.08$
(Four intervals of the form $\overline{X} \pm (1.96)\, \sigma_{\overline{X}}$ **have been indicated.)**

According to Appx. 2, the probability of obtaining a CR between -1.96 and $+1.96$ is .95; therefore, the probability that a sample interval of the form $\overline{X} \pm 1.96\sigma_{\overline{X}}$ will overlap or "include" the population mean is also .95.

Instead of using the value of 1.96 for CR in the previous paragraphs, we could have used the value 2.58. According to Appx. 2, the probability of obtaining a CR between -2.58 and $+2.58$ is .9902 (i.e., .4951 + .4951). Thus, it similarly can be shown that the probability that a sample interval of the form $\overline{X} \pm 2.58\sigma_{\overline{X}}$ includes the population mean is approximately .99. Furthermore, by using the appropriate CR in the formula $\overline{X} \pm (CR)\, \sigma_{\overline{X}}$, a sample interval could be determined that has any desired probability of including the population mean.

Confidence Interval for the Unknown Population Mean

In situations in which μ is unknown, σ is usually unknown as well. It would, in these circumstances, be impossible to obtain

$$\sigma_{\overline{X}} = \frac{\sigma}{\sqrt{N}}$$

and an interval of the form $\overline{X} \pm (CR)\, \sigma_{\overline{X}}$. If $s_{\overline{X}}$ is used as an estimate of $\sigma_{\overline{X}}$, an analogous interval can be derived from the ratio:

$$t = \frac{\overline{X} - \mu}{s_{\overline{X}}} \qquad (12\text{-}1)$$

The interval involves the use of Student's t distribution rather than the normal curve and is of the form:

$$\overline{X} \pm (t)\, s_{\overline{X}} \qquad (15\text{-}2)$$

The value of t obtained from Appx. 3 would be the value such that the area under the t distribution ($df = N - 1$) between $-t$ and $+t$ is equal to the desired probability (e.g., .95 or .99). For instance, if the degrees of freedom were 30, the appropriate value for a desired probability of .95 would be 2.042. It can easily be demonstrated with a little algebra (although no attempt to do so will be made here), that a sample interval of this form has the desired probability of including the unknown population mean, if the distribution of scores for the population is normal. This is the same assumption that underlies the use of the t ratio for testing hypotheses about population means. The assumption is of little or no practical importance unless the sample size is small.

At this point, the reader can begin to see how an interval could be used as an estimate of an unknown population mean.

Example 15-1. Suppose we wished to estimate the mean of the population of eighth-graders in county A (a very populous county) on the reading-achievement test previously discussed. The following are the data from a random sample of sixteen eighth-graders.

$$\overline{X} = 62.24, \quad \sum x^2 = 2235, \quad s_{\overline{X}} = \sqrt{\frac{\sum x^2}{N(N-1)}} = \sqrt{\frac{2235}{(16)(15)}} = 3.05$$

In this case, there are 15 (i.e., $16 - 1$) degrees of freedom. According to Appx. 3, .95 is the probability of obtaining a t ratio between -2.131 and $+2.131$. A sample interval of the form

$$\overline{X} \pm (2.131)\, s_{\overline{X}}$$

could be constructed. This interval would run between 55.74 and 68.74.

$$62.24 - (2.131)(3.05) = 55.74$$
$$62.24 + (2.131)(3.05) = 68.74$$

We know that, if the population distribution does not depart widely from normality, a sample interval constructed around the sample mean in this way has a .95 chance of including the unknown population mean; therefore, in one sense, we can be 95 per cent "sure" or "confident" that the interval does include the unknown population mean.

Such an interval is referred to as a *95 per cent confidence interval for the unknown population mean.* The 95 per cent is the *level of confidence,* and the limits of the interval are known as *confidence limits*. If we had used the value 2.947 (see Appx. 3) rather than 2.131 in the above example, the resulting interval estimate would have been a 99 per cent confidence interval for the population mean.

In more general terms, a confidence interval for an unknown parameter is a sample interval used as an estimate of that parameter. The interval is constructed from sample data in such a way that it has a certain probability of including the unknown parameter. This probability is known as *the level of confidence*.

Any value between 0 and 1 can be used as the level of confidence, depending on how "confident" the researcher wishes to be that the interval includes the unknown parameter. One might reasonably wonder why a higher level of confidence, such as .99 or even .9999, is not always preferable to a lower level of confidence, such as .95. The answer to this can be illustrated by a comparison of the 95 per cent, the 99 per cent, and the 99.9 per cent confidence intervals for the unknown population mean. The sample data from Ex. 15-1 will be used.

$$95 \text{ per cent} \quad 62.24 - (2.131)(3.05) = 55.74$$
$$\text{to}$$
$$62.24 + (2.131)(3.05) = 68.74$$
$$99 \text{ per cent} \quad 62.24 - (2.947)(3.05) = 53.25$$
$$\text{to}$$
$$62.24 + (2.947)(3.05) = 71.23$$
$$99.9 \text{ per cent} \quad 62.24 - (4.073)(3.05) = 49.82$$
$$\text{to}$$
$$62.24 + (4.073)(3.05) = 74.66$$

It can be seen that the 99.9 per cent confidence interval is much wider than the 99 per cent and the 99 per cent is wider than the 95 per cent. That is, the higher the level of confidence that is used, the wider will be the confidence interval. Thus, if a very high level of confidence is used, the unknown value of the parameter is not "pinned down" to the degree that it would have been had a lower level of confidence been used. Ninety-five per cent and 99 per cent seem to be the compromise values settled upon by most research workers in education and psychology.

There is a common misunderstanding of the meaning of *level of confidence* among beginning students. When asked for a definition, a beginning student will often give an answer such as the following: "The level of confidence is the probability that the population mean falls within the obtained confidence interval." This definition is incorrect in that it involves a probability statement about the unknown parameter, which has only *one* value. If we had all of the scores in the population and made no mistakes in computing μ, the probability of obtaining that particular value would be 1.00 or 100 per cent. The probability of obtaining any other value for μ would be 0. On the other hand, for a given level of confidence such as .95, there are *many* possible sample intervals that might be obtained. Of such sample intervals, 95 per cent would include the *one* population mean; therefore, the level of confidence is the probability that a sample interval constructed in a particular way (e.g., $\overline{X} \pm t\, s_{\overline{X}}$) will include the parameter.

Confidence Intervals for Differences between Two Population Means (Using Independent Samples)

The confidence interval for a single mean can be derived from the t ratio used for testing hypotheses about a single population mean and involves the same assumptions as the t ratio. The same is true for confidence intervals for the difference between two population means. If small samples are randomly selected from two populations, the ratio

$$t = \frac{(\overline{X}_1 - \overline{X}_2) - (\mu_1 - \mu_2)}{s_{\overline{X}_1 - \overline{X}_2}}$$

$$\text{where} \quad s_{\overline{X}_1 - \overline{X}_2} = \sqrt{\frac{s_c^2}{N_1} + \frac{s_c^2}{N_2}}$$

$$\text{and} \quad s_c^2 = \frac{\sum x_1^2 + \sum x_1^2}{N_1 + N_2 - 2}$$

will follow Student's t distribution for $N_1 + N_2 - 2$ degrees of freedom if (1) the population distributions of scores are normal and (2) the population variances are approximately equal. These assumptions have practical importance only when the samples are small. The confidence interval for $\mu_1 - \mu_2$ would involve the same assumptions and would be of the following form.

$$(\overline{X}_1 - \overline{X}_2) \pm (t)\, s_{\overline{X}_1 - \overline{X}_2} \tag{15-3}$$

$$\text{where} \quad s_{\overline{X}_1 - \overline{X}_2} = \sqrt{\frac{s_c^2}{N_1} + \frac{s_c^2}{N_2}}$$

Example 15-2. Mr. Brown wishes to estimate the difference between mean reading-achievement scores for seventh- and eighth-graders in his county. He administers the achievement test to random samples of ten and fifteen seventh- and eighth-graders, respectively. He plans to construct a 95 per cent confidence interval for the difference between the population means (i.e., $\mu_8 - \mu_7$). The two populations in this case are, of course, all the seventh-graders in his county and all the eighth-graders in his county. The following are the sample data.

Seventh-graders	Eighth-graders
$N_7 = 10$	$N_8 = 15$
$\overline{X}_7 = 51.59$	$\overline{X}_8 = 62.41$
$\sum x_7^2 = 1287$	$\sum x_8^2 = 2163$

$$s_c^2 = \frac{1287 + 2163}{23} = \frac{3450}{23} = 150$$

$$s_{\overline{X}_8 - \overline{X}_7} = \sqrt{\frac{s_c^2}{N_7} + \frac{s_c^2}{N_8}} = \sqrt{\frac{150}{10} + \frac{150}{15}} = 5.00$$

For $10 + 15 - 2 = 23df$, the appropriate t would be 2.069. The confidence interval for $\mu_8 - \mu_7$ would run from $+0.47$ to $+21.17$.

$$(62.41 - 51.59) - (2.069)(5.00) = 10.82 - 10.35 = +0.47$$
$$(62.41 - 51.59) + (2.069)(5.00) = 10.82 + 10.35 = +21.17$$

Thus, Mr. Brown can be 95 per cent confident that the population difference ($\mu_8 - \mu_7$) is somewhere between $+.47$ and $+21.17$.

If the samples are both large, the homogeneity of variance assumption need not be made, and an approximate t ratio of the form

$$t = \frac{\overline{X}_1 - \overline{X}_2 - (\mu_1 - \mu_2)}{s_{\overline{X}_1 - \overline{X}_2}}$$

where $\quad s_{\overline{X}_1 - \overline{X}_2} = \sqrt{\frac{s_1^2}{N_1} + \frac{s_2^2}{N_2}} = \sqrt{\frac{\sum x_1^2}{N_1(N_1 - 1)} + \frac{\sum x_2^2}{N_2(N_2 - 1)}}$

can be used to test hypotheses about the difference between two unknown population means. A confidence interval derived from this ratio would be of the form:

$$(\overline{X}_1 - \overline{X}_2) \pm (t) s_{\overline{X}_1 - \overline{X}_2}$$

where $\quad s_{\overline{X}_1 - \overline{X}_2} = \sqrt{\frac{\sum x_1^2}{N_1(N_1 - 1)} + \frac{\sum x_2^2}{N_2(N_2 - 1)}}$

Example 15-3. A pharmaceutical firm wishes to test the effectiveness of a fairly expensive weight-reducing capsule. Two hundred overweight men who are trying to reduce are divided at random into two groups of 100 each. Each member of group A receives a bottle of the weight-reducing capsules, whereas each member of group B receives a bottle of capsules which resemble the weight-reducing capsules but contain a neutral substance instead. None of the 200 individuals is aware of which group he is in, but all agree to take the capsules—in addition to any other weight-

reducing activities in which they might be engaged—for a six-month period. At the beginning and at the end of that period, each individual is
weighed, and his final weight is subtracted from his initial weight to determine his weight loss over the period. The following are the results in terms
of weight loss in pounds:

Group A (weight-reducing capsules)	Group B (neutral capsules)
$N_A = 100$	$N_B = 100$
$\overline{X}_A = 9.38$	$\overline{X}_B = 6.23$
$\sum x_A^2 = 4,892$	$\sum x_B^2 = 4,661$

$$s_{\overline{X}_A - \overline{X}_B} = \sqrt{\frac{\sum x_A^2}{N_A (N_A - 1)} + \frac{\sum x_B^2}{N_B (N_B - 1)}} = \sqrt{\frac{4,892}{100 (99)} + \frac{4,661}{100 (99)}} = .982$$

A 99 per cent confidence interval for the difference between the means of
the hypothetical treatment populations will be constructed.

Either Appx. 2 or Appx. 3 tells us that 2.576, or approximately 2.58, is
the appropriate t value. The confidence interval would run from $+.61$ lb.
to $+5.69$ lbs.

$$(9.38 - 6.23) = (2.58)(.982) = 3.15 - 2.54 = +.61$$
$$(9.38 - 6.23) = (2.58)(.982) = 3.15 + 2.54 = +5.69$$

It could be concluded that, on the average, an overweight individual similar to those used in the weight-reduction experiment would lose between
$+.61$ and $+5.69$ more pounds over a six-month period if he had taken
the capsule than if he had not.

Confidence Intervals for Differences between Two Population Means (Using Dependent Samples)

In Chap. 13, two different but equivalent approaches were discussed
for dealing with the difference between two population means when dependent samples are used (i.e., when every score in one of the samples is
matched with a score from the other sample). In one of these approaches
($\overline{X}_1 - \overline{X}_2$ method), the difference between the means is dealt with directly,
and the fact of dependent samples is taken into consideration in the standard-error term. This approach utilizes the following t ratio.

$$t = \frac{(\overline{X}_1 - \overline{X}_2) - (\mu_1 - \mu_2)}{s_{\overline{X}_1 - \overline{X}_2}(\text{dep.})} \qquad (13\text{-}4)$$

where $s_{\overline{X}_1 - \overline{X}_2}(\text{dep.}) = \sqrt{\dfrac{\sum x_1^2 + \sum x_2^2 - 2 \sum x_1 x_2}{N (N - 1)}}$ $\qquad (13\text{-}3)$

and N is the number of pairs

Using this approach, a confidence interval for the difference between two population means would be of the following form.

$$\overline{X}_1 - \overline{X}_2 \pm (t)\, s_{\overline{X}_1 - \overline{X}_2} \,(\text{dep.}) \qquad (15\text{-}4)$$

In the other approach ($\overline{X}_D$ method), the difference between each pair of scores is obtained, and the mean of the difference scores for a single population is of direct concern. For this approach, a ratio of the form

$$t = \frac{\overline{X}_D - \mu_D}{s_{\overline{X}_D}}$$

$$\text{where} \quad s_{\overline{X}_D} = \frac{s_D}{N} = \sqrt{\frac{\sum x_D^2}{N(N-1)}}$$

can be used if the population distribution of D scores is normal. Again, the normality assumption is important for small samples only. A confidence interval for the mean of the population of difference scores would be of the following form.

$$\overline{X}_D \pm (t)\, s_{\overline{X}_D} \qquad (15\text{-}5)$$

Since $\mu_1 - \mu_2 = \mu_D$ for dependent samples, a confidence interval for the difference between the means of the two populations could be computed with the $\overline{X}_D$ approach as well as the $\overline{X}_1 - \overline{X}_2$ approach.

Example 15-4. Mrs. Cash, a school psychologist in a large high-school district, wants to determine how effective she can be in helping academically talented female underachievers by giving them special individual counselling. From a group of sophomore girls with very high aptitude-test scores and low grades, Mrs. Cash is able to form sixteen pairs on the basis of freshman grades. That is, both members of each pair obtained about the same grade-point average during the freshman year. GPA is computed on the basis of $A = 4$, $B = 3$, $C = 2$, $D = 1$, and $F = 0$. For each pair, Mrs. Cash randomly assigns one member to group A and the other to group B. Then, during the next three years, she devotes a large proportion of her time to giving special individual counselling to each member of group A. She gives none to any member of group B. At the end of the senior year, the three-year grade-point average of each of the thirty-two girls is computed. A 99 per cent confidence interval for the difference between the mean grade-point averages of the two hypothetical treatment populations is to be constructed using the $\overline{X}_D$ method. For each pair, a D-score is obtained by subtracting the grade-point average of the group B (non-counselled) member from that of the group A (counselled) member. The following are the results based on the sample of D-scores.

$$N = 16$$
$$\overline{X}_D = .302$$
$$\sum x_D^2 = 2.40$$

$$s_{\overline{X}_D} = \sqrt{\frac{\sum x_D^2}{N(N-1)}} = \sqrt{\frac{2.40}{(16)(15)}} = .100$$

For 15df, the appropriate t (from Appx. 3) is 2.947. The 99 per cent confidence interval for $\mu_A - \mu_B$ would be from .005 to .595.

$$.302 - (2.947)(.100) = .302 - .295 = .007$$
$$.302 + (2.947)(.100) = .302 + .295 = .597$$

Mrs. Cash would be "99 per cent sure" that the difference between the mean grade-point average of the two hypothetical treatment populations is somewhere between .007 and .597; therefore, she would probably conclude that, although her counselling has a beneficial effect (the entire confidence interval was in the positive range), the size of the effect may be anywhere from something negligible to over half a grade point. Thus, Mrs. Cash, if she wishes to remain 99% confident, cannot pin down the "true" average effect of her counselling with very much precision, using the data she has obtained from her two samples of 16 students.

Decreasing the Width of an Interval Estimate

It has already been pointed out that the higher the level of confidence the wider the confidence interval. That is, the more confident a researcher wishes to be that the sample interval he constructs includes the population value, the less the interval will pinpoint that value. Fortunately, there are two ways in which a researcher can decrease the width of a confidence interval and thus pinpoint the population value to a greater degree, without decreasing his level of confidence. Both involve decreasing the standard error.

Each of the confidence intervals discussed thus far is of the general form: point estimate $\pm$ (t) (standard error), where the point estimate is either the mean of a single sample or the difference between the means of two samples; therefore, decreasing the size of the standard error will result in a narrower confidence interval. Two methods of decreasing the standard error have previously been mentioned in the discussions of Type II error and power. To review, all of the standard errors discussed will be less if larger samples are used, and the standard error of the difference between sample means will usually be less if the scores are paired on some relevant basis.

Relationship between Interval Estimation and Hypothesis Testing

Each of the interval estimates discussed thus far is related to a t ratio involving the same parameter or parameters, for there is a relationship between interval estimation and hypothesis testing. The nature of the relationship can be illustrated with reference to the data of Ex. 15-1. In that example, we constructed a 95 per cent confidence interval for the average reading-achievement test score of the eighth-graders in the county. For our sample of sixteen individuals, the degrees of freedom were 15 (i.e., $16 - 1$). The other sample data were as follows.

$$\overline{X} = 62.24, \qquad s_{\overline{X}} = 3.05$$

According to Appx. 3, for $15df$, .95 is the probability of obtaining a t ratio between -2.131 and $+2.131$. This value of t was used with the sample data in determining the limits of the interval (confidence limits).

$$62.24 - (2.131)(3.05) = 55.74$$
$$62.24 + (2.131)(3.05) = 68.74$$

Suppose that instead of estimating μ, we had tested a null hypothesis about the value of μ with a two-tailed test and the .05 level of significance. For a two-tailed test at the .05 level of significance, a null hypothesis will be rejected if the obtained t ratio is greater than 2.131 or less than -2.131. Suppose we had tested the null hypothesis $H_o : \mu = 54$. We would have obtained a t of $+2.70$.

$$t = \frac{62.24 - (\mu)_{HYP}}{3.05} = \frac{62.24 - 54.00}{3.05} = +2.70$$

Consequently, we would have rejected $H_o : \mu = 54$ as unreasonable in the light of our sample results. Or, suppose we had wanted to test the null hypothesis $H_o : \mu = 59$. We would have obtained a t of $+1.06$:

$$t = \frac{62.24 - 59.00}{3.05} = +1.06$$

and we would have accepted $H_o : \mu = 59$ as reasonable in the light of our sample results. Using the same sample results (i.e., $N = 16$, $\overline{X} = 62.24$, $s_{\overline{X}} = 3.05$), there are many null hypotheses about μ that we could have tested. Let us consider some of them.

Possible null hypothesis	t ratio	Conclusion
$H_o : \mu = 54$	$t = \dfrac{62.24 - 54.00}{3.05} = 2.70$	54 is not a reasonable value for μ (reject H_o)
$H_o : \mu = 55.74$	$t = \dfrac{62.24 - 55.74}{3.05} = 2.13*$	55.74 is not a reasonable value for μ (reject H_o)
$H_o : \mu = 59$	$t = \dfrac{62.24 - 59.00}{3.05} = 1.06$	59 is a reasonable value for μ (accept H_o)
$H_o : \mu = 62$	$t = \dfrac{62.24 - 62.00}{3.05} = .08$	62 is a reasonable value for μ (accept H_o)
$H_o : \mu = 65$	$t = \dfrac{62.24 - 65.00}{3.05} = -.90$	65 is a reasonable value for μ (accept H_o)
$H_o : \mu = 68.74$	$t = \dfrac{62.24 - 68.74}{3.05} = -2.13*$	68.74 is not a reasonable value for μ (reject H_o)
$H_o : \mu = 71$	$t = \dfrac{62.24 - 71.00}{3.05} = -2.87$	71 is not a reasonable value for μ (reject H_o)

*Critical $t = 2.13$

It should be fairly evident from this illustration that any null hypothesis between the 95 per cent confidence limits of 55.74 and 68.74 would be accepted as reasonable on the basis of our sample results. On the other hand, any null hypothesis outside of those limits would be rejected.

This relationship can be stated in more general terms: *for a given set of sample results, every value within the 95 per cent confidence interval for an unknown parameter would be accepted as a reasonable value for that parameter if used as a null hypothesis in a two-tailed test at the .05 level of significance.* The same relationship would hold between a 99 per cent confidence interval and a two-tailed test at the .01 level of significance, between a 99.9 per cent interval and a test at the .001 level, and so on.

HYPOTHESIS TESTING OR ESTIMATION

Two related approaches to making inferences about unknown parameters, hypothesis testing and estimation, have been discussed. In order to compare these two approaches with regard to their usefulness as research tools, it is necessary to examine the nature of the inferences to which each leads. This will be done with reference to Ex. 15-3, which dealt with the effectiveness of the weight-reducing capsule.

Suppose the data for that sample had been analyzed with a hypothesis-testing approach. What inferences would have been drawn? A reasonable research hypothesis would be that the average weight loss of the hypothetical treatment population of individuals who took the weight-reducing capsule would be greater than the average weight loss of the hypothetical treatment population of individuals who took the neutral capsule. That is:

$$H_R : \mu_A \text{ (weight-reducing capsule)} > \mu_B \text{ (neutral capsule)}$$
$$\text{or} \quad H_R : \mu_A - \mu_B > 0$$

The appropriate null hypothesis would be $H_o : \mu_A - \mu_B = 0$, and the resulting t ratio (using the results from Ex. 15-3) would be:

$$t = \frac{(\overline{X}_A - \overline{X}_B) - 0}{\sqrt{s_{\overline{X}_A - \overline{X}_B}}} = \frac{9.38 - 6.23 - 0}{.982} = 3.21$$

$$P < .001 \text{ (one-tailed)}$$

For a one-tailed test, the null hypothesis would be rejected for a level of significance as low as .001, and the research hypothesis would be considered strongly supported. It would be concluded that, on the average, the capsules are effective in helping the type of individual used in the experiment lose weight.

Suppose the management of the pharmaceutical firm are in the process of deciding whether or not to produce and market the capsules on a large scale. Which approach, hypothesis testing or interval estimation, would provide the most useful information? If the only basis for their decision were the fact that $H_o : \mu_A - \mu_B = 0$ was rejected and $H_R : \mu_A - \mu_B > 0$ was supported with $P < .001$, they would probably decide to go ahead with the capsule. Notice, however, that the very low value of the P suggests only that the capsules are, on the average, effective; it says nothing about *how effective* they are. In order to obtain some notion of the magnitude of the average effect, one could examine the point estimate, $\overline{X}_A - \overline{X}_B$. Looking at the obtained value of $+3.15$ lbs., the management might decide that the average increase in weight loss due to the capsules is not quite large enough to justify the expense of the capsules or the occasional unpleasant side-effects. Thus, even though the observed effect is highly significant statistically, it may not be of practical importance.

Now, let us consider what decision might be made on the basis of the interval estimate which indicated that the average increase in weight loss due to the capsules might be anywhere between $+.61$ and $+5.69$ lbs. From a practical point of view, an additional weight loss of only .61 lb. would probably be considered negligible. Suppose, however, that the management agree, on the basis of other considerations, that an additional weight loss of 5 lbs. or more would justify the expense and possible side effects. The "true" effect of the capsules, then, might be anywhere from quite negligible to something of practical importance. Thus, on the basis of the confidence interval, it might be concluded that the obtained results are not sufficiently precise to warrant a decision on producing the capsule. Additional research using much larger samples would be appropriate.

This example illustrates the often overlooked distinction between statistical significance and practical importance. When the results of an experiment are statistically significant, as in this case (i.e., when H_o is rejected), they may or may not be of practical importance. In order to make a judgment about the latter, it is usually necessary to have some idea of the size of the effects involved. For such a purpose, interval estimation rather than hypothesis testing would be most useful.

Exercises and Problems

1. What value of t would be used in setting up a:
   a) 99 per cent confidence interval for $\mu_1 - \mu_2$ using independent samples ($N_1 = 8$; $N_2 = 10$)?
   b) 99.9 per cent confidence interval for μ, where $N = 6$?
   c) 80 per cent confidence interval for $\mu_1 - \mu_2$ using dependent samples ($N_1 = N_2 = 12$)?
2. For a sample of size 11, $S^2 = 9.0$. Compute an unbiased estimate of σ^2.
3. Using the data of Prob. 2, p. 229, set up the 95 per cent confidence interval for μ.
4. Using the data of Prob. 4, p. 230, set up the 95 per cent confidence interval for $\mu_Y - \mu_X$. Would you conclude that rats of strain X are, in general, brighter than rats of strain Y?
5. Using the data of Prob. 5, p. 230, set up the 99 per cent confidence interval for $\mu_B - \mu_A$. Judging from the sample results, is it possible that being tested after learning might actually decrease the amount of material remembered? Why or why not?
6. Using the data of Prob. 2, p. 243:
   a) Set up the 99 per cent confidence interval for the magnitude of the experimental effect.
   b) Compute an estimate of the size of the interval which would have been obtained had independent groups been used. Compare this value with the size of the interval obtained in (a).

7. *a)* Using the data of Prob. 4, p. 246, set up the 95 per cent confidence interval for the effect of the movie.

   b) If it were very important to ascertain the effect of the movie, what might you decide to do on the basis of the answer obtained in (*a*)?

8. Using the data of Prob. 5, p. 246, set up the 99 per cent confidence interval for the magnitude of the effect of the problem-solving instruction.

9. Suppose, in a large school district, thirty third-grade classes are divided into two groups of fifteen each. During the year, the classes in one group are taught math according to the older, conventional approach, and the classes in the other group are taught math according to a new, experimental approach. At the end of the year, a mathematics-achievement test is administered to all third-graders, and the mean score is obtained for each class in the two groups. As determined from the thirty class means, the 99 per cent confidence interval for $\mu_{\text{experimental}} - \mu_{\text{conventional}}$ runs from -1.02 to $+8.39$. Assume that the superintendent of the district is quite intelligent but unsophisticated with regard to statistical matters. How would you explain to him in simple but accurate terms:

   a) The nature of the hypothetical treatment populations and the meaning of $\mu_{\text{experimental}} - \mu_{\text{conventional}}$?

   b) The meaning of the 99 per cent confidence interval?

10. For a sample of size 9, the 99 per cent confidence interval for μ runs from 98.62 to 104.53. Suppose the following statement were made concerning this interval: "The probability is .99 that μ falls between 98.62 and 104.53."

    a) What is wrong with the above statement?

    b) Restate it in correct fashion.

Chapter 16

Inferences about Pearson Product Moment Correlation Coefficients

In earlier chapters, we treated the computation, use, and interpretation of the Pearson product moment correlation, r. The reader will recall that r is a measure of the relationship between two variables. Each pair of scores for the two variables may be based on the same individual or on a pair of individuals matched in some way. For instance, if we were interested in the correlation between the height and weight of American adult males, each pair of height and weight scores would be based on the same individual; whereas if we were concerned with the correlation between the IQ scores of husbands and wives, each pair of IQ scores would be based on two individuals, matched by marriage. In either case, the statistical treatment of the data would be the same.

In problems concerned with inferences about the correlation coefficient, it is necessary to distinguish between sample values and the population value. Normally, r is used to represent a sample value, and the Greek letter ρ (rho) is used to represent the population value. However, since ρ has also been used as a symbol for the Spearman rank-order correlation coefficient, we will depart from convention and use R to represent the Pearson product moment correlation for the population. In the sections which follow, several techniques will be presented for making statistical inferences about population correlations on the basis of correlations obtained for random samples.

Random-Sampling Distribution of the Correlation Coefficient, r

Suppose we were interested in the correlation, R, between two variables for a very large population of individuals. If we selected many random samples of size N and computed r for each sample, the frequency distribution of the sample r's would be a random-sampling distribution of r for samples of size N. The shape of this sampling distribution would depend upon the value of R. If the population value, R, were equal to zero, the sampling distribution of r would be symmetrical; but if R were greater than zero the sampling distribution would be negatively skewed, and if it were less than zero the sampling distribution would be positively skewed.

The fact of this skewness should not be difficult to understand. The value of a correlation coefficient can never be more than $+1.00$ or less than -1.00; therefore, if $R = .90$, the sample r's above R would be limited to the narrow range of values between .90 and 1.00, whereas the sample r's below R could range in value all the way from -1.00 to $+.90$. Consequently, the sampling distribution of r's would be negatively skewed. As the sample size is increased, the degree of skewness becomes less, and the shape of the sampling distribution of r approaches that of the normal curve. Nevertheless, for a value of R as extreme as .90, the sample size would have to be quite large indeed before the normal curve could safely be used as an approximation. On the other hand, if $R = 0$ or some value very close to 0, the normal curve would be a quite good approximation to the sampling distribution of r for samples as small as 30.

Fisher's z Transformation

Fortunately, the non-normality of sampling distributions of r offers no obstacle to testing hypotheses about, and constructing interval estimates for, population values of the correlation coefficient. A famous statistician, R. A. Fisher, developed a statistic, z_r, which does have a normal sampling distribution and can be used for making inferences about R. This statistic, known as Fisher's z, is a transformation of the sample correlation coefficient, r, according to the following formula.

$$z_r = \tfrac{1}{2} \log_e (1 + r) - \tfrac{1}{2} \log_e (1 - r)$$

If a large number of samples is selected from a population and if the r obtained for each is transformed to a z_r according to the above formula, the resulting sampling distribution of the statistic z_r can be closely approximated by a normal curve. The Fisher's z obtained by substituting the population value R in the formula can be used as the mean of the sampling distribution and $\sqrt{1/(N-3)}$ as the standard error. Thus, the sampling distribution of the ratio

$$CR = \frac{z_r - Z_R}{\sqrt{\dfrac{1}{(N-3)}}}$$

where Z_R is the Fisher's z corresponding to the population value R

can be approximated by the normal curve (Appx. 2) even for fairly small samples and extreme values of R. Therefore, it can be considered a critical ratio.

The formula for obtaining z_r from r requires the use of logarithms to the base e; however, the student who is unfamiliar with logarithms need have no concern, for the value of z_r which corresponds to each value of r between 0.00 and 1.00 (in steps of .01) is detailed in Appx. 4. For instance, according to this table, the value of z_r which corresponds to an r of .61 is .709. This is the same value of z_r which would have been obtained had .61 been substituted for r in the formula and the necessary computations performed.

Testing a Hypothesis about the Population Correlation, R

Since the sampling distribution of the ratio

$$CR = \frac{z_r - (Z_R)_{HYP}}{\sqrt{\dfrac{1}{N-3}}} \qquad (16\text{-}1)$$

is approximately normal, it can be used with Appx. 2 to test a null hypothesis about R. The Fisher's z for the sample r would be used as z_r, and the Fisher's z for the R specified in the null hypothesis would be used as $(Z_R)_{HYP}$.

Example 16-1. Professor Jackson, a psychologist, is interested in finding out if there is a positive correlation between general intelligence and the scores on a certain personality test. He administers an IQ test and the personality test to a group of twenty-five seniors from a local high school. The following are his results: $N = 25$, $r = .50$. The research hypothesis in this case would be $H_R : R > 0$. The null hypothesis $H_o : R = 0$ will be tested with the .01 level of significance. The corresponding Fisher's z's would be obtained from Appx. 4.

$$z_r = .549 \text{ for } r = .50, \quad \text{and} \quad Z_R = 0 \text{ for } H_o : R = 0$$

Then a critical ratio would be computed.

$$CR = \frac{z_r - 0}{\sqrt{\dfrac{1}{N - 3}}} = \frac{.549 - 0}{\sqrt{\dfrac{1}{22}}} = 2.59, \quad P < .005 \text{ (one-tailed)}$$

If Z_R for the population is equal to 0, the probability of obtaining a sample z_r as large as or larger than the .549 obtained is less than .005. Since $z_r = .549$ corresponds to $r = .50$ and $Z_R = 0$ corresponds to $R = 0$, the probability of obtaining a sample r as large as or larger than the .50 obtained (assuming $R = 0$) would also be less than .005. Thus, the null hypothesis would be rejected, and it would be concluded that there is a positive correlation in the population between IQ and scores on the personality test.

A comment should be made concerning the nature of the population about which the inference is made in Ex. 16-1. Professor Jackson is probably not primarily interested in the correlation for the particular twenty-five students in his sample or even the population of seniors in the high school. He probably is interested in the correlation "in general"; therefore, his *statistical inferences* would be for a hypothetical population of high-school seniors like those used in his research. Any non-statistical inferences to students outside of this population would be based on the assumption that differences between those students and the seniors used in the research are not important.

Interval Estimation of the Population Correlation Coefficient R

A confidence interval for R may be constructed indirectly by constructing one for the corresponding Fisher's z. Since the sampling distribution of the ratio

$$CR = \frac{z_r - Z_R}{\sqrt{\dfrac{1}{N - 3}}}$$

is normally distributed, a confidence interval for Z_R would be of the form:

$$z_r \pm (CR) \sqrt{\frac{1}{N - 3}} \tag{16-2}$$

where CR for the desired level of confidence is obtained from Appx. 2

Then the confidence limits for Z_R could be converted back to values of r, using Appx. 4. The resulting interval will be a fairly good approximation of the desired confidence interval for R.

Example 16-2.   A 95 per cent confidence interval for R will be constructed using the same data from Ex. 16-1. From Appx. 4, the Fisher's z corresponding to the sample r or .50 would be obtained.

$$z_r = .549$$

The standard error for z_r would be:

$$\sqrt{\frac{1}{N-3}} = \sqrt{\frac{1}{22}} = .212$$

Using the above values, the 95 per cent confidence limits for Z_R can be obtained.

$$.549 - (1.96)(.212) = .549 - .416 = .133$$
$$.549 + (1.96)(.212) = .549 + .416 = .965$$

Using Appx. 4, these limits can be converted to 95 per cent confidence limits for R.

$$z = .133 \quad \text{corresponds to } r = .13$$
$$z = .965 \quad \text{corresponds to } r = .75$$

We could, therefore, be "95 per cent confident" that the value of the population correlation is somewhere between .13 and .75.

In using Appx. 4 to convert the confidence limits for Z_R to those for R, there is no need to become concerned about not finding tabled values of Z_R exactly equal to those obtained. Using the closest values in the table should, for all practical purposes, result in sufficient accuracy.

Testing the Null Hypothesis that the Difference between Two Population Correlations Is Equal to Zero (Using Independent Samples)

Fisher's z transformation provides the key for testing hypotheses about the difference between two population correlation coefficients as well. If many pairs of independent samples are randomly selected from two populations and pairs of sample correlations are computed, the resulting sampling distribution of the differences between the two correlations in each pair cannot, in most circumstances, be approximated by a normal curve. If, however, all the sample correlations are converted to Fisher's z's, the resulting sampling distribution of the differences between the two z_r's in each pair will be approximately normal. The mean of the sampling distribution will be $Z_{R_1} - Z_{R_2}$ (where Z_{R_1} and Z_{R_2} are the Fisher's z's corresponding to the population correlations, R_1 and R_2), and the standard error will be:

$$\sqrt{\frac{1}{N_1 - 3} + \frac{1}{N_2 - 3}}$$

where N_1 and N_2 are the sizes of the samples selected from the two populations

Consequently, the critical ratio

$$CR = \frac{(z_{r_1} - z_{r_2}) - 0}{\sqrt{\frac{1}{N_1 - 3} + \frac{1}{N_2 - 3}}} \qquad (16\text{-}3)$$

can be used to test the null hypothesis that the difference between two population R's (i.e., $R_1 - R_2$) equals zero. The Fisher's z's corresponding to the two sample r's would be used for z_{r_1} and z_{r_2}.

Example 16-3. Professor Jackson of Ex. 16-2 wants to determine whether the correlation between general intelligence and the score on the personality test is different for males and females. He administers an IQ test and the personality test to all 210 juniors at a local high school. One hundred and ten of these are girls, and 100 are boys. The following are his results.

$$\begin{array}{cc} Boys & Girls \\ N_B = 100 & N_G = 110 \\ r_B = .61 & r_G = .47 \end{array}$$

The research hypothesis would be that the population correlation for boys is not equal to that for girls. That is:

$$H_R : R_B \neq R_G, \quad \text{or} \quad H_R : R_B - R_G \neq 0$$

The null hypothesis $H_o : R_B - R_G = 0$ will be tested directly using the .05 level of significance. The Fisher's z's would be obtained.

$$z_{r_B} = .709 \quad \text{for} \quad r_B = .61$$
$$z_{r_G} = .510 \quad \text{for} \quad r_G = .47$$

Then a critical ratio would be computed.

$$CR = \frac{(z_{r_B} - z_{r_G}) - 0}{\sqrt{\frac{1}{N_B - 3} + \frac{1}{N_G - 3}}} = \frac{.199}{\sqrt{.010 + .009}} = \frac{.199}{.138} = 1.44$$

For a two-tailed test, $P = .075 + .075 = .15$. Thus, on the basis of these sample results, there is no reason to believe that the population correlations for boys and girls are unequal.

What are the populations referred to in this example? Here again, Professor Jackson is probably not primarily interested in the correlations for the particular students used in the research. These students would be considered as random samples of very large hypothetical populations of similar boys and girls.

Testing the Null Hypothesis that the Difference between Two Population Correlations Is Equal to Zero (Using Dependent Samples)

The technique of the preceding section is appropriate only if the two sample correlations are based upon samples of *different individuals not matched in any way*. There is a fairly common situation in which the two sample correlations are based upon the same individuals. This is the situation where one desires to determine which of two variables correlates most highly with a third. For instance, in a certain school district, all eighth-graders are administered an academic-aptitude test, the results of which are used as an aid for programming into ninth-grade courses. The guidance director wants to determine whether the score from aptitude test A (variable No. 1) or the score from aptitude test B (variable No. 2) is more highly correlated with academic grade-point average in the ninth grade (variable No. 3). That is, his research hypothesis would be:

$$H_R : R_{13} \neq R_{23}, \quad \text{or} \quad H_R : R_{13} - R_{23} \neq 0$$

If r_{13} and r_{23} are based upon the same individuals and if $R_{13} = R_{23}$, the following sample ratio follows the t distribution with $N - 3$ degrees of freedom.

$$t = \frac{(r_{13} - r_{23}) \sqrt{(N - 3)(1 + r_{12})}}{\sqrt{2(1 - r_{12}^2 - r_{13}^2 - r_{23}^2 + 2r_{12} r_{13} r_{23})}} \qquad (16\text{-}4)$$

It can, therefore, be used to test the null hypothesis:

$$H_o : R_{13} = R_{23}, \quad \text{or} \quad R_{13} - R_{23} = 0$$

Example 16-4. Suppose the guidance director mentioned in the previous paragraph had both tests administered to a sample of 50 eighth-graders. Then, at the end of ninth grade, the scores from both tests are correlated with the ninth-grade academic grade-point averages for the sample of 50. The following are the results.

r_{13} (the r between test A and GPA) $= .70$

r_{23} (the r between test B and GPA) $= .50$

r_{12} (the r between test A and test B) $= .80$

Using the above formula, a t ratio could be obtained.

$$t = \frac{.20 \sqrt{(47)(1.80)}}{\sqrt{2(1 - .64 - .49 - .25 + .56)}} = +3.07 \qquad P < .01 \text{ (two-tailed)}$$

If the null hypothesis were true, the probability of obtaining a t as large as or larger than $+3.07$ would be less than .005 for $50 - 3 = 47$ degrees of freedom. Thus for a two-tailed test the probability would be less than $.005 + .005 = .01$. If a level of significance of .01 or more were used, the null hypothesis $H_o : R_{13} - R_{23} = 0$ could be rejected, and it would be concluded that aptitude test A is more highly related to GPA for the type of student used in the research.

Exact Method for Testing the Null Hypothesis that a Single Population Correlation Equals Zero

In a previous section, the use of Fisher's z transformation in testing the null hypothesis $H_o : R = 0$ was illustrated. There is an alternate method for testing this null hypothesis which involves the use of the sample t ratio.

$$t = \frac{r}{\sqrt{\dfrac{1 - r^2}{N - 2}}} \qquad (16\text{-}5)$$

If $R = 0$, the sampling distribution of this ratio follows the t distribution with $N - 2$ degrees of freedom.

Example 16-5. Let us consider again the data of Ex. 16-1 in which the null hypothesis $H_o : R = 0$ was tested using Fisher's z transformation.

$$N = 25, \qquad r = .50$$

The t ratio would be:

$$t = \frac{.50}{\sqrt{\dfrac{1 - (.50)^2}{23}}} = 2.793, \qquad P < .01 \text{ (one-tailed)}$$

If the null hypothesis were true, the probability of obtaining a sample r as large as or larger than that obtained would be less than .01. Thus, the null hypothesis would be rejected at the .01 level of significance.

These results are practically identical to those in Ex. 16-1, obtained using a critical ratio with Fisher's z transformation. This illustrates the fact that the two methods of testing $H_o : R = 0$ will, for all practical purposes, give the same results, even though a critical ratio with Fisher's z transformation is "approximate" and the t ratio is "exact."

Comments and Cautions

Excluding any non-statistical considerations, large samples are always preferable to small samples for making inferences about unknown population values. This is particularly true when the inferences are about population correlations because of the large sampling error involved in correlation coefficients based on small samples. For instance, if the correlation in a population were 0, it would be expected that 15 per cent of the correlations from random samples of size 10 would be greater than $+.50$ or less than $-.50$ and that over 42 per cent would be greater than $+.30$ or less than $-.30$. For samples of size 20, these figures would be 2 per cent and 20 per cent respectively. Because of this, one should rarely attempt any research based on samples of less than twenty or thirty individuals if correlations are to play a prominent part in the conclusions. Furthermore, if such research is performed, any conclusions drawn should be interpreted with extreme caution.

A second comment concerns testing the null hypothesis $H_o : R = 0$. The distinction between statistical significance and practical importance, pointed out in the last chapter, is all too often overlooked when this null hypothesis is rejected. For instance, consider some research dealing with the relationship between scores on a particular language-aptitude test and achievement during a subsequent course in a foreign language. Suppose that the aptitude test is administered to a sample of individuals just prior to the beginning of the course and that an achievement test in the language is administered at the end. The aptitude scores are correlated with the achievement scores, and the resulting sample correlation is statistically significant. That is, the sample correlation is large enough to lead to a rejection of the null hypothesis $H_o : R = 0$ and consequently to a demonstration of the research hypothesis $H_R : R < 0$. It is concluded that an individual's score on the aptitude test is definitely related to his performance in the course.

Just how valuable is this conclusion as far as any practical utilization (e.g., for selection or counselling) of the aptitude test is concerned? By itself it is not very valuable at all, for it tells us nothing about the *size* of the relationship. If, in fact, the "true" relationship or population correlation, R, were very small, but not 0, it is still quite likely that results based on large enough samples would lead to a rejection of the null hypothesis $H_o : R = 0$. For instance, suppose 200 individuals had been used in the research described. A sample correlation as low as .12 would have led to the rejection of $H_o : R = 0$ at the .05 (one-tailed) level of significance. Yet, for an obtained r of .12, the 95 per cent confidence interval for R would run from $-.02$ to .26, indicating that the "true" relationship is quite small; perhaps far too small to be of any importance.

It would appear then, that there are many situations in which the conclusions drawn upon rejecting the null hypothesis $H_o : R = 0$ are not very useful. This is particularly true when practical considerations are involved. The sensible alternative to hypothesis testing in these cases would be interval estimation.

Exercises and Problems

1. For a very large population of males, the correlation between variable X and variable Y, R_{XY}, is equal to $+.50$. Suppose 100 random samples, each of size 67, are selected from this population and that, for each sample, r_{XY} is computed. How many sample correlations would you expect to be:
   a) Greater than $+.60$?
   b) Less than $+.40$?
   c) Between $+.45$ and $+.55$?
2. Suppose for two different populations, A and B, the following are the correlations between two variables, X and Y.

Population A	Population B
$R_{XY} = .30$	$R_{XY} = .40$

Suppose a sample of size 203 is to be selected from each of the two populations and r_{XY} is to be computed for each of the two samples. What is the probability that the correlation computed for the sample from population A will be greater than the correlation computed for the sample from population B?

3. Professor Smith wishes to test the hypothesis that intelligence is negatively correlated with a certain personality variable. He administers an IQ test and a test to measure the personality variable to fifty-two students at a local high school. For this sample, the obtained correlation is $-.30$.
   a) Test the research hypothesis using Fisher's z transformation.
   b) Test the research hypothesis using the exact method discussed.
   c) Set up the 99 per cent confidence interval for R.
4. For a sample of size 39, $r_{XY} = +.60$.
   a) Test $H_R : R_{XY} > 0$
   b) Test $H_R : R_{XY} < +.85$
   c) Set up the 95 per cent confidence interval for R_{XY}.

5. Professor Jones wishes to determine whether or not two attitudinal variables, *A* and *B*, are more highly correlated for liberal-arts majors than for engineering majors. The following are the results for two samples obtained at his college.

Engineering majors	Liberal-arts majors
$N = 53$, $r_{AB} = .29$	$N = 153$, $r_{AB} = .48$

Test the research hypothesis.

6. For a sample of 28 children of age 7, $r_{AB} = .35$; and for a sample of 103 children of age 12, $r_{AB} = .61$. Test the hypothesis that the correlation between *A* and *B* increases as children grow older.

7. You wish to select the test which is the best predictor of reading-achievement level at the end of second grade. At the beginning of first grade, you administer each of 103 children two different reading-readiness tests (*X* and *Y*). Then at the end of the second grade you administer, to the same 103 children, a reading-achievement test (*Z*). The following are the results.

$$r_{XY} = .65, \qquad r_{XZ} = .40, \qquad r_{YZ} = .60$$

Test the appropriate research hypothesis.

8. Suppose you read in a research report that a certain personality scale is significantly correlated (in a positive direction) with intelligence.
   a) What null hypothesis was tested, and what conclusions were drawn?
   b) Comment on the usefulness of the assertion that the two variables are "significantly" correlated.

Chapter 17

Dichotomous Data: Normal Approximation to the Binomial

The inference procedures presented in previous chapters are appropriate only when the data to be analyzed consist of *numerical scores for individuals*—that is, when there is a score for each individual or element in the sample on each variable being studied. In many inference problems, however, the data are not numerical scores for individuals, but *numbers or frequencies of individuals* falling into various categories of the variables being studied. In research dealing with the variable of political affiliation, for example, each individual in a sample of adults might be placed in a category of the variable (e.g., "Republican," "Democratic," "other"). In such an investigation, the frequencies of individuals in the several categories become the "raw" numerical data for the analysis.

The present chapter will consider the principles underlying some of the inference techniques which are used with frequency data when the individuals are grouped into two categories (i.e., when there are two possible scores). The basis for classification in such instances is referred to as a *dichotomous variable*. One does not have to look far for examples of dichotomous variables; they are quite common. For instance, if a coin is flipped once, only two results are possible, heads or tails. Consider a single test item for which no partial credit is given. An individual attempting the item can obtain one of only two possible scores, pass or fail. In an election in which only two candidates are running for office, an individual voter has only two choices (barring a write-in vote), candidate *A* and candidate *B*. Finally, an obvious dichotomous variable is sex. There

299

are only two possibilities for an individual human; male and female—barring some extremely rare exceptions.

In many instances, a variable which takes on more than two values can be transformed into a dichotomous variable. For example, for a single roll of a die, there are six possible results, since any one of the six sides may come up; however, we could classify a single roll of a die into one of two categories according to whether a *particular* side came up or not. If the "six" side were the one we were interested in, a single roll of the die would fall in one category for a six and into the other category for any of the remaining five sides. Similarly, there might be many candidates running for a particular office in a forthcoming election, but we might be concerned mainly with candidate A. We could, therefore, consider those voting for candidate A as falling in one category and those not voting for candidate A (i.e., voting for any other candidate) as falling in the other category. Or, as a final example, we might be interested in the extent to which smokers smoke a particular brand of cigarettes, brand X. A smoker who smoked brand X would fall in one category, whereas a smoker who did not smoke brand X (i.e., smoked any of the other available brands) would fall in the other.

Dichotomous data are often summarized in terms of the *relative* frequencies or proportions of individuals falling in each of the two categories. For instance, consider the single test item. Meaningful summary measures for a population of individuals would be the proportion of the population who pass the item and the proportion who fail the item. Or, in the case of the election in which we are concerned with candidate A, the summary measures could be the proportion of eligible voters intending to vote for candidate A and the proportion of eligible voters intending not to vote for candidate A (i.e., the proportion intending to vote for any other candidate). From now on, P will represent the relative frequency or proportion of elements in the population falling in one of the two possible categories, and Q will represent the proportion falling in the other. If we are primarily concerned with one of the categories, it is conventional to use P as the proportion falling in it and to use Q as the proportion falling in the other. The corresponding proportions for a sample randomly selected from the population will be designated by p and q. In the remainder of this chapter we shall be concerned with the background necessary for making inferences about population proportions (P) on the basis of sample proportions (p).

Since for a dichotomous variable there will be only two possible categories, the proportions of individuals who fall in each must add to one. That is, $P + Q = 1$ and $p + q = 1$. If P is known, Q can always be obtained by using the relationship $Q = 1 - P$. For example, if .48 of eligible voters intend to vote for candidate A, .52 (i.e., $1.00 - .48 = .52$) must intend *not* to vote for candidate A; therefore, if statistical techniques are used in making inferences about P, the inferences about Q will follow automatically.

THE BINOMIAL DISTRIBUTION

In order to understand the techniques for making inferences about population proportions, the reader should have some familiarity with sampling distributions of proportions. Sampling distributions of proportions based on dichotomous data follow a theoretical probability distribution called the *binomial distribution*.

Consider coin flipping: for each individual flip of a coin there are two possibilities, heads or tails. Consider further the hypothetical population which would result from flipping the coin an infinite number of times. Let P equal the proportion of those flips which come up heads and Q equal the proportion which come up tails. Since a coin has two sides (each of which is equally likely to come up), we would expect that half the flips in the population would turn up heads and half would turn up tails. That is, $P = 1/2$ or .5 and $Q = 1/2$ or .5.

Suppose we flip a coin just 10 times and observe the number of heads which turn up. This amounts to selecting a random sample of 10 flips out of the infinitely large hypothetical population of flips. For such a sample there would be 11 possible results (in terms of the number of heads turning up): 0, 1, 2, 3, 4, 5, 6, 7, 8, 9, or 10 heads. These possible results could be converted to proportions by dividing by the sample size which, in this case, is 10. Then, in terms of the proportion (p) of heads for the sample, the 11 possible results would be $0/10 = 0$, $1/10 = .1$, $2/10 = .2$, .3, . . . , .9 or 1.0. Suppose now that an infinite number of samples of 10 flips each are selected and that for every one of these samples the number and proportion (p) of heads obtained are recorded. Even though the population proportion, P, equals $1/2$ or .5, we would certainly not expect that for every one of the samples of 10 flips exactly 5 or $1/2$ of the flips would turn up heads. Sometimes, because of chance factors, more than 5 heads or fewer than 5 heads would be obtained. Occasionally, although not very often, all 10 of the flips might come up heads or all 10 might come up tails.

Using the binomial distribution, it is possible to determine the theoretical relative frequencies of samples with no heads, with one head, with two heads, and so on that one would expect to obtain if an infinite number of samples of ten flips each were taken. These theoretical relative frequencies are presented in Table 17-1 and Fig. 17-1. A histogram rather than a smooth curve has been used because the sample results are discrete (there are only eleven different possibilities). Viewed in terms of the proportion of heads (p), the theoretical relative-frequency distribution of Table 17-1 would be referred to as a *random-sampling distribution of proportions*.

Table 17-1

Theoretical Relative-Frequency Distribution of the Results from an Infinite Number of Samples of 10 Flips Each of a Coin

Number of Heads Turning Up in the Sample	Proportion of Heads	Theoretical Relative Frequencies
10	1.0	.0010
9	.9	.0098
8	.8	.0439
7	.7	.1172
6	.6	.2051
5	.5	.2461
4	.4	.2051
3	.3	.1172
2	.2	.0439
1	.1	.0098
0	.0	.0010
		1.0000

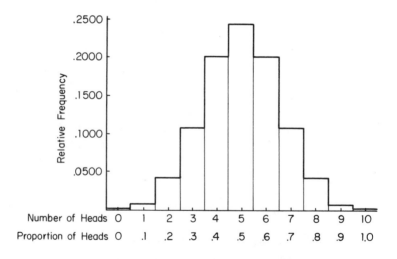

Figure 17-1. Histogram for the Theoretical Relative-Frequency Distribution Shown in Table 17-1

The mean and standard deviation of the theoretical sampling distribution of Table 17-1 can be obtained using the following general formulas for the binomial distribution.

<table>
<tr><td align="center">In terms of the
number of heads</td><td align="center">In terms of the
proportion of heads</td></tr>
<tr><td align="center">mean $= NP$</td><td align="center">mean $= P$</td></tr>
<tr><td align="center">$\sigma = \sqrt{NPQ}$ (17-1)</td><td align="center">$\sigma_p = \sqrt{\dfrac{PQ}{N}}$ (17-2)</td></tr>
</table>

For P and $Q = .5$ and $N = 10$:

$$\text{mean} = 10 \cdot \frac{1}{2} = 5 \qquad\qquad \text{mean} = \frac{1}{2}$$

$$\sigma = \sqrt{10 \cdot \frac{1}{2} \cdot \frac{1}{2}} = \sqrt{2.5} \qquad \sigma_p = \sqrt{\frac{\frac{1}{2} \cdot \frac{1}{2}}{10}} = \sqrt{\frac{1}{40}}$$

$$= 1.58 \qquad\qquad = \sqrt{.025} = .158$$

It is common to refer to σ_p as *the standard error of a proportion,* since it represents the standard deviation of a sampling distribution of proportions.

Using the theoretical sampling distribution of Table 17-1, it is possible to determine the probabilities of obtaining various results for a sample of ten flips. For example, if a coin is flipped ten times, the probability of obtaining exactly seven heads is .1172, and the probability of obtaining seven or more is .1719 (i.e., $.1172 + .0439 + .0098 + .0010 = .1719$). Thus, if 10,000 samples of ten flips each were taken, one would expect to obtain (on the average) 1,172 samples with exactly seven heads and 1,719 samples with seven or more heads. As was pointed out in Chap. 2, the relative frequencies and thus the probabilities are proportional to areas under the histogram. That is, the area of the bar for seven heads, or $p = .7$, would be .1172 of the total area under the histogram. Similarly, the area of the bar for five heads, or $p = .5$, would be .2461 of the total area. The importance of the relationships between the areas and the probabilities will become apparent when one of the approximate methods commonly used to obtain the probabilities is discussed.

The coin-tossing situation is one in which P and $Q = .5$. There are many situations in which P and Q do not $= .5$. Consider the hypothetical population of an infinite number of rolls of a die. Suppose we are concerned with how often a 6 comes up. We let P be the proportion of times 6 comes up in the population and Q be the proportion of times 6 does not come up (i.e., the proportion of times 1, 2, 3, 4, and 5 come up). Since a die is a cube with 6 sides, $P = 1/6$ and $Q = 5/6$ (if the die is not loaded). Suppose an infinite number of samples of 12 rolls each were taken and the number and proportion of 6's for each sample were recorded. For each sample of 12 rolls there would be 13 possible results. Each proportion of 6's would be obtained by dividing the corresponding number of 6's by the sample size of 12. That is, $0/12 = 0$, $1/12 = .083$, $2/12 = .167, \ldots, 12/12 = 1.00$. The theoretical sampling distribution (obtained using the binomial) is represented in Table 17-2 and in Fig. 17-2. The

Table 17-2

Theoretical Relative-Frequency Distribution of Results from an Infinite Number of Samples of Twelve Rolls Each of a Die, with Results in Terms of Number and Proportion of Sixes per Sample

Number of Sixes Turning Up in the Sample	Proportion of Sixes	Theoretical Relative Frequencies
12	1.000	<.0001
11	.917	<.0001
10	.833	<.0001
9	.750	<.0001
8	.667	.0001
7	.583	.0011
6	.500	.0066
5	.417	.0284
4	.333	.0888
3	.250	.1974
2	.167	.2961
1	.083	.2692
0	.000	.1122
		1.0000

mean and standard deviation of this theoretical sampling distribution would also be obtained by the formulas for the binomial distribution.

Number of sixes   *Proportion of sixes*

$$\text{mean} = NP = 12 \cdot \frac{1}{6} = 2.0 \qquad \text{mean} = P = \frac{1}{6}$$

$$\sigma = \sqrt{NPQ} = \sqrt{12 \cdot \frac{1}{6} \cdot \frac{5}{6}} \qquad \sigma_p = \sqrt{\frac{PQ}{N}} = \sqrt{\frac{\frac{1}{6} \cdot \frac{5}{6}}{12}}$$

$$= \sqrt{\frac{10}{6}} = 1.29 \qquad = \sqrt{\frac{5}{432}} = .108$$

Probabilities can be obtained from Table 17-2 as they were from Table 17-1, and the same relationships between the probabilities and the areas

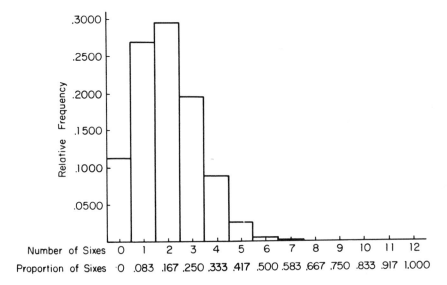

Figure 17-2. Histogram for the Theoretical Relative-Frequency Distribution Shown in Table 17-2

of the histogram would hold. It should be noted, however, that the histogram of Fig. 17-2 is highly skewed. This illustrates the fact that a sampling distribution of proportions will be skewed if $P \neq .5$. The importance of the skewness will soon become apparent.

NORMAL APPROXIMATION TO THE BINOMIAL

A more thorough discussion of the binomial distribution as well as its use to determine the exact probabilities of obtaining various sample results is beyond the scope of this book; however, a widely applicable approximate method for determining these probabilities which utilizes the normal distribution can be discussed. In Fig. 17-3, the sampling distribution of the number or proportion of heads for ten tosses of the coin is presented once again. The smooth curve in that figure represents a normal distribution with the same mean and standard deviation as the theoretical

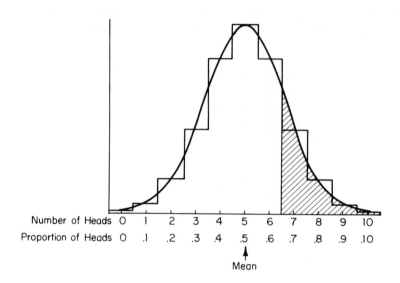

Number of Heads   O   1   2   3   4   5   6   7   8   9   10
Proportion of Heads   O   .1   .2   .3   4   .5   .6   .7   .8   .9   .10

↑
Mean

Figure 17-3. Normal-Curve Approximation of the Sampling Distribution of Figure 17-1 for Samples of Ten Flips Each of a Coin

sampling distribution represented by the histogram. That is, the parameters of the normal curve are as follows.

In terms of the number of heads	*In terms of the proportion of heads*
mean $= NP = 5$	mean $= P = .5$
$\sigma = \sqrt{NPQ} = 1.58$	$\sigma_p = \sqrt{\dfrac{PQ}{N}} = .158$

Notice that the superimposed normal curve is a fairly good approximation of the histogram; therefore, since the proportional area within each bar of the histogram represents the theoretical probability of obtaining that number or proportion of heads, the fraction of the area under the corresponding portion of the normal curve should be a fairly good approximation of this probability.

In order to illustrate, let us determine the probability of obtaining seven or more heads if a coin is flipped ten times. This is the same as the probability of obtaining a sample proportion (p) of .7 or more. The exact probability would be the fraction of the total area under the histogram for the bars for seven, eight, nine, and ten heads, and can be approximated by the shaded area under the normal curve in Fig. 17-3. The shaded area can be obtained using either the number of heads or the proportion of heads. We shall do it both ways, first using number of heads.

As has been pointed out, number of heads out of a sample of 10 throws is discrete. When the normal curve is used as an approximation with discrete variables, *a correction for continuity* should be applied. The correction for continuity involves considering each score as an interval including everything from half-way between it and the previous score to half-way between it and the succeeding score. That is, 6 heads would be considered as the interval between 5.5 and 6.5, 7 heads would be considered as the interval between 6.5 and 7.5, and so on. This is illustrated by the histogram of Fig. 17-3 where the bar for 6 heads is between 5.5 and 6.5, and that for 7 heads is between 6.5 and 7.5. Therefore, in using the normal curve to determine the probability of 7 or more heads, we search for the area which lies above the value 6.5 (shaded area in Fig. 17-3). If, instead, we were to use the area under the curve above 7, the obtained probability would be too small by the fraction of area between 6.5 and 7.

For a distribution with $\mu = 5$ and $\sigma_p = 1.58$, 6.5 would correspond to a *CR* of .95.

$$CR = \frac{6.5 - 5}{1.58} = +.95$$

According to Appx. 2, the area beyond a *CR* of .95 is .1711; therefore, the probability of 7 or more heads out of 10 is approximately .1711. This is quite close to the exact value of .1719 obtained from the sum of the theoretical relative frequencies in Table 17-1 for 7, 8, 9, and 10 heads.

In order to determine the probability of obtaining a sample *proportion* of heads of .7 or more, we would again want to determine the amount of the shaded area in Fig. 17-3. This is the area under the curve above 6.5 heads. In order to convert the number of heads to the proportion of heads, it is necessary to divide by the sample size; therefore, the shaded area above 6.5 heads would be the area beyond the proportion of .65 (i.e., 6.5/10 = .65). For a distribution with a mean of .5 and $\sigma_p = .158$, a proportion of .65 would correspond to:

$$CR = \frac{.65 - .5}{.158} = +.95$$

This is exactly the same value of *CR* which we obtained when solving the problem in terms of the number of heads; consequently, the probability would be the same. We would, of course, expect to obtain identical results, since for 10 tosses of a coin, 7 heads corresponds to a sample proportion of .7.

What would be the probability of obtaining 4 or fewer heads? Applying the correction for continuity, exactly 4 heads would be considered to include everything between 3.5 and 4.5. Consequently, we would want to determine the area under the curve below 4.5.

$$CR = \frac{4.5 - 5}{1.58} = \frac{-.5}{1.58} = -.32$$

Using Appx. 2, we find that the appropriate area is .3745; therefore, the probability of 4 or fewer heads out of 10 flips is approximately .3745. Again, this is quite close to the exact value obtained by summing the theoretical relative frequencies in Table 17-1 for 0, 1, 2, 3, and 4 heads.

In order to determine the probability of obtaining 4 heads or fewer out of 10 tosses of a coin, we determined the area below 4.5 heads. Similarly, if we wanted to determine the probability of obtaining a proportion of heads of .4 or less we would determine the area under the curve below a proportion of .45 (i.e., $4.5/10 = .45$). The critical ratio would be obtained as follows.

$$CR = \frac{.45 - .5}{.158} = \frac{-.05}{.158} = -.32$$

When Can the Normal Approximation Be Used?

A probability obtained by using the normal curve with dichotomous data is only an approximation of the exact value which would be determined by using the binomial distribution. Whether or not it is a close approximation depends upon two factors, the value of P and the size of the sample. When $P = .5$ or is quite close to .5, the normal approximation to the binomial will give fairly accurate results for samples as small as 10. This was demonstrated in the coin-tossing example. If, however, P is extreme (i.e., close to 0 or to 1), the sampling distribution for small samples is quite skewed and cannot be approximated with any degree of accuracy by a normal curve. As sample size is increased, the normal-curve approximation becomes increasingly accurate. The following rule of thumb, sometimes used as a basis for deciding whether or not the normal curve is a good approximation, incorporates these generalizations. If both NP and NQ are greater than 5, the use of the normal curve to approximate the binomial should give fairly accurate results.

Correction for Continuity

In the next chapter, a technique for testing hypotheses about a population proportion will be discussed. This technique will require the use of the normal curve to determine either (1) the probability of obtaining a sample proportion as large as or larger than that actually obtained (in those cases in which the obtained sample proportion, p, is greater than P) or (2) the probability of obtaining a sample proportion as small as or smaller than that actually obtained (in those cases in which p is less than P). When using the normal curve for this purpose, one should correct for continuity. In the following paragraphs, the nature of the correction for continuity will be made more explicit.

We earlier determined the probability of obtaining 7 or more heads or 4 or fewer heads if a coin is tossed 10 times. Correcting for continuity, 4 or fewer was considered as 4.5 or fewer and 7 or more as 6.5 or more. The corrected number of heads in each case was .5 closer to the mean of the sampling distribution than was the uncorrected number. That is, 6.5 is .5 closer to 5 than is 7, and 4.5 is .5 closer to 5 than is 4; therefore, *in terms of the number of heads*, correcting for continuity amounts to adding .5 to or subtracting .5 from the numerator of the uncorrected critical ratio.

	4 or fewer heads	*7 or more heads*
uncorrected	$CR = \dfrac{4 - 5}{1.58} = -.63$	$CR = \dfrac{7 - 5}{1.58} = 1.27$
corrected	$CR = \dfrac{4 - 5 + (.5)}{1.58} = -.32$	$CR = \dfrac{7 - 5 - (.5)}{1.58} = .95$

It can be seen that the absolute values (i.e., values without regard to sign) of both critical ratios are smaller after correction. Whether the .5 should be added or subtracted depends on which tail of the curve we are concerned with. If we are concerned with the upper tail as in the case of 7 or more heads, the .5 should be subtracted; if we are concerned with the lower tail as in the case of 4 or fewer heads, the .5 should be added.

In order to convert the number of heads to a proportion of heads, it is necessary to divide by the sample size, N; therefore, in terms of proportions, the correction for continuity is $.5/N$ rather than .5. This amount is added to or subtracted from the numerator of the uncorrected critical ratio.

	.4 or fewer heads *(4 or fewer out of 10)*	*.7 or more heads* *(7 or more out of 10)*
uncorrected	$CR = \dfrac{.4 - .5}{.158} = -.63$	$CR = \dfrac{.7 - .5}{.158} = 1.27$
corrected	$CR = \dfrac{.4 - .5 + \left(\frac{.5}{10}\right)}{.158} = -.32$	$CR = \dfrac{.7 - .5 - \left(\frac{.5}{10}\right)}{.158} = .95$

Again, both critical ratios are smaller (ignoring signs) than if the correction of .05 (i.e., $.5/N = .5/10 = .05$) had not been applied.

Correcting for continuity has a far greater effect on the size of the critical ratio for small samples than for large samples. That this is true should be evident after considering the nature of the correction; however, it is recommended that the correction be routinely applied regardless of sample size.

Summary

At this point, it might be well to summarize some of the central ideas discussed thus far concerning dichotomous variables. For a random sample of individuals, we can determine either the number or proportion falling in one of the two possible categories. If many, many random samples of the same size are selected from the population, the sampling distribution of the numbers and the sampling distribution of the proportions will follow a theoretical probability distribution known as the *binomial distribution*. Under most conditions (i.e., N large enough and P not too extreme), these sampling distributions can be closely approximated by normal curves. The following example will further illustrate how these notions may be used to determine the probabilities of obtaining certain sample results.

Example 17-1. In 36 tosses of a die, the 3 side appeared four times. If the die is not loaded, what is the probability of obtaining a sample proportion of 3's equal to or less than the .111 (4 out of 36) actually obtained? Since the die has 6 sides, the population proportion of times the 3 side would come up is .167, and the proportion of times it would not come up is .833. This information can be summarized as follows.

$$\text{Population} \qquad\qquad \text{Sample}$$

$$P = \frac{1}{6} = .167 \qquad\qquad N = 36$$

$$Q = \frac{5}{6} = .833 \qquad\qquad p = \frac{4}{36} = .111$$

Since both NP and NQ are greater than 5, the sampling distribution of p can be considered normal.

$$NP = 36\left(\frac{1}{6}\right) = 6, \qquad NQ = 36\left(\frac{5}{6}\right) = 30$$

The correction for continuity would be:

$$\frac{.5}{N} = \frac{.5}{36} = .014$$

The standard error of the proportion:

$$\sigma_p = \sqrt{\frac{PQ}{N}} = \sqrt{\frac{\frac{1}{6} \cdot \frac{5}{6}}{36}} = \sqrt{\frac{5}{1296}} = \sqrt{.00386} = .0621$$

and a critical ratio:

$$CR = \frac{.111 - .167 + (.014)}{.0621} = \frac{.125 - .167}{.0621} = \frac{-.042}{.0621} = -.68$$

are obtained. The correction was added because we are concerned with the area in the lower tail of the curve. From Appx. 2, we find that the probability of obtaining a sample critical ratio of less than $-.68$ is .2483. Thus the probability of obtaining four or fewer 3's in 36 throws of the die is approximately .25.

Exercises and Problems

1. A coin is to be flipped sixty-four times. What is the probability of obtaining each of the following results (solve in terms of the *number* of heads or tails)?
   a) More than thirty-six heads
   b) Thirty-six or more heads
   c) Between thirty and thirty-six tails (inclusive)
   d) Exactly thirty-two heads
2. Obtain the answer to each part of Prob. 1 using the *proportion* of heads or tails.
3. A die is to be rolled thirty-six times. What is the probability of obtaining each of the following results (solve in terms of the *number*)?
   a) The six side coming up on five or more rolls
   b) The six side coming up on more than five rolls
   c) The two side coming up on exactly six rolls
4. Obtain the answer to each part of Prob. 3 using *proportions*.
5. A bond issue is to be voted on in a forthcoming statewide election; and, at this time, exactly half the voters favor the bond issue, and half opposite it.
   a) Suppose many random samples of 100 voters each are to be polled. In what proportion of the samples would we expect to find 60 per cent or more favoring the bond issue?
   b) Suppose many random samples of ten voters each are to be polled. In what proportion of the samples would we expect to find 60 per cent (six out of ten) or more favoring the bond issue?
6. Suppose an individual makes a random guess on each item of a thirty-six-item true-or-false test. What is the probability that he will obtain a score of:

   a)   Twenty or more?
   b)   Either less than 15 or more than 21?
7. Suppose an individual makes a random guess on each item of a forty-eight-item multiple-choice test. There are four alternatives for each item. What is the probability that he will obtain a score of:
   a)   Fourteen or more?
   b)   Less than 9?
8. Suppose for a certain population $P = Q = .5$. Explain why the normal-curve approximation to the binomial will give more accurate probabilities for samples of size 12 than for samples of size 6. Illustrate your explanation with a rough sketch.
9. The following are the parameters of two populations.

Population A	Population B
$P_A = .5$	$P_B = .95$
$Q_A = .5$	$Q_B = .05$

   Explain why a much larger sample size would be required if the normal-curve approximation to the binomial were used with samples from population *B* than if it were used with samples from population *A*. Illustrate your explanation with a rough sketch.
10. Suppose you wish to use the normal-curve approximation to the binomial. What is the minimum sample size which should be used if:

   a) $P = .5$ *d)* $Q = .9$
   b) $P = .8$ *e)* $Q = .95$
   c) $P = .2$ *f)* $Q = .05$

Chapter 18

Dichotomous Data: Inferences about Proportions

TESTING HYPOTHESES ABOUT PROPORTIONS FROM SINGLE POPULATIONS

It was pointed out in the previous chapter that if the population proportion, P, is not too extreme and if the sample size, N, is large enough, the sampling distribution of proportions, p, can be closely approximated by a normal distribution. More specifically, the approximation tends to be good if NP and NQ are both greater than 5. Under these conditions, a critical ratio of the following form can be used in conjunction with Appx. 2 to test a null hypothesis about P:

$$CR = \frac{p - P_H + (\text{or } -)\frac{.5}{N}}{\sigma_p} \qquad (18\text{-}1)$$

where $\sigma_p = \sqrt{\frac{(P_H)(Q_H)}{N}}$

P_H is the value of P specified in the null hypothesis

and $\frac{.5}{N}$ is the correction for continuity

Correcting for continuity will always result in decreasing the absolute value (i.e., value without regard to sign) of the critical ratio. If, therefore, the sign of the numerator is positive before correcting, the correction should be subtracted; if the sign is negative, the correction should be added.

Notice that P_H is to be used in computing $_p\sigma$. This is because the formula for σ_p involves P, the parameter with which the null hypothesis is concerned. In testing a null hypothesis about P, the hypothesis is first assumed to be true; therefore, the value of P specified in the null hypothesis should be used as the population value for purposes of the test.

Example 18-1. On the basis of casual observations over a long period of time, a gambler insists that a particular die is biased in that the 4 side comes up "more often than it should." In order to check on that possibility, the die is rolled 54 times, and it is observed that the 4 side comes up .296 of the time (16 times out of 54). If the die is not biased, the 4 side theoretically should come up 1/6, or .167, of the time. The following are the appropriate hypotheses.

$$H_R : P > .167, \quad \text{and} \quad H_o : P = .167$$

Assuming H_o to be true, σ_p can be determined:

$$\sigma_p = \sqrt{\frac{(P_H)(Q_H)}{N}} = \sqrt{\frac{(.167)(.833)}{54}} = \sqrt{\frac{.139}{54}} = \sqrt{.00257} = .0507$$

and a critical ratio computed.

$$CR = \frac{p - P_H - \dfrac{.5}{N}}{\sigma_p} = \frac{.296 - .167 - .009}{.0507} = \frac{.120}{.0507} = +2.37$$

Since the obtained p of .296 is greater than the value $P_H = .167$, the sign of the numerator will be positive; therefore, the correction for continuity of .009 is subtracted. For a $CR = +2.37$, $P = .0089$ (one-tailed). Using the .01 level of significance, the null hypothesis would be rejected, and it would be concluded that the die is probably biased in the direction specified by the gambler.

Two comments should be made concerning this example. First, the use of the normal curve approximation is appropriate, because both NP_H and NQ_H are larger than 5 (i.e., 54 [.167] = 9; 54 [.833] = 45). Second, the symbol P is used in this chapter to designate two different things, population proportions and probabilities obtained as a result of hypothesis testing. No confusion should result, however, if the reader examines the context in which P is used.

Example 18-2. A market-research firm is interested in determining whether or not a new brand of margarine can be distinguished from butter. Each of a sample of 100 customers at a nearby supermarket is blindfolded and asked to taste five small "pats," four of which are butter and one of which is the new margarine. Twenty-four out of the 100 are able to identify correctly which of the five pats is margarine.

If an individual were unable to distinguish between the butter and the margarine, he would have a 1-in-5 chance of making a correct identification. Therefore, if *more* than 1/5 of the hypothetical population of which the 100 customers could be considered a random sample were able to make a correct identification, one would conclude that at least some individuals can taste the difference. The following, then, would be the appropriate research and null hypotheses, in terms of the proportion making a correct identification.

$$H_R : P > .2$$
$$H_o : P = .2$$

Assuming H_o to be true, σ_p can be determined:

$$\sigma_p = \sqrt{\frac{(P_H)(Q_H)}{N}} = \sqrt{\frac{(.2)(.8)}{100}} = .0400$$

and a critical ratio computed.

$$CR = \frac{p - P_H - \frac{.5}{N}}{\sigma_p} = \frac{.240 - .2 - .005}{.0400} = .0350 = +.87$$

For a CR of .87, the null hypothesis would be accepted ($P = .1922$). Thus, the sample results do not support the hypothesis that people (like those used in the research) can taste the difference between butter and the new margarine.

Hypotheses about Differences between P and Q

In a number of the situations that involve dichotomous variables and single populations of individuals, the major concern is with the difference between P and Q. For instance, suppose you are interested in predicting the outcome of a particular election in which the candidate who obtains the most votes will win. There are only two candidates, candidate A and candidate B. If P and Q are the proportions of voters who will vote for A and B respectively, the outcome of the election depends on the difference between P and Q. If P is greater than Q, candidate A will win; whereas if Q is greater than P, candidate B will win.

The usual approach to testing a hypothesis about the difference between P and Q for a single population involves recasting the hypothesis into a form which involves only P. Since $P + Q$ must equal 1, P and Q will be equal to each other only if both are equal to 1/2 or .5. If P were greater than .5, Q would necessarily have to be less than .5; or if P were less than .5, Q would have to be greater. Consequently, one of the following three research hypotheses would be formulated when the concern is with the difference between P and Q.

$$H_R : P \neq .5 \text{ (equivalent to } H_R : P \neq Q)$$
$$H_R : P > .5 \text{ (equivalent to } H_R : P > Q)$$
$$H_R : P < .5 \text{ (equivalent to } H_R : P < Q)$$

The appropriate null hypothesis would be $H_o : P = .5$.

Example 18-3. A professor is investigating various aspects of the psychology of humor. He wishes to determine which of two jokes seems funnier to male college students. He presents both jokes to a sample of twenty-eight males from his elementary-psychology classes and asks each individual in the sample to indicate which of the two jokes appears to be the funnier. Eight favor joke A, and twenty favor joke B. In terms of the proportion who believe joke A is the funnier, the following would be appropriate hypotheses.

$$H_R : P \neq .5 \quad \text{and} \quad H_o : P = .5$$

Assuming H_o to be true, σ_p can be determined:

$$\sigma_p = \sqrt{\frac{(P_H)(Q_H)}{N}} = \sqrt{\frac{(.5)(.5)}{28}} = .0945$$

and a critical ratio computed.

$$CR = \frac{p - P_H + \frac{.5}{N}}{\sigma_p} = \frac{.286 - .5 + .005}{.0945} = \frac{-.209}{.0945} = -2.21$$

Since the sample p of .286 (i.e., $8/28 = .286$) is smaller than P_H (i.e., .5), the numerator would be negative. Thus, the correction for continuity of .005 is *added*. For a $CR = -2.21$, $P = .0272$ (two-tailed). Using the .05 level of significance, H_o would be rejected, and it would be concluded that the jokes are not equally funny (for the hypothetical population implied). Furthermore, it would be concluded that joke B is funnier than joke A.

The reader should be aware that identical conclusions would have been reached had P been used to represent the proportion of individuals favoring joke B rather than the proportion of individuals favoring joke A. He should satisfy himself of this fact by carrying the example through, using P to represent the proportion of individuals favoring joke B.

Confidence Interval for *P*

The appropriate statistic to use as a point estimate of the population proportion, P, is the sample proportion, p. Since the mean of the sampling distribution of p equals P, p is an unbiased estimator of P. In constructing a confidence interval for P, the same general approach can be used as was used previously with means, standard deviations, and correlation coefficients. If both Np and Nq are larger than 5, a confidence interval for P could be constructed using the normal curve. It would have the following limits.

$$\text{lower confidence limit} = p - (CR)\,\sigma_p - \frac{.5}{N}$$

$$\text{upper confidence limit} = p + (CR)\,\sigma_p + \frac{.5}{N}$$

(18-2)

where $\sigma_p = \sqrt{\frac{pq}{N}}$ and $\frac{.5}{N}$ is the correction for continuity

The sample proportions (p and q) are used in the formula for σ_p, because the population proportions P and Q are unknown and there are no hypothetical values P_H and Q_H which can be used. It should be pointed out that the use of the normal curve to approximate the binomial as well as the use of p and q in the formula for σ_p result in a confidence interval which is only approximate; however, for most practical purposes, the approximation is quite good, particularly for large samples. If either Np or Nq is 5 or less, more exact methods should be used for constructing the interval.

Example 18-4. The curriculum director of a large school district wants to construct a 95 per cent confidence interval for the proportion of second-graders in his district who can pass a particular item on a reading-achievement test. Of a random sample of 40 second-graders to whom the item is given, .80 (i.e., 32 out of 40) passed the item, and .20 (i.e., 8 out of 40) failed it. First, σ_p can be computed.

$$\sigma_p = \sqrt{\frac{pq}{N}} = \sqrt{\frac{(.800)(.200)}{40}} = \sqrt{\frac{.160}{40}} = .0632$$

Using $CR = 1.96$, the confidence limits can then be determined.

$$\text{lower confidence limit} = .800 - 1.96\,(.0632) - \frac{.5}{40} = .66$$

$$\text{upper confidence limit} = .800 + 1.96\,(.0632) + \frac{.5}{40} = .94$$

On the basis of these results the curriculum director can be "95 per cent confident" that the proportion of second-graders in the district who can pass the item is somewhere between .66 and .94.

DIFFERENCES BETWEEN PROPORTIONS FROM TWO POPULATIONS

Sampling Distribution of $p_1 - p_2$

Let us consider two populations, the population of all second-grade boys in the United States and the population of all second-grade girls in the United States. Suppose it were possible to select a random sample of 200 boys and a random sample of 100 girls from these two populations. All the individuals in both samples are administered an item from a standardized reading test. The proportion passing in the female sample is determined (p_2) and subtracted from the proportion passing in the male sample (p_1). Suppose an infinite number of pairs of random samples of 200 boys and 100 girls is selected and for each pair $p_1 - p_2$ is determined. The theoretical relative-frequency distribution of the sample differences ($p_1 - p_2$) would be known as a *sampling distribution of differences between proportions*. For sufficiently large samples, such a sampling distribution is approximately normal with the following mean and standard deviation.

$$\text{mean} = P_1 - P_2 \qquad\qquad (18\text{-}3)$$

$$\sigma_{p_1-p_2} = \sqrt{\frac{P_1 Q_1}{N_1} + \frac{P_2 Q_2}{N_2}} \qquad\qquad (18\text{-}4)$$

where P_1 and P_2 are the proportions for Populations 1 and 2 and N_1 and N_2 are the sample sizes

(The standard deviation of the sampling distribution is, of course, the *standard error of the difference between independent proportions*.) Consequently, the ratio

$$CR = \frac{(p_1 - p_2) - (P_1 - P_2) + (\text{or } -)\dfrac{.5\,(N_1 + N_2)}{N_1\,N_2}}{\sqrt{\dfrac{P_1 Q_1}{N_1} + \dfrac{P_2 Q_2}{N_2}}} \qquad\qquad (18\text{-}5)$$

can be used to determine the probability of obtaining a difference between two sample proportions as large as (or as small as) any sample difference actually obtained, if N_1 and N_2 are sufficiently large. How large is "sufficiently large" again depends on the population proportions and the sample sizes. If $N_1 P_1$, $N_1 Q_1$, $N_2 P_2$, and $N_2 Q_2$ are all greater than 5, the normal approximation will give fairly accurate results.

The appropriate correction for continuity:

$$\frac{.5\,(N_1 + N_2)}{N_1\,N_2}$$

is either subtracted from or added to the numerator of the above critical ratio. When we are concerned with the upper tail of the sampling distribution (i.e., when we are concerned with a difference as large as or larger than a certain value), the correction should be subtracted. Although the correction will have a negligible effect on the size of the CR for large samples, it is recommended that it be routinely applied unless the samples are quite large.

Example 18-5. The proportion of second-grade boys in the U.S. who can pass the reading-test item referred to earlier is .80, and the proportion of second-grade girls is .60. A pair of random samples of 200 boys and 100 girls is selected and administered the item. The following are the sample results.

$$Girls\ N_2 = 100 \qquad\qquad Boys\ N_1 = 200$$

$$\text{Pass 59:}\quad p_2 = \frac{59}{100} = .590 \qquad \text{Pass 164:}\quad p_1 = \frac{164}{200} = .820$$

$$\text{Fail 41:}\quad q_2 = \frac{41}{100} = .410 \qquad \text{Fail 36:}\quad q_1 = \frac{36}{200} = .180$$

What is the probability of obtaining a difference between sample proportions $(p_1 - p_2)$ as large as or larger than the .23 (i.e., $.820 - .590 = .230$) actually obtained? First, $\sigma_{p_1 - p_2}$ and the correction for continuity can be determined.

$$\sigma_{p_1 - p_2} = \sqrt{\frac{P_1\,Q_1}{N_1} + \frac{P_2\,Q_2}{N_2}} = \sqrt{\frac{(.800)\,(.200)}{200} + \frac{(.600)\,(.400)}{100}} = .0566$$

$$\text{correction} = \frac{.5\,(N_1 + N_2)}{N_1\,N_2} = \frac{.5\,(200 + 100)}{(200)\,(100)} = .0075$$

Then a critical ratio can be computed.

$$CR = \frac{(p_1 - p_2) - (P_1 - P_2) - .0075}{\sigma_{p_1 - p_2}}$$

$$= \frac{(.820 - .590) - (.800 - .600) - .0075}{.0566} = \frac{.0225}{.0566} = +.40$$

According to Appx. 2, the probability of obtaining a sample critical ratio as large as or larger than the $+.40$ obtained is approximately .3446. Consequently, the probability of obtaining a difference between sample proportions as large as or larger than the .23 obtained is approximately .34.

Testing the Null Hypothesis H_o: $P_1 - P_2 = 0$, or $P_1 = P_2$

Example 18-5 is obviously unrealistic for several reasons. First, it would be impossible, for all practical purposes, to select random samples from the populations specified. Second, in a real inference problem concerned with the difference $P_1 - P_2$, the values of these two parameters would be unknown. In cases in which P_1 and P_2 are unknown, the investigator will often be concerned with testing one of the following research hypotheses.

$$H_R : P_1 - P_2 > 0 \quad (P_1 > P_2)$$
$$H_R : P_1 - P_2 < 0 \quad (P_1 < P_2)$$
$$H_R : P_1 - P_2 \neq 0 \quad (P_1 \neq P_2)$$

Each of these research hypotheses can be tested indirectly by testing directly the null hypothesis $H_o : P_1 - P_2 = 0$ (i.e., $P_1 = P_2$).

The characteristics of sampling distributions of $p_1 - p_2$, discussed in the previous section, offer a basis for testing $H_o : P_1 - P_2 = 0$. If N_1 and N_2 are large enough, the following variation of Form. (18-5) can be used in conjunction with Appx. 2 for this purpose.

$$CR = \frac{(p_1 - p_2) - 0 + (\text{or} -) \dfrac{.5(N_1 + N_2)}{N_1 N_2}}{\sigma_{p_1 - p_2}} \quad (18\text{-}6)$$

$$\text{where} \quad \sigma_{p_1 - p_2} = \sqrt{\frac{p_c q_c}{N_1} + \frac{p_c q_c}{N_2}}$$

As was noted in the previous section, the unknown population values P_1, Q_1, P_2, and Q_2 are necessary in order to obtain the value of $\sigma_{p_1 - p_2}$. Under the assumption, however, that the null hypothesis is true (i.e., that $P_1 - P_2 = 0$ or $P_1 = P_2$), it is possible to obtain estimates of P_1, Q_1, P_2, and Q_2 from the sample results. These estimates are p_c and q_c.

Under the assumption that the null hypothesis is true, P_1 and P_2 would have the *same numerical value*, and p_1 and p_2 would both be estimates of this *single* numerical value; however, p_1 is based only on the N_1 cases from the first sample, and p_2 is based only on the N_2 cases from the second sample. A better estimate of the value of P_1 and P_2 (assuming H_o to be true) would be a combined estimate, p_c, based on all the cases in both samples. The combined estimate, p_c, would be based on $N_1 + N_2$ cases; consequently, it would have less of a standard error than either p_1 or p_2. The method of obtaining p_c is straightforward. It is merely the proportion of the total $N_1 + N_2$ individuals in both samples who fall in one of the two possible categories. The estimate of Q_1 and Q_2 would be the proportion of the total $N_1 + N_2$ individuals who fall in the other category. This is q_c. Of course, $p_c + q_c = 1$.

As in problems dealing with single population proportions, correcting for continuity will reduce the absolute value of the critical ratio; therefore, if the sign of the numerator of the obtained critical ratio is positive, the correction should be subtracted. If the sign is negative, the correction should be added. If any of the four values $N_1 p_c$, $N_1 q_c$, $N_2 p_c$, or $N_2 q_c$ is 5 or less, this approach to testing $H_o : P_1 - P_2 = 0$ should not be used.

Example 18-6. Dr. Greene is concerned with differences between college men and college women with regard to their attitudes toward dating. He presents a statement about dating to samples of sixty freshman boys and seventy-five freshman girls at his university and asks each individual to indicate whether he or she agrees or disagrees with the statement. The following are the results for the two samples.

Males $N_M = 60$	*Females* $N_F = 75$
Agree 33: $p_M = \dfrac{33}{60} = .550$	Agree 36: $p_F = \dfrac{36}{75} = .480$
Disagree 27: $q_M = \dfrac{27}{60} = .450$	Disagree 39: $q_F = \dfrac{39}{75} = .520$

The appropriate hypotheses to be tested are:

$$H_R : P_M - P_F \neq 0 \quad \text{and} \quad H_o : P_M - P_F = 0$$

where P_M is the proportion of the hypothetical male population who would agree with the statement and P_F is the proportion of the hypothetical female population who would agree with the statement

First, p_c and q_c should be obtained.

$$p_c = \frac{33 + 36}{60 + 75} = \frac{69}{135} = .511 \quad \binom{\text{proportion of those who agree,}}{\text{for both samples \textit{combined}}}$$

$$q_c = \frac{27 + 39}{60 + 75} = \frac{66}{135} = .489$$

Then $\sigma_{p_M - p_F}$ can be determined.

$$\sigma_{p_M - p_F} = \sqrt{\frac{p_c q_c}{N_M} + \frac{p_c q_c}{N_F}} = \sqrt{\frac{(.511)(.489)}{60} + \frac{(.511)(.489)}{75}} = .0866$$

The normal-curve approximation can be used, because $N_M \, p_c$, $N_M \, q_c$, $N_F \, p_c$, and $N_F \, q_c$ are all greater than 5. The correction for continuity and the critical ratio would be obtained as follows.

$$\text{correction} = \frac{.5 \, (N_M + N_F)}{N_M \, N_F} = \frac{.5 \, (60 + 75)}{(60) \, (75)} = .015$$

$$CR = \frac{p_M - p_F - 0 - .015}{\sigma_{p_M - p_F}} = \frac{.550 - .480 - .015}{.0866} = +.64$$

From Appx. 2, we find that $P = .5222$ (two-tailed); thus, we conclude that these sample data do not support the contention that the sexes differ with regard to agreement with the statement used. Of course any *statistical* inferences would be limited to the hypothetical populations implied by the sampling procedure.

Confidence Intervals for $P_1 - P_2$

The general approach used previously may be applied here as well. That is, if $N_1 \, p_1$, $N_1 \, q_1$, $N_2 \, p_2$, and $N_2 \, q_2$ are all greater than 5, an approximate confidence interval for $P_1 - P_2$ would have the following limits.

$$\text{lower confidence limit} = p_1 - p_2 - (CR) \, \sigma_{p_1 - p_2} - \frac{.5 \, (N_1 + N_2)}{N_1 \, N_2}$$

$$\text{upper confidence limit} = p_1 - p_2 + (CR) \, \sigma_{p_1 - p_2} + \frac{.5 \, (N_1 + N_2)}{N_1 \, N_2}$$

(18-7)

$$\text{where} \quad \sigma_{p_1 - p_2} = \sqrt{\frac{p_1 \, q_1}{N_1} + \frac{p_2 \, q_2}{N_2}}$$

$$\text{and} \quad \frac{.5 \, (N_1 + N_2)}{N_1 \, N_2} \quad \text{is the correction for continuity}$$

The sample proportions (p_1, q_1, p_2, and q_2), rather than p_c and q_c, are used in the formula for σ_p, since there is no reason for assuming P_1 and P_2 to be equal.

Example 18-7. Dr. Greene decides to set up a 99 per cent confidence interval for the difference between the proportion of boys and the proportion of girls who agree with the statement on dating. Using the data from Ex. 18-6, $\sigma_{p_M - p_F}$ can be determined.

$$\sigma_{p_M - p_F} = \sqrt{\frac{p_M \, q_M}{N_M} + \frac{p_F \, q_F}{N_F}} = \sqrt{\frac{(.550) \, (.450)}{60} + \frac{(.480) \, (.520)}{75}} = .0863$$

The correction for continuity would be the same as in Ex. 18-6. The following would be the confidence limits.

lower confidence limit $= (.550 - .480) - (2.58) (.0863) - .015 = -.17$
upper confidence limit $= (.550 - .480) + (2.58) (.0863) + .015 = +.31$

Thus, Dr. Greene can be 99 per cent sure that the difference between the hypothetical population proportions of boys and girls who agree with the statement (i.e., $P_M - P_F$) is somewhere between $-.17$ and $+.31$. The minus sign merely indicates that, for the lower limit, P_M would be $.17$ *smaller* than P_F, whereas for the upper limit it would be $.31$ larger.

TESTING THE NULL HYPOTHESIS
$H_o: P_1 - P_2 = 0$, OR $P_1 = P_2$
(DEPENDENT SAMPLES)

In Ex. 18-5, Ex. 18-6, and Ex. 18-7, the individuals in one sample were not paired in any way with the individuals in the other sample. That is, the samples were selected independently of each other. There are many situations in which this is not true. In these cases, either the same individuals are used in both samples or each individual in one of the samples is paired in some way with an individual in the other sample. For instance, in Ex. 18-6, Dr. Greene administered the statement about dating to a sample of boys and a sample of girls. No individual in either sample was paired in any way with an individual in the other. Suppose now that Dr. Greene wishes to determine the effect of a certain film about love and marriage on attitudes toward dating. He shows the film to the sixty males of Ex. 18-6 and, after the film, asks them to react once again to the statement. The sample proportions of males agreeing with the statement before and after the film, p_1 and p_2, would be based on the same sixty individuals; and, as a consequence, they would be considered *dependent* sample proportions.

The appropriate null hypothesis for checking on the effect of the film would be $H_o : P_1 - P_2 = 0$. In testing this null hypothesis, using dependent samples, the critical ratio would take the same general form as Form. (18-6) for independent samples.

$$CR = \frac{p_1 - p_2 - 0 + (\text{or} -) \text{ correction}}{\sigma_{p_1 - p_2}}$$

As the reader might suspect, however, the standard error of the difference between dependent proportions (assuming $H_o : p_1 - p_2 = 0$ is true) is not equal to the standard error of the difference between independent proportions as computed by Form. (18-6). It will be recalled that the standard error of the difference between dependent sample means is usually less than the standard error of the difference between independent sample means. To review, the two formulas which are pertinent are as follows.

Independent

$$\sigma_{\overline{X}_1 - \overline{X}_2} = \sqrt{\sigma_{\overline{X}_1}^2 + \sigma_{\overline{X}_2}^2}$$ (10-3)

Dependent

$$\sigma_{\overline{X}_1 - \overline{X}_2} = \sqrt{\sigma_{\overline{X}_1}^2 + \sigma_{\overline{X}_2}^2 - 2r\,\sigma_{\overline{X}_1}\,\sigma_{\overline{X}_2}}$$ (13-1)

In the formula for the dependent case, a term involving the correlation between the two sets of scores was subtracted. The reason that standard errors of differences based on dependent samples are usually smaller than those based on independent samples was discussed in Chap. 13.

For proportions, similarly, the standard error of a difference based on two dependent samples tends to be less than the standard error of a difference based on two independent samples. A simple procedure for obtaining $\sigma_{p_1 - p_2}$ for dependent samples will be presented, although a discussion of the rationale for this procedure will not be attempted. For each male student in his sample, Dr. Greene would have two scores, the score on the statement before the film and the score after the film. If a $+$ is used to indicate agreement with the statement and a $-$ is used to indicate disagreement, a list such as the following could represent Dr. Greene's results for the 60 male students.

Name	Before the film	After the film
1. Don Jones	$-$	$+$
2. Tom Smith	$-$	$-$
3. Phil Robinson	$+$	$-$
4. George Williams	$-$	$+$
. . .		
58. George Powell	$+$	$+$
59. Bernard Clark	$+$	$-$
60. Axel Swenson	$+$	$+$

Suppose that the total number of pluses was 33 before the film and 19 after. The sample proportions of those agreeing with the statement would be:

$$p_1 = \frac{33}{60} = .550 \quad \text{and} \quad p_2 = \frac{19}{60} = .317$$

In order to determine the standard error of $p_1 - p_2$, a four-fold table such as the following would be constructed.

After the Film

		Disagree $(-)$	Agree $(+)$
Before	Agree $(+)$	$A = 20$	$B = 13$
the Film	Disagree $(-)$	$C = 21$	$D = 6$

Each individual in the sample of sixty would be tallied in one of the four boxes according to his agreement with the statement before and after the film. For instance, Phil Robinson and Bernard Clark showed agreement before the film but disagreement after; therefore, they would fall in box A. Tom Smith disagreed on both occasions; he would fall in box C. George Powell and Axel Swenson, on the other hand, agreed on both occasions; they would fall in box B. Finally, Don Jones and George Williams disagreed before and agreed after; they would fall in box D. Let A, B, C, and D represent the numbers of individuals falling in the respective boxes. That is, for this example, there were twenty students who agreed before but disagreed after, thirteen who agreed on both occasions, twenty-one who disagreed on both occasions, and six who disagreed before but agreed after. It should be apparent that the following relationships hold.

$$A + B + C + D = N \qquad (20 + 13 + 21 + 6 = 60)$$
$$A + B = \text{total number agreeing before} \qquad (20 + 13 = 33)$$

$$\frac{A + B}{N} = p_1 \qquad \frac{33}{60} = .550$$

$$B + D = \text{total number agreeing after} \qquad (13 + 6 = 19)$$

$$\frac{B + D}{N} = p_2 \qquad \frac{19}{60} = .317$$

It could be shown that the standard error of the difference between the two dependent sample proportions can be obtained from the four-fold table by means of the following formula.

$$\sigma_{p_1 - p_2} = \sqrt{\frac{(A + D)}{N^2}} = \sqrt{\frac{(20 + 6)}{(60)^2}} = \sqrt{.00722} = .0850 \qquad (18\text{-}8)$$

The critical ratio, therefore, for testing the null hypothesis $H_o : P_1 - P_2 = 0$, using dependent sample proportions, would be of the form:

$$CR = \frac{p_1 - p_2 - 0 + (\text{or} -)\dfrac{.5}{N}}{\sigma_{p_1 - p_2}} = \frac{\dfrac{A+B}{N} - \dfrac{B+D}{N} + (\text{or} -)\dfrac{.5}{N}}{\sqrt{\dfrac{A+D}{N^2}}}$$

$$= \frac{.550 - .317 - .008}{.0850} = \frac{.225}{.0850} = 2.65$$

where $\dfrac{.5}{N}$ is the correction for continuity

The formula for the critical ratio above can be simplified for easy computations by multiplying the numerator and denominator by N and combining terms.

$$CR = \frac{A - D + (\text{or} -).5}{\sqrt{A+D}} = \frac{20 - 6 - .5}{\sqrt{20+6}} = 2.65 \qquad (18\text{-}9)$$

The correction for continuity of .5 was subtracted from the numerator of the CR, because the numerator was positive; if the numerator had been negative, the correction would have been added. If $A + D$ is greater than 10, as it is in this case, the sampling distribution of the ratio can be considered normal for most practical purposes; therefore, for this example, $P = .0080$ (two-tailed), and the null hypothesis would certainly be rejected, using either the .05 or the .01 levels of significance. It would be concluded that a smaller proportion of the hypothetical population of male students would be in agreement with the statement after seeing the film than before. If $A + D$ had been equal to 10 or less, exact methods not covered by this text would have been appropriate.

A few additional words regarding the format of the four-fold table should be mentioned. Whether or not the table is set up and labelled exactly as illustrated is not important. What is important is that A and D represent the boxes containing those individuals who agreed on one occasion and disagreed on the other.

Exercises and Problems

1. A school bond issue is to be voted on in the next election. Of a random sample of 100 voters polled, sixty indicate that they are in favor of the issue, and forty indicate that they are opposed.
   a) Test the hypothesis that the population proportion favoring the issue differs from the proportion opposed to the issue.
   b) Set up a 95 per cent confidence interval for the proportion favoring the issue.

2. In an attempt to demonstrate ESP (extra-sensory perception), a regular deck of playing cards is used. A card is drawn from a well shuffled deck and presented face down to Mr. Smith, who makes a guess as to whether the card is a spade, heart, diamond, or club. The card is then replaced in the deck, the deck is thoroughly shuffled, and another card is selected. Out of sixty cards presented in this way, Mr. Smith is able to guess correctly the suit of twenty cards. Do these results support the hypothesis that Mr. Smith has the power of ESP?

3. According to extensive experience with a certain disease, one out of five who contracts it is dead within a year after positive diagnosis. A new serum is administered to a sample of 100 individuals who have contracted the disease. At the end of a year after positive diagnosis, ninety-two out of the sample are still alive. Test the hypothesis that the serum is effective.

4. A sample of forty-eight students is administered a multiple-choice test with four alternatives per item. Seventeen of the forty-eight students choose the correct alternative to Item 12.

   a) Test the hypothesis that students of this type do better on Item 12 than would be expected on the basis of chance alone.

   b) Set up the 95 per cent confidence interval for the proportion of students of this type who would choose the correct alternative.

5. One hundred rats are randomly divided into two groups of fifty each. The rats in group A are given a series of training trials that differ in several respects from the training trials given to the rats of group B. Then each rat is given a test trial in which it has the choice of leaving the maze through either one of two exits. Just above one of the exits is a card with a white circle on it, and just above the other is a card with a black square on it. The following are the results of the test trial.

| | Exit selected | |
	White circle	Black square
Group A	15	35
Group B	22	28

   a) Test the hypothesis that the type of training given to group A leads to a preference for the black square.

   b) Consider the hypothetical population of rats trained like those in group A. Set up the 95 per cent confidence interval for the proportion who would select the black square.

   c) Suppose a certain theory predicts that the rats trained like those in group A should have a greater preference for the black square than rats trained like those in group B. Do the above data support the theory?

   d) Set up the 95 per cent confidence interval for the difference in the effects of the two types of training on preferences for the black square.

6. Out of a recent graduating class at Lincoln High School, 79 of the 120 male graduates went on to college, and 51 of the 105 female graduates went on to college.

    a) Is there evidence for a "real" sex difference with regard to the proportions going on to college from Lincoln High School?

    b) Set up the 99 per cent confidence interval for the difference between the proportions of males and females going on to college from Lincoln High School.

    c) How would you describe the hypothetical populations with which (*a*) and (*b*) are concerned?

7. Dr. Jones, a sociology professor, is constructing a scale to measure attitudes toward minority groups. He administers two trial items to his elementary-sociology classes. Each item is in the form of a statement about minority groups, and the students are asked to indicate whether they agree or disagree. His sample results, divided according to sex, are presented in Table 18-1.

    a) Dr. Smith hypothesized that more males would disagree with Item *H* than would agree with it. Test this hypothesis.

    b) Set up the 95 per cent confidence interval for the proportion of males agreeing with Item *H*.

    c) Test the hypothesis that the proportion of females which would agree with Item *G* differs from the proportion which would disagree.

    d) Set up the 95 per cent confidence interval for the proportion of females agreeing with Item *G*.

    e) Do males and females differ with regard to their responses to Item *G*? Test the appropriate hypothesis.

    f) Set up the 99 per cent confidence interval for the difference in the proportions of males and females who would agree with Item *G*.

    g) Test the hypothesis that more males would agree with Item *G* than with Item *H*.

    h) Test the hypothesis that Items *G* and *H* differ with regard to the proportions of females who would agree with them.

    i) How would you describe the hypothetical populations to which the statistical inferences made in (*a*) through (*h*) would be limited?

8. You administer several aptitude-test items to a sample of eighty fourth-graders. Of the sample, thirty-five pass item *A*; thirty pass item *B*; and thirty-five fail both. Are the items of unequal difficulty? Test the appropriate hypothesis.

9. For the same sample of eighty fourth-graders mentioned in Prob. 8, the following are the results for items *C* and *D*: twenty passed both items, twenty-five failed both, and twenty-five passed item *C* but failed item *D*.

    a) Test the hypothesis that item *C* is easier than item *D*.

    b) Compute a point estimate of the population value with which the hypothesis in (*a*) is concerned.

10. In what way does the standard error to be used in the solution of part (*a*) of Prob. 1 differ from the standard error to be used in part (*b*)? Why does it differ?

11. In what way does the standard error to be used in the solution of (*a*) of Prob. 6 differ from the standard error to be used in (*b*)? Why does it differ?

Table 18-1

Results for Two Attitude Items Presented to Dr. Jones's Sociology Classes
(*A indicates agreement, and D indicates disagreement.*)

Males

Student	Item G	Item H	Student	Item G	Item H
1	D	D	21	A	A
2	A	A	22	A	D
3	D	A	23	D	D
4	D	D	24	D	D
5	D	D	25	D	D
6	D	D	26	A	A
7	A	D	27	A	D
8	D	D	28	A	D
9	A	D	29	D	D
10	D	D	30	D	A
11	A	D	31	D	D
12	A	A	32	A	A
13	D	D	33	D	D
14	A	D	34	A	A
15	D	D	35	A	D
16	A	A	36	D	A
17	D	D			
18	D	D			
19	D	D			
20	D	D			

Females

Student	Item G	Item H	Student	Item G	Item H
1	A	D	21	A	D
2	A	A	22	D	D
3	D	A	23	A	D
4	A	A	24	D	D
5	D	A	25	A	A
6	D	D	26	A	A
7	A	A	27	A	A
8	A	A	28	A	A
9	A	D	29	A	D
10	D	D	30	A	A
11	D	D	31	A	A
12	D	D	32	A	A
13	A	A	33	A	D
14	A	A	34	A	D
15	D	D	35	D	D
16	A	D	36	A	A
17	D	D	37	A	D
18	A	A	38	A	D
19	A	A	39	A	D
20	D	D	40	D	A

12. The correction for continuity to be used when making inferences about $P_1 - P_2$ makes very little difference when the samples are both large. Illustrate this fact by substituting the following pairs of sample sizes into the formula for the correction.

$$N_1 = N_2 = 10, \quad N_1 = N_2 = 20, \quad N_1 = N_2 = 40,$$
$$N_1 = N_2 = 100, \quad N_1 = N_2 = 1,000$$

13. Suppose you are using the technique described in this chapter to test the hypothesis $H_R : P_1 - P_2 \neq 0$ at the .05 level of significance. Suppose furthermore that your samples are both relatively small and that you forget to incorporate a correction for continuity in the computation of your critical ratio.

   a) What effect will your forgetting to use the correction for continuity have on the probability of making a Type II error? Explain.

   b) Will the probability of making a Type I error equal .05; will it be greater than .05; or will it be less than .05? Explain.

Chapter 19

Chi Square

In the previous chapter, we considered some common techniques for making statistical inferences from frequency data based on variables for which there are two possible categories or scores. Such variables were referred to as *dichotomous variables*, and the data were referred to as *dichotomous data*. In the present chapter, more general techniques which are applicable to a wide variety of frequency data will be discussed. These techniques are relevant not only to dichotomous data, but also to frequency data based on variables for which there are more than two possible categories or scores. For instance, such techniques are applicable to course grades (each individual is placed in one of five possible categories, *A*, *B*, *C*, *D*, and *F*) and to the results of rolling a die (each roll obtains one of six possible scores).

The techniques to be presented utilize a theoretical probability distribution known as the χ^2 (*chi* square) distribution.

THE χ^2 DISTRIBUTION

Let us consider once again the data which result from tossing a coin. If a coin is tossed many times, we would expect that approximately half of the tosses would turn up heads and half would turn up tails. For an infinitely large population of flips, the proportion (*P*) of tosses that will turn up heads is .5 and the proportion (*Q*) of tosses that will turn up tails, similarly, is .5; therefore, if a coin were tossed 40 times (i.e., a random sample of 40 tosses), we would *expect* to obtain 20 heads and 20 tails. Suppose, however, that we actually *observed* 23 heads and 17 tails. The observed number of heads is 3 more than the expected number, whereas the observed number of tails is 3 less. These discrepancies between observed and expected values would be attributed to the chance factors involved in random sampling. The observed results, the expected results, and the discrepancies between the observed and expected are shown below.

	Heads	Tails
a) Observed	23	17
b) Expected	20	20
c) Discrepancy	+3	-3

The degree of discrepancy presented here can be expressed in terms of a statistic, χ^2, obtained using the formula:

$$\chi^2 = \sum \frac{(O - E)^2}{E} \qquad (19\text{-}1)$$

where O and E represent the observed and expected frequencies, respectively

The operations indicated by the formula are as follows.

1) For each category the discrepancy is squared and divided by the expected frequency for that category.

$$\text{For heads:} \quad \frac{(O - E)^2}{E} = \frac{(+3)^2}{20} = \frac{+9}{20} = +.45$$

$$\text{For tails:} \quad \frac{(O - E)^2}{E} = \frac{(-3)^2}{20} = \frac{+9}{20} = +.45$$

2) The results from Step 1 are added to obtain the χ^2.

$$\chi^2 = \sum \frac{(O - E)^2}{E} = (+.45) + (+.45) = +.90$$

If another sample of forty tosses were taken and fifteen heads and twenty-five tails were observed, the χ^2 would be computed as follows.

$$\chi^2 = \sum \frac{(O - E)^2}{E} = \overset{\text{heads}}{\frac{(15 - 20)^2}{20}} + \overset{\text{tails}}{\frac{(25 - 20)^2}{20}} = +2.50$$

Suppose, now, that we produced an infinite number of samples of 40 flips each and, for each sample, recorded the results and computed the χ^2. The theoretical relative-frequency distribution of the obtained χ^2 statistics is presented in Table 19-1. This distribution, known as a *random-sampling distribution of χ^2 statistics*, could be used to determine the probability of obtaining various results for a single sample of 40 flips. For instance, it can be seen from the table that the probability of obtaining a sample with

Table 19-1

Theoretical Relative-Frequency Distribution of χ^2's Each Based on Forty Tosses of a Coin

Number of Heads	χ^2	Rel. f
28+ or 12−	6.4 and up	.014
27 or 13	4.9	.026
26 or 14	3.6	.042
25 or 15	2.5	.074
24 or 16	1.6	.112
23 or 17	0.9	.162
22 or 18	0.4	.206
21 or 19	0.1	.240
20	0	.124
		1.000

a χ^2 of 6.4 or more is .014, the probability of obtaining a sample with a χ^2 of 4.9 or more is .040 (i.e., .014 + .026 = .040), and so on; thus, if 10,000 samples of 40 flips each were taken, one would expect to obtain about 140 with χ^2's of 6.4 or more (.014 × 10,000 = 140), 400 with χ^2's of 4.9 or more (.040 × 10,000 = 400), and so on.

Consider the rolling of a die. Since there are six sides to a die, there are six possible results for a single roll of the die. We saw earlier that the results obtained from rolling dice may be considered dichotomous data by treating one of the six possible results as one category and the other five as the second category. Now, however, we shall treat each of the six possible results as a separate category. The probability of obtaining any one of these results is 1/6. For instance, if the die were rolled thirty-six times, we would expect on the average to obtain six *ones* (36 × 1/6 = 6), six *twos*, six *threes*, six *fours*, six *fives*, and six *sixes*. Suppose the following are the results actually observed for a sample of thirty-six rolls.

Side Coming Up

	1	2	3	4	5	6	Total
a)	8	3	6	4	9	6	36

The tables for the expected results and for the discrepancies would be as follows.

Side Coming Up

		1	2	3	4	5	6	Total
b)	Expected	6	6	6	6	6	6	36
c)	Discrepancies	+2	−3	0	−2	+3	0	0

A χ^2 statistic can be computed from these results.

$$\chi^2 = \sum \frac{(O - E)^2}{E} = \frac{(+2)^2}{6} + \frac{(-3)^2}{6} + \frac{(0)^2}{6} + \frac{(-2)^2}{6} + \frac{(+3)^2}{6} + \frac{(0)^2}{6}$$

$$= 4.33$$

Suppose, now, that we produced an infinite number of samples of 36 rolls each and, for each sample, recorded the results and computed the χ^2. The theoretical relative-frequency distribution of the obtained χ^2 statistics for this type of situation is presented in Table 19-2. The table can be used in the same way as Table 19-1 to determine the probabilities of obtaining various results for samples of size 36. For example, for a sample of 36

Table 19-2

Theoretical Relative-Frequency Distribution of χ^{2}'s, Each Based on Thirty-six Rolls of a Die

χ^2	Rel. f
14.01 and up	.017
12.01–14.00	.018
10.01–12.00	.041
8.01–10.00	.081
6.01– 8.00	.149
4.01– 6.00	.244
2.01– 4.00	.300
0 – 2.00	.150
	1.000

rolls of a die, the probability of obtaining a χ^2 larger than 14.00 is .017. Thus, for 10,000 samples of 36 rolls each, one would expect to obtain about 170 with χ^2's of 14.01 or more.

The discussion thus far illustrates several points which should be emphasized. First, a χ^2 can be used with variables for which there are two *or more* possible scores or categories. Second, the χ^2 statistic for a sample reflects the discrepancies between the observed and expected frequencies of individuals falling in the various categories. The larger the discrepancies between the observed and expected frequencies, the larger will be the resulting χ^2 statistic. Third, since the computations involve squaring each of the discrepancies between observed and expected frequencies, a χ^2 statistic will never be negative. Furthermore, because of squaring, discrepancies of equal amounts, regardless of direction, will add equal contributions to a χ^2 statistic. For instance, referring to the example in which 40 coins were tossed, twenty-four heads (four above the expected twenty) would add the same contribution to a χ^2 as sixteen heads (four below the expected twenty).

$$\frac{(24 - 20)^2}{20} = \frac{16}{20} = .80, \qquad \frac{(16 - 20)^2}{20} = \frac{16}{20} = .80$$

Fourth, the sum of the observed frequencies will always equal the sum of the expected frequencies, and thus the sum of the discrepancies will equal zero. This is illustrated by both the coin-tossing and die-rolling examples.

Finally, it can be seen from a comparison of Tables 19-1 and 19-2 that the two sampling distributions represented there are not the same. This is so because the two situations for which the tables were derived involve different numbers of degrees of freedom, and there is a unique sampling distribution of χ^2 associated with each number of degrees of freedom. The reader will recall that this is the case for sampling distributions of t ratios as well; there is a unique t distribution for each number of degrees of freedom. The degrees of freedom for a χ^2 depend upon the number of possible categories or score values rather than the sample size. Consider, for instance, the die-rolling example. Once the discrepancies $(O - E)$ are known for any five of the categories, the sixth discrepancy can be determined from the fact that all six must total zero. In this sense then, only five of the six discrepancies are "free to vary," and the number of degrees of freedom involved is five. Similarly, in the coin-tossing example, only one of the two discrepancies is free to vary, since the two must total zero. Thus, only one degree of freedom is involved. The general rule in cases like those described is that the number of degrees of freedom is equal to the number of possible categories minus one.

A sampling distribution of χ^2 statistics obtained from frequency data can, with certain exceptions to be discussed, be closely approximated by one of the theoretical distributions presented in the table shown in Appx. 5 for one through thirty degrees of freedom. The format of the table shown there is similar to that of Appx. 3, in which a number of the t distributions are represented. The numbers across the top of Appx. 5 are *areas in the upper tail* of the χ^2 distribution, and the numbers in the left column are degrees of freedom. Each row of the table represents the χ^2 distribution for a unique number of degrees of freedom. Each entry in a particular row is the value of χ^2 to the right of which lies the tail area specified at the top of the table. The table is easily read. Consider an example in which $\chi^2 = 11.07$ and $df = 5$. Refer to the df column; find the row for $df = 5$; and, in that row, locate the χ^2 value closest to 11.07. For $df = 5$, 11.07 itself is one of the table entries. Now move up the column containing 11.07 and identify the proportion at the top. We find it to be .05, which is the proportion of the area in this χ^2 distribution lying to the right of the value 11.07 (see Fig. 19-1).

Sampling distributions of χ^2 are not symmetric; they are positively skewed. Consequently, Appx. 5 (which deals with areas in the upper tail

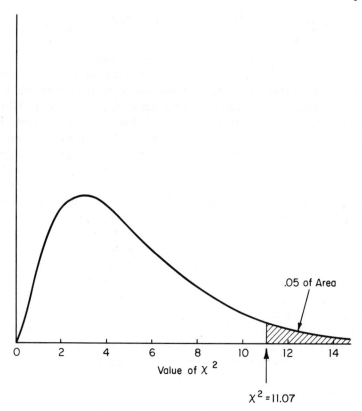

.05 of Area

Value of X ^{2}

X ^{2} = 11.07

Figure 19-1. χ^2 Distribution for Five Degrees of Freedom

only) does not permit us to find areas in the lower tail. The table is still sufficient for our purposes, however, because in the applications of χ^2 discussed in this text, we shall not be concerned with areas in the lower tail. Rather, the interest will be in determining the probability of obtaining discrepancies between the observed sample frequencies and the expected frequencies *as large as or larger than* those discrepancies actually obtained. This would be equivalent to the probability of obtaining a χ^2 as large as or larger than that actually obtained. The determination of such a probability requires a knowledge of the area relationships for the upper tail of the distribution only.

Let us illustrate the use of Appx. 5 further, using the coin-tossing example discussed previously. Out of 40 tosses of a coin, we would expect to obtain 20 heads and 20 tails; however, in our second sample, 15 heads and 25 tails were observed. The discrepancies of -5 for heads and $+5$

for tails were used in Form. (19-1) to obtain a χ^2 of 2.50. For this situation, there is only 1 degree of freedom. In the first row of Appx. 5 ($df = 1$), we find that a χ^2 of 2.50 falls between the tabled values of 1.64 and 2.71. Since .20 of the area lies beyond $\chi^2 = 1.64$ and .10 of the area lies beyond $\chi^2 = 2.71$, the probability of obtaining a χ^2 as large as or larger than our 2.50 is somewhere between .20 and .10. We can say, therefore, that the probability of obtaining discrepancies as large as or larger than those actually obtained for our sample of 40 tosses is also somewhere between .20 and .10. This may be stated symbolically as $P > .10$ or, more precisely, $.20 > P > .10$.

In the die-rolling example, the discrepancies between the observed frequencies and the expected frequencies for the sample of 36 rolls led to a χ^2 of 4.33. For this situation there are 5 degrees of freedom. Using the row for 5 degrees of freedom in Appx. 5, it can be seen that 4.33 is smaller than the smallest tabled value of 6.06. Since .30 of the area lies beyond a χ^2 of 6.06, the probability of obtaining a χ^2 as large as or larger than the 4.33 obtained must be greater than .30. Thus, the probability of obtaining results as discrepant as or more discrepant than those actually obtained would also be greater than .30 (i.e., $P > .30$).

APPLICATIONS OF χ^2: THE ONE-VARIABLE CASE

Distinction between One-Variable and Two-Variable Cases

In some of the situations in which the use of χ^2 is appropriate, we may be concerned with how individuals score on a *single* variable. We might, for example, be interested in hair color for a group of children, utilizing as the "score" categories the colors blonde, brown, black, and red, and placing each individual in one of these four possible categories. In other situations, our interest may be in the relationship between individuals' scores on *two* variables or characteristics. For instance, if hair color and eye color were the variables of interest, we would obtain *two* "scores" for each child, the color of his eyes and the color of his hair. Applications of χ^2 to situations involving single variables will be discussed first. In later sections of the chapter, the techniques for analyzing the relationship between two variables will be presented.

Hypotheses in the One-Variable Case

When we are interested in a single variable, our hypotheses will be in terms of the proportions of individuals in the population who fall into the various categories. The null hypothesis to be tested directly will be that the population proportions equal certain values determined beforehand. As illustrated, the degrees of freedom will equal the number of categories minus one.

For instance, suppose we have reason to believe that the die used by a gambler is "loaded." We decide to check on this possibility by rolling the die a number of times and observing how often each of the sides comes up. If the die were not loaded, we would expect any given side of the die to come up 1/6 of the time. That is, for an infinitely large hypothetical population of rolls of a fair die, we would expect P_1 (the proportion of individual rolls on which the "one" side came up) to equal 1/6, P_2 to equal 1/6, and so on. If the die were loaded, not all six of the population proportions would be equal to 1/6. The null and research hypotheses could be stated explicitly as follows.

General form of hypothesis	*Specific hypothesis for this example*
H_o : The population proportions equal certain values.	H_o : $P_1 = \dfrac{1}{6}, \quad P_2 = \dfrac{1}{6}, \cdots$ (The die is not loaded.)
H_R : The population proportions do *not* equal the values specified in the null hypothesis.	H_R : The population proportions $(P_1, P_2, P_3, P_4, P_5,$ and $P_6)$ do not all equal 1/6. (The die is loaded.)

Example 19-1. Suppose the die is rolled 48 times with the following results.

	\multicolumn{6}{c}{Side coming up}	

	1	2	3	4	5	6	Total
Observed frequencies	6	8	4	12	10	8	48

What do we conclude? Is the die loaded?

If the null hypothesis were true, the expected frequencies would be those obtained by multiplying the sample size (48) by each of the hypothesized population proportions.

| | \multicolumn{6}{c}{Side coming up} | |

	1	2	3	4	5	6	Total
Expected frequencies	$\frac{1}{6}(48) = 8$	$\frac{1}{6}(48) = 8$	$\frac{1}{6}(48) = 8$	$\frac{1}{6}(48) = 8$	$\frac{1}{6}(48) = 8$	$\frac{1}{6}(48) = 8$	48

The table of discrepancies could then be determined:

	Side coming up					
	1	2	3	4	5	6
Discrepancies $(O - E)$	$6 - 8 = -2$	$8 - 8 = 0$	$4 - 8 = -4$	$12 - 8 = 4$	$10 - 8 = 2$	$8 - 8 = 0$

and a χ^2 computed.

$$\chi^2 = \sum \frac{(O - E)^2}{E} = \frac{(-2)^2}{8} + \frac{(0)^2}{8} + \frac{(-4)^2}{8} + \frac{(+4)^2}{8} + \frac{(+2)^2}{8} + \frac{(0)^2}{8}$$
$$= 5.00$$

For 5 degrees of freedom $(6 - 1 = 5)$, the probability of obtaining a χ^2 as large as or larger than the 5.00 actually obtained is greater than .30 (Appx. 5). That is, if the null hypothesis is true, the probability of obtaining sample results as discrepant as those obtained is greater than .30; therefore, we certainly would accept H_o and conclude that the observed sample discrepancies are not large enough to support the contention that the die is loaded.

The hypothesized proportions for the various categories need not all be equal as in Ex. 19-1. Consider the following situation in which they differ from one another.

Example 19-2. The U.S. Department of Labor has predicted that by 1965, the labor force in this country will be distributed as follows.

Professional and technical occupations............10 per cent
Proprietary, managerial, and official occupations.... 9 per cent
Clerical and sales occupations....................20 per cent
Industrial occupations...........................41 per cent
Service occupations............................. 9 per cent
Agriculture..................................... 8 per cent
Unclassified occupations........................ 3 per cent

Mr. Green, the vocational-guidance coordinator of county X, a very populous county, wishes to determine whether the occupational aspirations of male high-school seniors in his county are inconsistent with these predictions. He selects a random sample of 210 male high-school seniors from the county population and identifies their vocational aspirations. The following are the results.

	Prof. and Tech.	Prop., Manag., and Off.	Clerical and Sales	Indust.	Service	Agri.	Unclass.	Total
Observed frequencies	92	41	10	22	40	2	3	210

The research and null hypotheses can be stated:

H_R : The proportions of seniors in the county population whose aspirations fall into the various categories mentioned are *not* all equal to those predicted by the U.S. Department of Labor.

H_o : The proportions of seniors in the county population whose aspirations fall into the various categories are equal to those predicted by the U.S. Department of Labor.

Assuming the null hypothesis to be true, the following are the expected frequencies for the sample of 210.

	Prof. and Tech.	Prop., Manag., and Off.	Clerical and Sales	Indust.	Service	Agri.	Unclass.
Expected frequencies	.10 × 210 = 21	.09 × 210 = 18.9	.20 × 210 = 42	.41 × 210 = 86.1	.09 × 210 = 18.9	.08 × 210 = 16.8	.03 × 210 = 6.3

The discrepancies between observed and expected can then be obtained.

	Prof. and Tech.	Prop., Manag., and Off.	Clerical and Sales	Indust.	Service	Agri.	Unclass.
Discrepancies	92 − 21 = +71	41 − 18.9 = +22.1	10 − 42 = −32	22 − 86.1 = −64.1	40 − 18.9 = +21.1	2 − 16.8 = −14.8	3 − 6.3 = −3.3

A χ^2 is computed.

$$\chi^2 = \sum \frac{(O - E)^2}{E} = \frac{(71)^2}{21} + \frac{(22.1)^2}{18.9} + \frac{(-32)^2}{42} + \frac{(-64.1)^2}{86.1} + \frac{(21.1)^2}{18.9}$$

$$+ \frac{(-14.8)^2}{16.8} + \frac{(-3.3)^2}{6.3} = 376$$

Since there are 7 possible scores or categories, the number of degrees of freedom is 6 (i.e., $7 - 1 = 6$). The probability of a sample χ^2 as large as or larger than the 376 obtained, with $df = 6$, is less than .001; therefore, the probability of obtaining results as deviant as actually observed is less than .001 if H_o is true. H_o would most certainly be rejected, and it would be concluded that the aspirations of male high-school seniors from county X are not consistent with the Labor Department predictions.

Ex. 19-2 illustrates one point that is often overlooked. In and of itself, a statistically significant χ^2 indicates very little about the practical or theoretical significance of the results. For instance, Mr. Green would be unreasonable to expect the aspirations of high school senior males in his county to be *perfectly* consistent with Labor Department predictions. Whether or not the discrepancies are of importance depends upon their size, their pattern, and a host of factors external to the data.

The Correction for Continuity when $df = 1$

In situations in which there are only two possible categories (i.e., when $df = 1$), slightly more accurate probabilities can be obtained from Appx. 5 if a correction for continuity is used when computing χ^2. The correction involves subtracting .5 from the absolute value (value without regard to sign) of each of the two discrepancies before squaring. A modified χ^2 formula, incorporating the correction, is as follows.

$$\chi^2 = \sum \frac{(|O - E| - .5)^2}{E} = \frac{(|O_1 - E_1| - .5)^2}{E_1} + \frac{(|O_2 - E_2| - .5)^2}{E_2} \quad (19\text{-}2)$$

The vertical bars indicate that the absolute values of the enclosed discrepancies are to be used. Although the correction will have only a slight effect on the value of χ^2 if N is very large, the authors recommend that it be routinely applied when $df = 1$. In situations involving more than one degree of freedom the correction is not appropriate.

Example 19-3. We wish to determine whether or not rats of a particular strain used in the laboratory have a direction bias. If no bias exists, we would expect half the rats of this strain to turn right and half to turn left at the choice point in a *T*-maze; however, if the majority favor one direction over the other, the strain would be considered to be biased in that direction. We use as subjects in an experiment 100 naive rats (i.e., rats of this strain who have never had any training). Each rat is placed in the *T*-maze only once, and the direction he turns at the choice point is recorded. Of the sample, thirty-six turn right, and sixty-four turn left.

If P_R and P_L represent the proportions of the hypothetical population of rats of this strain who would turn right and who would turn left, respectively, the hypotheses would be as follows.

$H_R : P_R$ and $P_L \neq .5$ (The strain is biased toward one direction.)
$H_o : P_R$ and $P_L = .5$ (The strain is not biased in either direction.)

Assuming H_o to be true, the expected frequencies can be determined.

	Right	Left	Total
Expected frequencies	.5 (100) = 50	.5 (100) = 50	100

Then the discrepancies are computed:

	Right	Left
Discrepancies $(O - E)$	36 − 50 = −14	64 − 50 = 14

and a χ^2 obtained.

$$\chi^2 = \frac{(|O_1 - E_1| - .5)^2}{E_1} + \frac{(|O_2 - E_2| - .5)^2}{E_2}$$

$$= \frac{(|-14| - .5)^2}{50} + \frac{(|+14| - .5)^2}{50}$$

$$= \frac{(14 - .5)^2}{50} + \frac{(14 - .5)^2}{50} = \frac{364.50}{50} = 7.29$$

Appendix 5 tells us that the probability of obtaining a χ^2 as large as or larger than the 7.29 obtained is between .001 and .01. If the .01 level of significance were used, H_o would be rejected, and it would be concluded that rats of this strain tend to turn left rather than right.

Relationship between χ^2 for One Degree of Freedom and *CR*

When there are only two possible values for the variable, $df = 1$. In these situations, either a χ^2 or a critical ratio may be used. For instance, as the reader may well have recognized, the data of Ex. 19-3 could be analyzed in terms of the proportion of rats who turn in one of the two directions.

Example 19-4.   According to the results presented in Ex. 19-3, thirty-six of the sample of 100 rats turned right; the remainder turned left. The research and null hypotheses could be represented in terms of the proportion of the population of rats which would turn right.

$$H_R : P \neq .5$$
$$H_o : P = .5$$

Using the techniques for testing hypotheses about a single population proportion, a critical ratio can be obtained.

$$CR = \frac{P - P_H + (\text{or} \ -)\frac{.5}{N}}{\sigma_p} = \frac{.360 - .5 + .005}{.0500}$$

$$= \frac{-.135}{.0500} = -2.70$$

$$\text{where} \quad \sigma_p = \sqrt{\frac{P_H Q_H}{N}} = \sqrt{\frac{(.5)(.5)}{100}} = .0500$$

From Appx. 2, we find that $P = .0070$ (two-tailed). Using the .01 level of significance, H_o would be rejected, and it would be concluded that rats of this strain tend to turn left rather than right.

It can be seen that identical conclusions were reached in Ex. 19-3 and Ex. 19-4. Furthermore, if a more detailed table of χ^2 were used, we would discover that the probability of obtaining a χ^2 as large as or larger than 7.29 ($df = 1$) is .007, exactly the same as the probability obtained in Ex. 19-4 using a *CR*. This illustrates the fact that *when only a single variable is involved and when that variable has only two possible values (i.e., when $df = 1$), the CR and the χ^2 techniques will give identical results. In addition, when df = 1, the relationship $(CR)^2 = \chi^2$ will hold.* This is confirmed by Ex. 19-3 and Ex. 19-4, for $(-2.70)^2 = 7.29$.

χ^2 and Direction of Differences

The probability obtained in Ex. 19-3 was equivalent to that obtained in Ex. 19-4 for a *two-tailed test*. The reason for this is that a χ^2 does not take the direction of the results into account, whereas a critical ratio does. The same χ^2 value (i.e., $+7.29$) would be obtained for a 64–36 split, regardless of whether 64 out of the 100 rats turned right or 64 out of the 100 turned left. On the other hand, a critical ratio of $+2.70$ would have been obtained only if 64 out of the 100 rats had turned right. As it was, 64 out of the 100 turned left, and the critical ratio was equal to -2.70.

The χ^2 approach can nonetheless be used to test directional research hypotheses when only one degree of freedom is involved. For instance, suppose in Ex. 19-3 the research hypothesis had been that rats of the strain under consideration tend to turn left rather than right (i.e., $H_R : P_R < .5$ and $P_L > .5$). Since the probability from the χ^2 table is the probability of obtaining sample results as discrepant as those obtained, *in either direction*, the probability for only one direction would be half the tabled value. In this case, then, the probability for the one-tailed test would be between .0005 and .005 (i.e., $.001/2 = .0005, .01/2 = .005$). If a more detailed table of χ^2 were used, we would find the probability equal to .0035, the value which would be obtained from a one-tailed test using the *CR* approach.

Limitations on the Use of χ^2 in the One-Variable Case

The sampling distribution of the statistic $\chi^2 = \sum (O - E)^2/E$ can be accurately approximated by one of the theoretical χ^2 distributions in Appx. 5 only if the expected frequency in each category is large enough. In determining whether or not the expected frequencies are large enough, the following rules of thumb are often used: In situations involving only two possible scores (i.e., $df = 1$), each expected frequency should be at least 5. In situations in which the number of possible scores is greater than 2 (i.e., $df > 1$), the χ^2 technique should not be used if more than 1/5 of the expected frequencies are less than 5 or if any expected frequency is less than 1.

APPLICATIONS OF χ^2:
THE TWO-VARIABLE CASE

Many situations arise in which the relationship between two variables is of major interest. If it is reasonable to assume that the relationship is in the nature of a consistently increasing or decreasing trend, an analysis involving either a Pearson r or a Spearman ρ (rho) may be appropriate. The reader will recall that the basic data utilized in such an analysis consist of pairs of *scores* for individuals, one score for each individual on each variable. Often, when the number of possible score values or categories for each of the two variables is relatively small, an analysis based on the *frequencies* of individuals obtaining the various possible combinations of scores is useful. An important technique for analyzing such bivariate frequency data involves the use of χ^2. This technique does not assume linearity, because the results obtained are independent of any sort of trend.

Contingency Tables

In situations where a χ^2 is to be used, the data for all individuals are summarized in a bivariate frequency distribution known as a *contingency table*. For instance, suppose we are interested in whether or not there is a relationship between the two variables *preferred candidate* and *sex* in a forthcoming election in which three candidates are running for mayor. For purposes of this discussion, assume that there are 6,000 eligible male voters and 4,000 eligible female voters and that we know the voting preference of each. The data for this entire population of eligible voters are presented in Table 19-3, in the form of a contingency table. Note that a

Table 19-3

Illustration of a Contingency Table, Containing the Voting Preferences by Sex for a Population of 10,000 Voters

Preferred Candidate	Sex Female	Male	
Smith	2,000	1,000	3,000 (total for Smith)
Jones	500	2,500	3,000 (total for Jones)
Phillips	1,500	2,500	4,000 (total for Phillips)
	4,000	6,000	10,000 (grand total)
	(total female)	(total male)	

contingency table is a two-dimensional table with the categories or scores for one variable (preferred candidate) along the vertical axis and for the other variable (sex) along the horizontal axis. Each individual is tallied in one of the six boxes according to his combination of "scores" on the two variables. We can see, for instance, that 2,000 individuals are characterized as "Smith and female," 1,000 as "Smith and male," 500 as "Jones and female," and so on. The row totals along the right side and the column totals along the bottom are known as *marginal totals*. The total (10,000) in the lower right corner is the grand total of all of the individuals represented in the table.

Relationship between the Variables: Dependence

The terms *relationship* and *dependence* are used here as synonyms. If, in general, how the individuals score on one variable is related to how they score on the other, the two variables are said to be dependent. For instance, consider again the data in Table 19-3. Of the 3,000 who prefer Smith, .67 (i.e., 2000/3000 = .67) are female and .33 are male. Of the 3,000 who prefer Jones, .17 are female and .83 are male. Of the 4,000 who prefer Phillips, .38 are female and .62 are male. Finally, of the total 10,000 individuals, .40 are female and .60 are male. These proportions are represented in Table 19-4. We can see that an individual selected from among those who prefer Smith is more likely to be a female, whereas an

Table 19-4

Data of Table 19-3 Expressed as Proportions of the Row Totals

Preferred Candidate	Sex Female	Male	Totals
Smith	.67	.33	1.00
Jones	.17	.83	1.00
Phillips	.38	.62	1.00
Totals	.40	.60	1.00

individual selected from among those who prefer Jones is more likely to be a male. An individual selected from among those who prefer Phillips is more likely to be a male, but to a lesser degree than if he had been selected from among those who preferred Jones. In this sense, then, *sex* and *preferred candidate* are "dependent" on each other. It is important to notice that dependence does not necessarily imply causality. For instance, it would be absurd to say that an individual who prefers Jones is more likely to be a male than a female *because* he prefers Jones.

It should now be clear why Table 19-3 is called a *contingency table*. It shows the extent to which scores on one variable are *contingent upon*, or related to scores on the other.

No Relationship between the Variables: Independence

Consider now the contingency table shown in Table 19-5, which, for a population of 10,000 eligible voters, shows a somewhat different pattern of voting preferences than that represented in Table 19-3. Notice that the marginal totals are the same in both tables but that the frequencies in the cells are different. For the situation represented in Table 19-5, are the two variables dependent or independent?

Table 19-5

Voting Preference by Sex for a Population of 10,000 Voters

Preferred Candidate	Sex Female	Male	Totals
Smith	1,200	1,800	3,000
Jones	1,200	1,800	3,000
Phillips	1,600	2,400	4,000
Totals	4,000	6,000	10,000

The answer to the question may be determined by first expressing the frequencies as proportions. This is done in Table 19-6. We can see from these proportions that, of the 3,000 who prefer Smith, .40 are female and .60 are male; of the 3,000 who prefer Jones, .40 are female and .60 are male; and of the 4,000 who prefer Phillips, .40 are female and .60 are male. Finally, of the total 10,000, .40 are female and .60 are male. Thus, an individual selected from among those who prefer Smith is more likely to

Table 19-6

Data of Table 19-5 Expressed as Proportions of the Row Totals

Preferred Candidate	Sex Female	Male	Totals
Smith	.40	.60	1.00
Jones	.40	.60	1.00
Phillips	.40	.60	1.00
Totals	.40	.60	1.00

be a male than a female; however, an individual selected from among those who prefer Jones or Phillips is also more likely, and to the same degree, to be a male. That is, the proportions or relative frequencies of males and females among those who prefer each candidate are equal to the proportions of females and males (.40 and .60) in the entire population. Sex and candidate preference, in this instance, are in no way related; they are independent.

To summarize, independence may be defined specifically in the following way. *Two variables are independent if, for each category on the first variable, the porportions of individuals falling in the various categories on the second variable are the same as the proportions of the total group falling in the various categories on the second variable.* Thus, a contingency table shows independence if the proportions in each row equal the proportions along the bottom margin (e.g., Tables 19-5 and 19-6). For the population represented in Tables 19-3 and 19-4, sex and preferred candidate are dependent, because, of the individuals who prefer each candidate, the proportions of females and males (i.e., .67 and .33, .17 and .83, .38 and .62) are not the same as the proportions of females and males for the entire group of 10,000 (i.e., .40 and .60 as determined from the marginal frequencies at the bottom of the table).

The Null Hypothesis of Independence

A researcher may have the research hypothesis that, in an entire population of individuals, two variables are related. The usual procedure is to select a random sample of individuals from that population, and, using the data from that sample, test the null hypothesis that the two variables are independent. If the sample results lead to a rejection of the null hypothesis, the researcher will conclude that, in the entire population, the two variables are indeed dependent or related.

The null hypothesis of independence may be tested through the use of χ^2 as a measure of discrepancy between observed sample frequencies and expected sample frequencies. That is, assuming independence of the two variables for the entire population, the expected sample frequencies for each part of the contingency table are determined. These frequencies are then compared with the sample frequencies actually observed, and a χ^2 based on the discrepancy between observed and expected is computed. If the discrepancies are large, the χ^2 will be large, and the null hypothesis of independence will be rejected. On the other hand, if the discrepancies are small, the χ^2 will be small, and it will be concluded that the data do not support the hypothesis that the two variables are related.

When testing the null hypothesis of independence using a χ^2, the degrees of freedom depend on the numbers of rows and columns of the contingency table. The degrees of freedom can be obtained by the following formula.

$$df = (\text{number of rows} - 1)(\text{number of columns} - 1)$$

The contingency table in Table 19-7, for example, has three rows and three columns; thus, $df = 4$.

Example 19-5. Mr. James, the guidance director of a very large high-school district, wishes to determine whether, for a hypothetical population of ninth-grade boys like those in his district, the amount of formal education of a student's father is related to the type of high-school curriculum the student has selected. A random sample of 100 ninth-grade boys is selected from those in the district, and each boy is assigned two scores according to (a) the formal education of his father and (b) the curriculum he has selected. The results for the sample are represented in Table 19-7.

Table 19-7

Curriculum Choice and Father's Educational Level for 100 Ninth-Grade Boys

	High-School Curriculum			
	Commercial	Technical	College Prep	Totals
College	4	5	26	35
High School	18	7	15	40
Non-HS	8	13	4	25
Totals	30	25	45	100

The research and null hypotheses can be specified.

H_R : High-school curriculum is related to the education of the father for the population of ninth-grade boys under consideration.

H_o : High-school curriculum is independent of the education of the father.

Assuming the null hypothesis to be true, the expected sample frequency for each cell of the contingency table can be determined. The lower marginal totals tell us that .30 of the sample of 100 students are in the commercial program, .25 are in the technical program, and .45 are in the college preparatory program. If the two variables are independent, one would expect .30 of the 35 students whose fathers graduated from college to be in the commercial program, .25 to be in the technical program, and .45 to be in the college-preparatory program. The same proportions would be expected for the students whose fathers fall into each of the other two educational categories. Thus, as illustrated in Table 19-8, the expected frequencies for each row can be obtained by multiplying the total frequency for the row by the proportions .30, .25, and .45. Note that the

Table 19-8

*Expected Frequencies for Table 19-7, Assuming Independence
of Curriculum Choice and Father's Education*

		Curriculum Choice		
	Commercial	Technical	College Prep	Totals
College	.30 (35) = 10.50	.25 (35) = 8.75	.45 (35) = 15.75	35
High School	.30 (40) = 12.00	.25 (40) = 10.00	.45 (40) = 18.00	40
Non-HS	.30 (25) = 7.50	.25 (25) = 6.25	.45 (25) = 11.25	25
Totals	30	25	45	100

(Row labels under "Father's Education")

expected frequencies add up to the marginal totals shown for the observed
frequencies. It is now possible to construct a table of the discrepancies
and then to use χ^2 as a test of independence. This is done in Table 19-9,

Table 19-9

Discrepancies between Observed and Expected Frequencies

	High-School Curriculum Selected		
	Commercial	Technical	College Prep
College	4 − 10.50 = **−6.50**	5 − 8.75 = **−3.75**	26 − 15.75 = **+10.25**
High School	18 − 12.00 = **+6.00**	7 − 10.00 = **−3.00**	15 − 18.00 = **−3.00**
Non-HS	8 − 7.50 = **+.50**	13 − 6.25 = **+6.75**	4 − 11.25 = **−7.25**

(Row labels under "Education of Father")

which shows in each cell the discrepancy between observed and expected
frequencies. Employing Form. (19-1), a χ^2 can be computed.

$$\chi^2 = \frac{(-6.50)^2}{10.50} + \frac{(-3.75)^2}{8.75} + \frac{(10.25)^2}{15.75}$$

$$+ \frac{(6.00)^2}{12.00} + \frac{(-3.00)^2}{10.00} + \frac{(-3.00)^2}{18.00}$$

$$+ \frac{(.50)^2}{7.50} + \frac{(6.75)^2}{6.25} + \frac{(-7.25)^2}{11.25}$$

$$= 28.70$$

For this particular situation, there are four degrees of freedom
$[(3 − 1)(3 − 1) = 4]$. Appendix 5 informs us that the probability of obtaining a χ^2 as large as or larger than the χ^2 obtained is less than .001.
Consequently, the null hypothesis would be rejected. We conclude that,
for a hypothetical population of ninth-grade boys selected in the same
way as those used in the research, the chosen curriculum is related to the
education of the father. The observed frequencies of Table 19-7 suggest
that boys whose fathers have graduated from college tend to select the

college-prep program, those whose fathers graduated from high school tend to select the commercial and college-prep programs more than the technical program, and those whose fathers did not graduate from high school tend to select the technical program.

It should be pointed out that this procedure will lead to the same χ^2 regardless of which variable is placed along the vertical axis and which along the horizontal axis. It is left as an exercise for the student to show that the same expected frequencies, and thus the same χ^2 of 28.70, would be obtained if the table were set up with curriculum along the vertical axis and education of father along the horizontal axis.

Computation Formula for 2 × 2 Tables

Regardless of the number of categories for each of the two variables, a χ^2 can be computed using the procedures illustrated in Ex. 19-5. That is, the expected frequencies can be determined and used with the observed frequencies in Form. (19-1).

$$\chi^2 = \sum \frac{(O - E)^2}{E}$$

For dichotomous variables, the χ^2 can also be computed without determining the expected frequencies. Formula (19-3), appropriate only for 2 × 2 tables, involves somewhat simpler computations and gives exactly the same results as Form. (19-1).

$$\chi^2 = \frac{N(AD - BC)^2}{(A + B)(C + D)(A + C)(B + D)} \tag{19-3}$$

where A, B, C, and D stand for the four cell frequencies of the contingency table:

A	B	$(A + B)$
C	D	$(C + D)$

$(A + C)$ $(B + D)$

Slightly more accurate results can be obtained if a correction for continuity is used. The correction can be incorporated into Form. (19-3) as follows.

$$\chi^2 = \frac{N\left(|AD - BC| - \frac{N}{2}\right)^2}{(A + B)(C + D)(A + C)(B + D)} \tag{19-4}$$

The vertical bars indicate that the correction $N/2$ is to be subtracted from the absolute value (value without regard to sign) of the difference

$(AD - BC)$. Although the correction will have little effect on the χ^2 if N is large, it is recommended that it be used routinely when analyzing 2×2 contingency tables. No correction is appropriate for contingency tables involving more than one degree of freedom.

Example 19-6.   We wish to test the research hypothesis that sex and ability to pass a particular item on an IQ test are related among fourth-grade pupils. The null hypothesis to be tested directly would be that the two variables are independent in that population. The item is administered to samples of fifty fourth-grade girls and forty fourth-grade boys drawn from a local school district, and the results are summarized in the following contingency table.

	Fail	Pass		
Girls	17	33	50	$(A + B)$
Boys	20	20	40	$(C + D)$
	37	53	90	(N)
	$(A + C)$	$(B + D)$		

Using Form. (19-4), χ^2 can be computed.

$$\chi^2 = \frac{N\left(|AD - BC| - \frac{N}{2}\right)^2}{(A + B)(C + D)(A + C)(B + D)}$$

$$= 90\frac{\left(|(17)(20) - (33)(20)| - \frac{90}{2}\right)^2}{(50)(40)(37)(53)}$$

$$= \frac{90(|-320| - 45)^2}{3,922,000} = \frac{90(320 - 45)^2}{3,922,000} = 1.74$$

The probability of obtaining a χ^2 as large as 1.74 for $df = 1$, is between .10 and .20. Consequently, the null hypothesis of independence would probably be accepted. It would be concluded that the results do not support the research hypothesis that sex and ability to pass the item are related for the population.

Limitations on the Use of χ^2 for Tests of Independence

It was pointed out in the discussion of the one-variable case that sampling distributions of the statistic $\chi^2 = \sum (O - E)^2/E$ are closely approximated by the theoretical distributions of Appx. 5 only if the expected frequencies are large enough. The same is true for sampling distributions of χ^2 statistics computed from contingency tables. When analyzing the bivariate frequency data of a contingency table, the following rules of thumb are sometimes used. If, in a 2 × 2 table, the smallest *expected* cell frequency is 5 or less, the technique discussed is inappropriate. The smallest expected frequency can easily be determined by dividing the product of the two smaller marginal totals by N (the total number of cases). In Ex. 19-6, for instance, the smallest row marginal was 40, the smallest column marginal was 37, and N was 90; therefore, the smallest expected frequency equals 16.45 [i.e., $(40 \times 37)/90 = 16.45$]. For 2 × 2 tables in which the smallest expected frequency is 5 or less, an exact method commonly referred to as *Fisher's exact test* is appropriate. The reader is referred to a more advanced text for a discussion of this method.

For contingency tables larger than 2 × 2, one rule of thumb is that χ^2 should not be used if more than 1/5 of the cells have expected frequencies less than 5 or if any cell has an expected frequency of less than 1.

Relationship between CR and χ^2 for 2 × 2 Contingency Tables

The null hypothesis of independence for 2 × 2 contingency tables is equivalent to another null hypothesis discussed in an earlier chapter. Consider Ex. 19-6. If sex and ability to pass an item were independent, the proportions of boys passing and failing the item would equal the proportions of girls passing and failing the item. This is equivalent to saying that the proportion of boys passing the item would equal the proportion of girls passing the item, for if the proportions passing are equal, the proportions failing must be equal; therefore, the null hypothesis of independence tested in Ex. 19-6 is equivalent to the null hypothesis that the proportion of boys in the population who can pass the item is equal to the proportion of girls in the population who can pass the item. The technique for testing the latter null hypothesis was discussed in the previous chapter.

Example 19-7. The problem of Ex. 19-6 can be solved using methods of the previous chapter. In terms of the difference between two populations proportions, the null hypothesis of independence is:

$$H_o : P_M - P_F = 0$$

and the research hypothesis is:

$$H_R : P_M - P_F \neq 0$$

Since the boys and girls were not matched in any way, the appropriate formula would be that for independent samples.

$$CR = \cfrac{(P_M - P_F) - 0 + (\text{or} -) \cfrac{.5\,(N_M + N_F)}{N_M\,N_F}}{\sqrt{\cfrac{p_c\,q_c}{N_M} + \cfrac{p_c\,q_c}{N_F}}}$$

The combined proportions, p_c and q_c, could be determined using the data from Ex. 19-6.

$$p_c \text{ (proportion of total group passing item)} = \frac{53}{90} = .589$$

$$q_c \text{ (proportion of total group failing item)} = \frac{37}{90} = .411$$

Similarly, the proportions of boys and girls passing the item can be computed.

$$P_M = \frac{20}{40} = .500, \qquad P_F = \frac{33}{50} = .660$$

Then:

$$CR = \cfrac{.500 - .660 + \cfrac{.5\,(40 + 50)}{(40)\,(50)}}{\sqrt{\cfrac{(.589)\,(.411)}{40} + \cfrac{(.589)\,(.411)}{50}}} = \frac{-.160 + .022}{.104} = -1.32$$

From Appx. 2, we find $P = .19$ (two-tailed). Consequently, our conclusion is the same as was drawn in Ex. 19-6. In fact, using a more detailed χ^2 table than is included in this text, the probability of obtaining a χ^2 as large as or larger than the 1.74 obtained in Ex. 19-6 is also equal to .19. Furthermore, since a χ^2 for a 2 × 2 table involves only one degree of freedom $[(2 - 1)\,(2 - 1) = 1]$, the relationship $(CR)^2 = \chi^2$ must hold. That is, $(-1.32)^2 = 1.74$.

A comparison of Ex. 19-6 and Ex. 19-7 illustrates once again that a χ^2 does not take direction into account. The probability obtained in Ex. 19-6 is equal to that obtained in Ex. 19-7, *for a two-tailed test* (i.e., for $H_R : P_M - P_F \neq 0$). In the case of 2 × 2 tables, however, the χ^2 approach can be used to test a directional research hypothesis, if the probability obtained from the χ^2 table (Appx. 5) is divided in half. For instance, suppose our research hypothesis had been that the item was easier for girls than for boys (i.e., $H_R : P_M - P_F < 0$). A χ^2 could have been computed as in Ex. 19-6. According to Appx. 5, the probability of obtaining a χ^2 as large as or larger than the obtained 1.74 is between .10 and .20. The actual probability to be used in this instance, however, is found by taking half of the tabled probabilities. That is, since our hypothesis specifies *direction* ($H_R : P_M - P_F < 0$), P is between .05 and .10.

Dependence and Correlation: Similarities and Differences

The χ^2 techniques described in this chapter are appropriately used with nominal as well as ordered variables. A nominal variable, it will be recalled, was described in Chap. 1 as one for which the possible scores or categories do not represent different amounts or degrees of the underlying characteristic. Thus, there is inherent in the scores themselves no basis for ordering or ranking the scores. An illustration would be the variable *preferred candidate*, referred to earlier in this chapter. Obviously, the three possible scores, *Smith*, *Jones*, and *Phillips*, cannot be ranked according to degree or amount of *preferred candidate*.

An ordered variable, on the other hand, was described as one for which the possible scores or categories do represent different amounts or degrees of the underlying characteristic. For instance, *course grade* would be considered an ordered variable because the possible letter grades (e.g., *A*, *B*, *C*, *D*, and *F*) represent different degrees of academic accomplishment and can be ordered or ranked from high to low.

For χ^2 tests of independence, the research and null hypotheses, as well as the specific procedures for testing the hypotheses, do not depend on whether the variables involved are ordered or not; however, if *both* variables are ordered, there is a similarity between the notion of dependence as defined in this chapter and the concept of correlation as represented by a Pearson r or a rank-order correlation coefficient. Suppose, for instance, we are interested in whether or not the educational aspirations of male high-school seniors are related to the formal educations of their respective fathers. Each of a sample of 200 senior boys is asked to check one of the following categories according to how much formal education he plans to receive after graduation from high school: (1) no formal education beyond high school, (2) some but not enough to obtain a college degree, (3) enough to obtain a bachelor's degree, (4) formal education beyond a bachelor's degree. Then he is asked to indicate the amount of formal education of his father. The results are presented in the contingency Table 19-10. Notice that the possible scores for each of the two variables are ordered from small to large according to the amount of education each represents. Inspection of this contingency table strongly suggests that education of father and student educational aspirations may not be independent in the population from which the sample was selected. Using the procedures illustrated in Ex. 19-5, a χ^2 of 128.16 is obtained in this case, and we find from Appx. 5 that the associated probability is less than .001.

Table 19-10

Educational Aspirations of 200 High-School Seniors, by Father's Level of Education

		Aspiration of Student				
		Finish High School	HS plus Some College	Finish College	Graduate School	Totals
Education of Father	College	0	5	22	25	52
	High School	42	47	14	2	105
	Non-HS	30	8	5	0	43
	Totals	72	60	41	27	200

The null hypothesis of independence would be rejected, and we would conclude that the two variables are related in the population.

Inspection of Table 19-10 suggests that the greater the education of the father, the higher the educational aspirations of the son tend to be. Therefore, if Table 19-10 were viewed as analogous to the scatter-diagrams used in the chapters on correlation and regression, the relationship between the two variables would be approximated by a "regression" line from the lower left to the upper right of the table. Such a relationship is of the general type which either a Pearson r or a rank-order correlation (rho) is often used to describe. Thus, in this situation the dependence could be interpreted as reflecting a positive correlation between the two variables.

Dependence as reflected by a χ^2 for a contingency table, however, involves a relationship between variables which is much more general in nature than the type of relationship usually implied by the term *correlation*. Whereas the correlation coefficients r and ρ are measures of the direction and degree of a consistent, increasing or decreasing trend, the size of a χ^2 for a contingency table does not depend on any sort of consistent trend at all. For instance, consider the contingency table shown in Table 19-11. This table differs from Table 19-10 in that the results for Cols. 1 and 3 have been reversed. Viewed as a scatter-diagram, this table shows essen-

Table 19-11

Table 19-10 with Cols. 1 and 3 Interchanged

		Aspiration of Student				
		Finish HS	HS plus Some College	Finish College	Graduate School	Totals
Education of Father	College	22	5	0	25	52
	HS	14	47	42	2	105
	Non HS	5	8	30	0	43
	Totals	41	60	72	27	200

tially no consistent increasing or decreasing trend; the fathers of the students with either extremely high or extremely low aspirations show far more formal education than the fathers of the students in the middle columns; however, the χ^2 computed for this table would be identical to that obtained for Table 19-10. Thus, the null hypothesis of independence would be rejected, even though there appears to be little or no correlation.

To summarize, both dependence and correlation involve relationships between variables; however, correlation of the type measured by r or ρ is a special type of dependence. If two variables are positively correlated, they are dependent in such a way that individuals who obtain high scores on one tend to obtain high scores on the other. If they are negatively correlated, the reverse is true. However, if two variables are dependent, as reflected by a large χ^2 for the contingency table, they may or may not be correlated in the above sense.

It may be well to emphasize, regarding the foregoing, that a trend of the type measured by a Pearson r or a rank-order correlation coefficient has meaning *only if both variables are ordered variables*. On the other hand, whether or not the variables are ordered is irrelevant to the concept of dependence.

χ^2 and Correlation for Ordered Dichotomous Variables

The statement that two dependent variables are not necessarily correlated needs to be modified in the case of two *ordered dichotomous variables*. If both variables are dichotomous, the appropriate contingency table would be a 2×2 table. Consequently, rejection of the null hypothesis of independence would imply that the variables are correlated, although the χ^2 would not reflect the *sign* (positive or negative) of the correlation. The contingency tables in Table 19-12 illustrate this. Use of the χ^2 formula

Table 19-12

Two Contingency Tables Showing Correlations
of Equal Magnitude but of Opposite Sign

Variable B	Variable A Low	High	Totals
High	15	35	50
Low	32	18	50
Totals	47	53	100

Positive corr. $\chi^2 = 10.28$

Variable B	Variable A Low	High	Totals
High	35	15	50
Low	18	32	50
Totals	53	47	100

Negative corr. $\chi^2 = 10.28$

for a 2 × 2 contingency table produces the same result in both cases: $\chi^2 = 10.28$. The probability of obtaining a χ^2 that large or larger, for $df = 1$, is less than .01. It would be concluded for either table that the two variables are dependent. Viewed as scatter diagrams, both tables represent the same *degree* of correlation. The correlation in the left-hand table, however, is positive, and that for the right-hand table is negative.

This relationship between χ^2 and correlation for 2 × 2 tables provides a basis for testing any of the following research hypotheses about the correlation between two ordered dichotomous variables.

a) H_R : Correlation $\neq 0$
b) H_R : Correlation > 0
c) H_R : Correlation < 0

It should be apparent that rejection of the null hypothesis of independence, for a 2 × 2 contingency table with ordered variables, would amount to support for the non-directional research hypothesis (*a*). In order to test research hypothesis (*b*) or (*c*), a variation must be added to the regular χ^2 test of independence, because hypotheses (*b*) and (*c*) are directional, or one-tailed. The variation amounts to dividing in half the probability figure obtained from Appx. 5—the same procedure described earlier in using χ^2 for a one-tailed test of the difference between independent proportions.

Example 19-8. A test developer wishes to test the research hypothesis that fifth- and sixth-graders' ability to pass a certain item in an arithmetic-achievement test is positively correlated with the grade placement of the pupil. He selects random samples of twenty fifth-graders and twenty sixth-graders from a particular school and administers the item to both samples. The following are the results and the hypotheses.

Grade Placement

		5	6	
Performance on	Pass	7	14	21
the item	Fail	13	6	19
		20	20	40

H_R : The variables are positively correlated (i.e., people in the higher grade have greater ability to pass the item).

H_o : The variables are independent or not correlated.

A χ^2 can be obtained, using Form. (19-4) for a 2 × 2 table.

$$\chi^2 = \frac{N\left(|AD - BC| - \dfrac{N}{2}\right)^2}{(A + B)(C + D)(A + C)(B + D)} = \frac{40\,(|42 - 182| - 20)^2}{(21)(19)(20)(20)} = 3.60$$

We find in Appx. 5 that for $df = 1$ the probability of obtaining a χ^2 as large as or larger than 3.60 is between .10 and .05. Since the research hypothesis is directional, these probability values must be divided in half. Hence, the probability of obtaining sample results which reflect this degree or a greater degree of positive correlation between the variables is between .05 and .025. If the .05 level were used, the null hypothesis would be rejected, and it would be concluded that the two variables are positively correlated for the entire population.

The Contingency Coefficient

The χ^2 for a contingency table increases in size as the degree of dependence or relationship between the two variables increases. Consequently, one might be tempted to use the value of χ^2 as a measure of the degree of the relationship between two variables; however, this practice would be quite misleading, because it could be shown that the size of a χ^2 statistic depends not only on the degree of relationship but on the size of the sample as well. An index that depends only on the degree of relationship is referred to as the *contingency coefficient* and is obtained by the following formula.

$$C = \sqrt{\frac{\chi^2}{N + \chi^2}} \qquad (19\text{-}5)$$

where the χ^2 for the contingency table is computed using any of the methods previously discussed and N is the total number of individuals represented in the table

The computation of C is straightforward and needs no illustration; however, interpreting the obtained value of a contingency coefficient in terms of the degree of relationship it indicates is somewhat more difficult. Several things should be kept in mind. First, C is not comparable to a correlation coefficient (i.e., r or ρ). It is a measure of a much more general type of relationship. Second, it is never negative. Third, the maximum possible size of a contingency coefficient depends on the number of possible scores for each of the two variables. The maximum possible value of C *for any square table* can be obtained by the formula $\sqrt{(K - 1)/K}$, in which K is the number of possible score values for each variable. For a 2×2 table, the maximum possible C which can be obtained is $\sqrt{1/2} = .707$; for a 3×3 table it is $\sqrt{2/3} = .816$; and for a 4×4 table it is $\sqrt{3/4} = .866$. Thus, it should be apparent that two contingency coefficients can be compared only if they are based upon tables of the same size. Unfortunately, the maximum C possible for a rectangular table is not determinable. The smallest possible C for any contingency table is .00, indicating that the two variables are completely independent.

ADDITIONAL CAUTIONS IN THE USE OF χ^2

Already it has been pointed out that sampling distributions of χ^2 statistics computed from frequency data are closely approximated by the theoretical distributions of Appx. 5 only if the expected frequencies are large enough. Two additional restrictions on the use of χ^2 should also be emphasized.

The Sum of the Observed Frequencies Must Equal the Sum of the Expected

This restriction implies that the observations in all categories should be included in the analysis. For instance, consider Ex. 19-2. Suppose Mr. Green was interested only in the professional and technical category. That is, suppose he was interested in whether or not the proportion of students in his county who aspired to occupations in that category was consistent with Labor Department predictions. A "χ^2" based on the frequency in that category alone would be computed as follows.

$$\text{``}\chi^2\text{''} = \frac{(O - E)^2}{E} = \frac{(92 - 21)^2}{21} = 240.0$$

Such a "χ^2" would be incorrect because the sum of the observed frequencies (i.e., 92) does not equal the sum of the expected frequencies (i.e., 21). The correct analysis would be based on the 210 cases from all seven categories. If Mr. Green was concerned only with the professional and technical occupations, he could combine all the remaining occupations into a single catch-all category. The observed and expected frequencies based on the data of Ex. 19-2 would be as follows.

	Professional and Technical	Other	Total
Observed..........	92	118	210
Expected...........	21	189	210

The appropriate χ^2 could then be computed.

$$\chi^2 = \sum \frac{(O - E)^2}{E} = \frac{(92 - 21)^2}{21} + \frac{(118 - 189)^2}{189} = 266.7$$

The Observations Must Be Independent of One Another

This is a requirement of random sampling as discussed in Chap. 9 and as such is an assumption underlying all the inference procedures described in this text; however, all too often in the past, investigators have used χ^2 techniques to analyze observations which are not independent. For example, suppose you wish to determine whether or not there is a relationship between sex and agreement with a set of three attitude statements. For each of the three statements a positive response indicates a favorable attitude toward encouraging competition when a child is young. You present the statements to 100 male and 100 female college students and obtain the following results.

	Agree	*Disagree*	*Total*
Male............	212	88	300
Female.........	180	120	300

That is, of the 300 responses ($100 \times 3 = 300$) made by the males, 212 were agreements and 88 were disagreements. The 600 observations are not all independent of one another because each group of three observations is based upon the same individual. Thus, in this case it would be incorrect to use a χ^2 to test whether or not the observed contingency table shows a significant relationship between the two variables. Whenever the number of observations (i.e., the sum of the observed frequencies) is greater than the number of individuals in the sample, the requirement of independence of observations has not been met, and the use of any of the χ^2 techniques discussed is incorrect.

Exercises and Problems

1. For sixty rolls of a die, the following are the results.

   Side coming up

1	2	3	4	5	6
9	8	3	10	14	16

   Is the die a fair die?

2. A botanist plants a group of hybrid flower seeds he has developed. On the basis of a certain genetic theory, he predicts that, on the average, 1/4 of the flowers grown from this type of seed will be red, 1/4 will be blue, and 1/2 will be purple. The following are the results for the seeds he planted.

   Color of flower

Red	Blue	Purple
28	35	57

   Do the results tend to support or disprove the theory?

3. You wish to determine whether or not the sample of 100 cases of which the scores are presented below might have been selected from a normal population with a mean of 100.00 and a standard deviation of 15.00.

	f
115.00 and above	20
100.00–114.99	41
85.00–99.99	25
below 85.00	14
	100

a) State the null hypothesis in terms of expected frequencies.

b) Test the null hypothesis. What do you conclude?

4. Use the χ^2 technique to solve (c) of Prob. 1, p. 326.

5. Use the χ^2 technique to solve (a) of Prob. 4, p. 327.

6. Each of a sample of 100 college students responds to a particular attitude statement by checking either *agree, disagree,* or *no opinion.* The following are the sample results.

	Agree	Disagree	No opinion	
Male	8	12	20	40
Female	12	38	10	60
	20	50	30	

a) State the null hypothesis of independence in terms of population proportions.

b) Compute the expected frequencies under the null hypothesis of independence.

c) Is response to the attitude statement related to sex?

7. The same attitude statement described in Prob. 6 is administered to samples of male engineering majors, male liberal-arts majors, and male business majors. The following are the results.

	Agree	Disagree	No opinion	
Engineer	15	20	5	40
Liberal Arts	10	65	5	80
Business	35	15	30	80
	60	100	40	

a) Is response to the attitude statement related to academic major?

b) Compute a contingency coefficient and compare it with the maximum possible value.

8. Use the χ^2 technique to solve (c) of Prob. 5, p. 327.
9. Use the χ^2 technique to solve (a) of Prob. 6, p. 327.
10. For each of the following contingency tables, state whether or not you would use the χ^2 technique to test the null hypothesis of independence and why.

(a)

2	4	2	8
19	20	3	42
24	21	5	50

45 45 10

(b)

20	0	0	20
20	20	20	60
20	40	60	120

60 60 80

11. For a 2×2 contingency table, the obtained χ^2 equals 2.03.
    a) Determine, accurate to two decimal places, the probability of obtaining results as deviant as or more deviant than those obtained (assuming independence for the population). Do not use interpolation.
    b) Could (a) have been answered for a 2×3 contingency table? Why or why not?
12. Consider two ordered variables, A and B. Suppose we group the scores on A into three categories and those on B into four categories and summarize the data for a sample of 200 cases in a 3×4 contingency table.
    a) Suppose furthermore that a χ^2 test of independence leads us to reject the null hypothesis. Does this suggest that $R_{AB} \neq 0$? (where R_{AB} is the Pearson correlation between A and B for the entire population) Why or why not?
    b) Suppose that $R_{AB} = 0$. If A and B are dependent in the population, what must be true about the nature of the relationship between A and B? Illustrate your answer with a rough sketch.
    c) Suppose $R_{AB} > 0$. Does this imply anything about the independence or dependence of A and B? Explain.

APPENDICES
and
INDEX

Appendix 1. Squares and Square Roots*

N	N^2	$\sqrt{N}$	$\sqrt{10N}$
1.00	1.0000	1.00000	3.16228
1.01	1.0201	1.00499	3.17805
1.02	1.0404	1.00995	3.19374
1.03	1.0609	1.01489	3.20936
1.04	1.0816	1.01980	3.22490
1.05	1.1025	1.02470	3.24037
1.06	1.1236	1.02956	3.25576
1.07	1.1449	1.03441	3.27109
1.08	1.1664	1.03923	3.28634
1.09	1.1881	1.04403	3.30151
1.10	1.2100	1.04881	3.31662
1.11	1.2321	1.05357	3.33167
1.12	1.2544	1.05830	3.34664
1.13	1.2769	1.06301	3.36155
1.14	1.2996	1.06771	3.37639
1.15	1.3225	1.07238	3.39116
1.16	1.3456	1.07703	3.40588
1.17	1.3689	1.08167	3.42053
1.18	1.3924	1.08628	3.43511
1.19	1.4161	1.09087	3.44964
1.20	1.4400	1.09545	3.46410
1.21	1.4641	1.10000	3.47851
1.22	1.4884	1.10454	3.49285
1.23	1.5129	1.10905	3.50714
1.24	1.5376	1.11355	3.52136
1.25	1.5625	1.11803	3.53553
1.26	1.5876	1.12250	3.54965
1.27	1.6129	1.12694	3.56371
1.28	1.6384	1.13137	3.57771
1.29	1.6641	1.13578	3.59166
1.30	1.6900	1.14018	3.60555
1.31	1.7161	1.14455	3.61939
1.32	1.7424	1.14891	3.63318
1.33	1.7689	1.15326	3.64692
1.34	1.7956	1.15758	3.66060
1.35	1.8225	1.16190	3.67423
1.36	1.8496	1.16619	3.68782
1.37	1.8769	1.17047	3.70135
1.38	1.9044	1.17473	3.71484
1.39	1.9321	1.17898	3.72827
1.40	1.9600	1.18322	3.74166
1.41	1.9881	1.18743	3.75500
1.42	2.0164	1.19164	3.76829
1.43	2.0449	1.19583	3.78153
1.44	2.0736	1.20000	3.79473
1.45	2.1025	1.20416	3.80789
1.46	2.1316	1.20830	3.82099
1.47	2.1609	1.21244	3.83406
1.48	2.1904	1.21655	3.84708
1.49	2.2201	1.22066	3.86005
1.50	2.2500	1.22474	3.87298
N	N^2	$\sqrt{N}$	$\sqrt{10N}$

N	N^2	$\sqrt{N}$	$\sqrt{10N}$
1.50	2.2500	1.22474	3.87298
1.51	2.2801	1.22882	3.88587
1.52	2.3104	1.23288	3.89872
1.53	2.3409	1.23693	3.91152
1.54	2.3716	1.24097	3.92428
1.55	2.4025	1.24499	3.93700
1.56	2.4336	1.24900	3.94968
1.57	2.4649	1.25300	3.96232
1.58	2.4964	1.25698	3.97492
1.59	2.5281	1.26095	3.98748
1.60	2.5600	1.26491	4.00000
1.61	2.5921	1.26886	4.01248
1.62	2.6244	1.27279	4.02492
1.63	2.6569	1.27671	4.03733
1.64	2.6896	1.28062	4.04969
1.65	2.7225	1.28452	4.06202
1.66	2.7556	1.28841	4.07431
1.67	2.7889	1.29228	4.08656
1.68	2.8224	1.29615	4.09878
1.69	2.8561	1.30000	4.11096
1.70	2.8900	1.30384	4.12311
1.71	2.9241	1.30767	4.13521
1.72	2.9584	1.31149	4.14729
1.73	2.9929	1.31529	4.15933
1.74	3.0276	1.31909	4.17133
1.75	3.0625	1.32288	4.18330
1.76	3.0976	1.32665	4.19524
1.77	3.1329	1.33041	4.20714
1.78	3.1684	1.33417	4.21900
1.79	3.2041	1.33791	4.23084
1.80	3.2400	1.34164	4.24264
1.81	3.2761	1.34536	4.25441
1.82	3.3124	1.34907	4.26615
1.83	3.3489	1.35277	4.27785
1.84	3.3856	1.35647	4.28952
1.85	3.4225	1.36015	4.30116
1.86	3.4596	1.36382	4.31277
1.87	3.4969	1.36748	4.32435
1.88	3.5344	1.37113	4.33590
1.89	3.5721	1.37477	4.34741
1.90	3.6100	1.37840	4.35890
1.91	3.6481	1.38203	4.37035
1.92	3.6864	1.38564	4.38178
1.93	3.7249	1.38924	4.39318
1.94	3.7636	1.39284	4.40454
1.95	3.8025	1.39642	4.41588
1.96	3.8416	1.40000	4.42719
1.97	3.8809	1.40357	4.43847
1.98	3.9204	1.40712	4.44972
1.99	3.9601	1.41067	4.46094
2.00	4.0000	1.41421	4.47214
N	N^2	$\sqrt{N}$	$\sqrt{10N}$

* From Table G of McNemar: *Psychological Statistics*, John Wiley and Sons Inc., New York, 1962, by permission of the author and publishers.

Squares and Square Roots (*continued*)

N	N²	√N	√10N	N	N²	√N	√10N
2.00	4.0000	1.41421	4.47214	**2.50**	6.2500	1.58114	5.00000
2.01	4.0401	1.41774	4.48330	2.51	6.3001	1.58430	5.00999
2.02	4.0804	1.42127	4.49444	2.52	6.3504	1.58745	5.01996
2.03	4.1209	1.42478	4.50555	2.53	6.4009	1.59060	5.02991
2.04	4.1616	1.42829	4.51664	2.54	6.4516	1.59374	5.03984
2.05	4.2025	1.43178	4.52769	2.55	6.5025	1.59687	5.04975
2.06	4.2436	1.43527	4.53872	2.56	6.5536	1.60000	5.05964
2.07	4.2849	1.43875	4.54973	2.57	6.6049	1.60312	5.06952
2.08	4.3264	1.44222	4.56070	2.58	6.6564	1.60624	5.07937
2.09	4.3681	1.44568	4.57165	2.59	6.7081	1.60935	5.08920
2.10	4.4100	1.44914	4.58258	**2.60**	6.7600	1.61245	5.09902
2.11	4.4521	1.45258	4.59347	2.61	6.8121	1.61555	5.10882
2.12	4.4944	1.45602	4.60435	2.62	6.8644	1.61864	5.11859
2.13	4.5369	1.45945	4.61519	2.63	6.9169	1.62173	5.12835
2.14	4.5796	1.46287	4.62601	2.64	6.9696	1.62481	5.13809
2.15	4.6225	1.46629	4.63681	2.65	7.0225	1.62788	5.14782
2.16	4.6656	1.46969	4.64758	2.66	7.0756	1.63095	5.15752
2.17	4.7089	1.47309	4.65833	2.67	7.1289	1.63401	5.16720
2.18	4.7524	1.47648	4.66905	2.68	7.1824	1.63707	5.17687
2.19	4.7961	1.47986	4.67974	2.69	7.2361	1.64012	5.18652
2.20	4.8400	1.48324	4.69042	**2.70**	7.2900	1.64317	5.19615
2.21	4.8841	1.48661	4.70106	2.71	7.3441	1.64621	5.20577
2.22	4.9284	1.48997	4.71169	2.72	7.3984	1.64924	5.21536
2.23	4.9729	1.49332	4.72229	2.73	7.4529	1.65227	5.22494
2.24	5.0176	1.49666	4.73286	2.74	7.5076	1.65529	5.23450
2.25	5.0625	1.50000	4.74342	2.75	7.5625	1.65831	5.24404
2.26	5.1076	1.50333	4.75395	2.76	7.6176	1.66132	5.25357
2.27	5.1529	1.50665	4.76445	2.77	7.6729	1.66433	5.26308
2.28	5.1984	1.50997	4.77493	2.78	7.7284	1.66733	5.27257
2.29	5.2441	1.51327	4.78539	2.79	7.7841	1.67033	5.28205
2.30	5.2900	1.51658	4.79583	**2.80**	7.8400	1.67332	5.29150
2.31	5.3361	1.51987	4.80625	2.81	7.8961	1.67631	5.30094
2.32	5.3824	1.52315	4.81664	2.82	7.9524	1.67929	5.31037
2.33	5.4289	1.52643	4.82701	2.83	8.0089	1.68226	5.31977
2.34	5.4756	1.52971	4.83735	2.84	8.0656	1.68523	5.32917
2.35	5.5225	1.53297	4.84768	2.85	8.1225	1.68819	5.33854
2.36	5.5696	1.53623	4.85798	2.86	8.1796	1.69115	5.34790
2.37	5.6169	1.53948	4.86826	2.87	8.2369	1.69411	5.35724
2.38	5.6644	1.54272	4.87852	2.88	8.2944	1.69706	5.36656
2.39	5.7121	1.54596	4.88876	2.89	8.3521	1.70000	5.37587
2.40	5.7600	1.54919	4.89898	**2.90**	8.4100	1.70294	5.38516
2.41	5.8081	1.55242	4.90918	2.91	8.4681	1.70587	5.39444
2.42	5.8564	1.55563	4.91935	2.92	8.5264	1.70880	5.40370
2.43	5.9049	1.55885	4.92950	2.93	8.5849	1.71172	5.41295
2.44	5.9536	1.56205	4.93964	2.94	8.6436	1.71464	5.42218
2.45	6.0025	1.56525	4.94975	2.95	8.7025	1.71756	5.43139
2.46	6.0516	1.56844	4.95984	2.96	8.7616	1.72047	5.44059
2.47	6.1009	1.57162	4.96991	2.97	8.8209	1.72337	5.44977
2.48	6.1504	1.57480	4.97996	2.98	8.8804	1.72627	5.45894
2.49	6.2001	1.57797	4.98999	2.99	8.9401	1.72916	5.46809
2.50	6.2500	1.58114	5.00000	**3.00**	9.0000	1.73205	5.47723
N	N²	√N	√10N	N	N²	√N	√10N

Squares and Square Roots (*continued*)

N	N²	√N	√10N	N	N²	√N	√10N
3.00	9.0000	1.73205	5.47723	**3.50**	12.2500	1.87083	5.91608
3.01	9.0601	1.73494	5.48635	3.51	12.3201	1.87350	5.92453
3.02	9.1204	1.73781	5.49545	3.52	12.3904	1.87617	5.93296
3.03	9.1809	1.74069	5.50454	3.53	12.4609	1.87883	5.94138
3.04	9.2416	1.74356	5.51362	3.54	12.5316	1.88149	5.94979
3.05	9.3025	1.74642	5.52268	3.55	12.6025	1.88414	5.95819
3.06	9.3636	1.74929	5.53173	3.56	12.6736	1.88680	5.96657
3.07	9.4249	1.75214	5.54076	3.57	12.7449	1.88944	5.97495
3.08	9.4864	1.75499	5.54977	3.58	12.8164	1.89209	5.98331
3.09	9.5481	1.75784	5.55878	3.59	12.8881	1.89473	5.99166
3.10	9.6100	1.76068	5.56776	**3.60**	12.9600	1.89737	6.00000
3.11	9.6721	1.76352	5.57674	3.61	13.0321	1.90000	6.00833
3.12	9.7344	1.76636	5.58570	3.62	13.1044	1.90263	6.01664
3.13	9.7969	1.76918	5.59464	3.63	13.1769	1.90526	6.02495
3.14	9.8596	1.77200	5.60357	3.64	13.2496	1.90788	6.03324
3.15	9.9225	1.77482	5.61249	3.65	13.3225	1.91050	6.04152
3.16	9.9856	1.77764	5.62139	3.66	13.3956	1.91311	6.04979
3.17	10.0489	1.78045	5.63028	3.67	13.4689	1.91572	6.05805
3.18	10.1124	1.78326	5.63915	3.68	13.5424	1.91833	6.06630
3.19	10.1761	1.78606	5.64801	3.69	13.6161	1.92094	6.07454
3.20	10.2400	1.78885	5.65685	**3.70**	13.6900	1.92354	6.08276
3.21	10.3041	1.79165	5.66569	3.71	13.7641	1.92614	6.09098
3.22	10.3684	1.79444	5.67450	3.72	13.8384	1.92873	6.09918
3.23	10.4329	1.79722	5.68331	3.73	13.9129	1.93132	6.10737
3.24	10.4976	1.80000	5.69210	3.74	13.9876	1.93391	6.11555
3.25	10.5625	1.80278	5.70088	3.75	14.0625	1.93649	6.12372
3.26	10.6276	1.80555	5.70964	3.76	14.1376	1.93907	6.13188
3.27	10.6929	1.80831	5.71839	3.77	14.2129	1.94165	6.14003
3.28	10.7584	1.81108	5.72713	3.78	14.2884	1.94422	6.14817
3.29	10.8241	1.81384	5.73585	3.79	14.3641	1.94679	6.15630
3.30	10.8900	1.81659	5.74456	**3.80**	14.4400	1.94936	6.16441
3.31	10.9561	1.81934	5.75326	3.81	14.5161	1.95192	6.17252
3.32	11.0224	1.82209	5.76194	3.82	14.5924	1.95448	6.18061
3.33	11.0889	1.82483	5.77062	3.83	14.6689	1.95704	6.18870
3.34	11.1556	1.82757	5.77927	3.84	14.7456	1.95959	6.19677
3.35	11.2225	1.83030	5.78792	3.85	14.8225	1.96214	6.20484
3.36	11.2896	1.83303	5.79655	3.86	14.8996	1.96469	6.21289
3.37	11.3569	1.83576	5.80517	3.87	14.9769	1.96723	6.22093
3.38	11.4244	1.83848	5.81378	3.88	15.0544	1.96977	6.22896
3.39	11.4921	1.84120	5.82237	3.89	15.1321	1.97231	6.23699
3.40	11.5600	1.84391	5.83095	**3.90**	15.2100	1.97484	6.24500
3.41	11.6281	1.84662	5.83952	3.91	15.2881	1.97737	6.25300
3.42	11.6964	1.84932	5.84808	3.92	15.3664	1.97990	6.26099
3.43	11.7649	1.85203	5.85662	3.93	15.4449	1.98242	6.26897
3.44	11.8336	1.85472	5.86515	3.94	15.5236	1.98494	6.27694
3.45	11.9025	1.85742	5.87367	3.95	15.6025	1.98746	6.28490
3.46	11.9716	1.86011	5.88218	3.96	15.6816	1.98997	6.29285
3.47	12.0409	1.86279	5.89067	3.97	15.7609	1.99249	6.30079
3.48	12.1104	1.86548	5.89915	3.98	15.8404	1.99499	6.30872
3.49	12.1801	1.86815	5.90762	3.99	15.9201	1.99750	6.31664
3.50	12.2500	1.87083	5.91608	**4.00**	16.0000	2.00000	6.32456
N	**N²**	**√N**	**√10N**	**N**	**N²**	**√N**	**√10N**

Squares and Square Roots (*continued*)

N	N²	√N	√10N	N	N²	√N	√10N
4.00	16.0000	2.00000	6.32456	**4.50**	20.2500	2.12132	6.70820
4.01	16.0801	2.00250	6.33246	4.51	20.3401	2.12368	6.71565
4.02	16.1604	2.00499	6.34035	4.52	20.4304	2.12603	6.72309
4.03	16.2409	2.00749	6.34823	4.53	20.5209	2.12838	6.73053
4.04	16.3216	2.00998	6.35610	4.54	20.6116	2.13073	6.73795
4.05	16.4025	2.01246	6.36396	4.55	20.7025	2.13307	6.74537
4.06	16.4836	2.01494	6.37181	4.56	20.7936	2.13542	6.75278
4.07	16.5649	2.01742	6.37966	4.57	20.8849	2.13776	6.76018
4.08	16.6464	2.01990	6.38749	4.58	20.9764	2.14009	6.76757
4.09	16.7281	2.02237	6.39531	4.59	21.0681	2.14243	6.77495
4.10	16.8100	2.02485	6.40312	**4.60**	21.1600	2.14476	6.78233
4.11	16.8921	2.02731	6.41093	4.61	21.2521	2.14709	6.78970
4.12	16.9744	2.02978	6.41872	4.62	21.3444	2.14942	6.79706
4.13	17.0569	2.03224	6.42651	4.63	21.4369	2.15174	6.80441
4.14	17.1396	2.03470	6.43428	4.64	21.5296	2.15407	6.81175
4.15	17.2225	2.03715	6.44205	4.65	21.6225	2.15639	6.81909
4.16	17.3056	2.03961	6.44981	4.66	21.7156	2.15870	6.82642
4.17	17.3889	2.04206	6.45755	4.67	21.8089	2.16102	6.83374
4.18	17.4724	2.04450	6.46529	4.68	21.9024	2.16333	5.84105
4.19	17.5561	2.04695	6.47302	4.69	21.9961	2.16564	6.84836
4.20	17.6400	2.04939	6.48074	**4.70**	22.0900	2.16795	6.85565
4.21	17.7241	2.05183	6.48845	4.71	22.1841	2.17025	6.86294
4.22	17.8084	2.05426	6.49615	4.72	22.2784	2.17256	6.87023
4.23	17.8929	2.05670	6.50384	4.73	22.3729	2.17486	6.87750
4.24	17.9776	2.05913	6.51153	4.74	22.4676	2.17715	6.88477
4.25	18.0625	2.06155	6.51920	4.75	22.5625	2.17945	6.89202
4.26	18.1476	2.06398	6.52687	4.76	22.6576	2.18174	6.89928
4.27	18.2329	2.06640	6.53452	4.77	22.7529	2.18403	6.90652
4.28	18.3184	2.06882	6.54217	4.78	22.8484	2.18632	6.91375
4.29	18.4041	2.07123	6.54981	4.79	22.9441	2.18861	6.92098
4.30	18.4900	2.07364	6.55744	**4.80**	23.0400	2.19089	6.92820
4.31	18.5761	2.07605	6.56506	4.81	23.1361	2.19317	6.93542
4.32	18.6624	2.07846	6.57267	4.82	23.2324	2.19545	6.94262
4.33	18.7489	2.08087	6.58027	4.83	23.3289	2.19773	6.94982
4.34	18.8356	2.08327	6.58787	4.84	23.4256	2.20000	6.95701
4.35	18.9225	2.08567	6.59545	4.85	23.5225	2.20227	6.96419
4.36	19.0096	2.08806	6.60303	4.86	23.6196	2.20454	6.97137
4.37	19.0969	2.09045	6.61060	4.87	23.7169	2.20681	6.97854
4.38	19.1844	2.09284	6.61816	4.88	23.8144	2.20907	6.98570
4.39	19.2721	2.09523	6.62571	4.89	23.9121	2.21133	6.99285
4.40	19.3600	2.09762	6.63325	**4.90**	24.0100	2.21359	7.00000
4.41	19.4481	2.10000	6.64078	4.91	24.1081	2.21585	7.00714
4.42	19.5364	2.10238	6.64831	4.92	24.2064	2.21811	7.01427
4.43	19.6249	2.10476	6.65582	4.93	24.3049	2.22036	7.02140
4.44	19.7136	2.10713	6.66333	4.94	24.4036	2.22261	7.02851
4.45	19.8025	2.10950	6.67083	4.95	24.5025	2.22486	7.03562
4.46	19.8916	2.11187	6.67832	4.96	24.6016	2.22711	7.04273
4.47	19.9809	2.11424	6.68581	4.97	24.7009	2.22935	7.04982
4.48	20.0704	2.11660	6.69328	4.98	24.8004	2.23159	7.05691
4.49	20.1601	2.11896	6.70075	4.99	24.9001	2.23383	7.06399
4.50	20.2500	2.12132	6.70820	**5.00**	25.0000	2.23607	7.07107
N	N²	√N	√10N	N	N²	√N	√10N

Squares and Square Roots (*continued*)

N	N²	√N	√10N	N	N²	√N	√10N
5.00	25.0000	2.23607	7.07107	**5.50**	30.2500	2.34521	7.41620
5.01	25.1001	2.23830	7.07814	5.51	30.3601	2.34734	7.42294
5.02	25.2004	2.24054	7.08520	5.52	30.4704	2.34947	7.42967
5.03	25.3009	2.24277	7.09225	5.53	30.5809	2.35160	7.43640
5.04	25.4016	2.24499	7.09930	5.54	30.6916	2.35372	7.44312
5.05	25.5025	2.24722	7.10634	5.55	30.8025	2.35584	7.44983
5.06	25.6036	2.24944	7.11337	5.56	30.9136	2.35797	7.45654
5.07	25.7049	2.25167	7.12039	5.57	31.0249	2.36008	7.46324
5.08	25.8064	2.25389	7.12741	5.58	31.1364	2.36220	7.46994
5.09	25.9081	2.25610	7.13442	5.59	31.2481	2.36432	7.47663
5.10	26.0100	2.25832	7.14143	**5.60**	31.3600	2.36643	7.48331
5.11	26.1121	2.26053	7.14843	5.61	31.4721	2.36854	7.48999
5.12	26.2144	2.26274	7.15542	5.62	31.5844	2.37065	7.49667
5.13	26.3169	2.26495	7.16240	5.63	31.6969	2.37276	7.50333
5.14	26.4196	2.26716	7.16938	5.64	31.8096	2.37487	7.50999
5.15	26.5225	2.26936	7.17635	5.65	31.9225	2.37697	7.51665
5.16	26.6256	2.27156	7.18331	5.66	32.0356	2.37908	7.52330
5.17	26.7289	2.27376	7.19027	5.67	32.1489	2.38118	7.52994
5.18	26.8324	2.27596	7.19722	5.68	32.2624	2.38328	7.53658
5.19	26.9361	2.27816	7.20417	5.69	32.3761	2.38537	7.54321
5.20	27.0400	2.28035	7.21110	**5.70**	32.4900	2.38747	7.54983
5.21	27.1441	2.28254	7.21803	5.71	32.6041	2.38956	7.55645
5.22	27.2484	2.28473	7.22496	5.72	32.7184	2.39165	7.56307
5.23	27.3529	2.28692	7.23187	5.73	32.8329	2.39374	7.56968
5.24	27.4576	2.28910	7.23878	5.74	32.9476	2.39583	7.57628
5.25	27.5625	2.29129	7.24569	5.75	33.0625	2.39792	7.58288
5.26	27.6676	2.29347	7.25259	5.76	33.1776	2.40000	7.58947
5.27	27.7729	2.29565	7.25948	5.77	33.2929	2.40208	7.59605
5.28	27.8784	2.29783	7.26636	5.78	33.4084	2.40416	7.60263
5.29	27.9841	2.30000	7.27324	5.79	33.5241	2.40624	7.60920
5.30	28.0900	2.30217	7.28011	**5.80**	33.6400	2.40832	7.61577
5.31	28.1961	2.30434	7.28697	5.81	33.7561	2.41039	7.62234
5.32	28.3024	2.30651	7.29383	5.82	33.8724	2.41247	7.62889
5.33	28.4089	2.30868	7.30068	5.83	33.9889	2.41454	7.63544
5.34	28.5156	2.31084	7.30753	5.84	34.1056	2.41661	7.64199
5.35	28.6225	2.31301	7.31437	5.85	34.2225	2.41868	7.64853
5.36	28.7296	2.31517	7.32120	5.86	34.3396	2.42074	7.65506
5.37	28.8369	2.31733	7.32803	5.87	34.4569	2.42281	7.66159
5.38	28.9444	2.31948	7.33485	5.88	34.5744	2.42487	7.66812
5.39	29.0521	2.32164	7.34166	5.89	34.6921	2.42693	7.67463
5.40	29.1600	2.32379	7.34847	**5.90**	34.8100	2.42899	7.68115
5.41	29.2681	2.32594	7.35527	5.91	34.9281	2.43105	7.68765
5.42	29.3764	2.32809	7.36206	5.92	35.0464	2.43311	7.69415
5.43	29.4849	2.33024	7.36885	5.93	35.1649	2.43516	7.70065
5.44	29.5936	2.33238	7.37564	5.94	35.2836	2.43721	7.70714
5.45	29.7025	2.33452	7.38241	5.95	35.4025	2.43926	7.71362
5.46	29.8116	2.33666	7.38918	5.96	35.5216	2.44131	7.72010
5.47	29.9209	2.33880	7.39594	5.97	35.6409	2.44336	7.72658
5.48	30.0304	2.34094	7.40270	5.98	35.7604	2.44540	7.73305
5.49	30.1401	2.34307	7.40945	5.99	35.8801	2.44745	7.73951
5.50	30.2500	2.34521	7.41620	**6.00**	36.0000	2.44949	7.74597
N	N²	√N	√10N	N	N²	√N	√10N

Squares and Square Roots (*continued*)

N	N²	√N	√10N	N	N²	√N	√10N
6.00	36.0000	2.44949	7.74597	**6.50**	42.2500	2.54951	8.06226
6.01	36.1201	2.45153	7.75242	6.51	42.3801	2.55147	8.06846
6.02	36.2404	2.45357	7.75887	6.52	42.5104	2.55343	8.07465
6.03	36.3609	2.45561	7.76531	6.53	42.6409	2.55539	8.08084
6.04	36.4816	2.45764	7.77174	6.54	42.7716	2.55734	8.08703
6.05	36.6025	2.45967	7.77817	6.55	42.9025	2.55930	8.09321
6.06	36.7236	2.46171	7.78460	6.56	43.0336	2.56125	8.09938
6.07	36.8449	2.46374	7.79102	6.57	43.1649	2.56320	8.10555
6.08	36.9664	2.46577	7.79744	6.58	43.2964	2.56515	8.11172
6.09	37.0881	2.46779	7.80385	6.59	43.4281	2.56710	8.11788
6.10	37.2100	2.46982	7.81025	**6.60**	43.5600	2.56905	8.12404
6.11	37.3321	2.47184	7.81665	6.61	43.6921	2.57099	8.13019
6.12	37.4544	2.47386	7.82304	6.62	43.8244	2.57294	8.13634
6.13	37.5769	2.47588	7.82943	6.63	43.9569	2.57488	8.14248
6.14	37.6996	2.47790	7.83582	6.64	44.0896	2.57682	8.14862
6.15	37.8225	2.47992	7.84219	6.65	44.2225	2.57876	8.15475
6.16	37.9456	2.48193	7.84857	6.66	44.3556	2.58070	8.16088
6.17	38.0689	2.48395	7.85493	6.67	44.4889	2.58263	8.16701
6.18	38.1924	2.48596	7.86130	6.68	44.6224	2.58457	8.17313
6.19	38.3161	2.48797	7.86766	6.69	44.7561	2.58650	8.17924
6.20	38.4400	2.48998	7.87401	**6.70**	44.8900	2.58844	8.18535
6.21	38.5641	2.49199	7.88036	6.71	45.0241	2.59037	8.19146
6.22	38.6884	2.49399	7.88670	6.72	45.1584	2.59230	8.19756
6.23	38.8129	2.49600	7.89303	6.73	45.2929	2.59422	8.20366
6.24	38.9376	2.49800	7.89937	6.74	45.4276	2.59615	8.20975
6.25	39.0625	2.50000	7.90569	6.75	45.5625	2.59808	8.21584
6.26	39.1876	2.50200	7.91202	6.76	45.6976	2.60000	8.22192
6.27	39.3129	2.50400	7.91833	6.77	45.8329	2.60192	8.22800
6.28	39.4384	2.50599	7.92465	6.78	45.9684	2.60384	8.23408
6.29	39.5641	2.50799	7.93095	6.79	46.1041	2.60576	8.24015
6.30	39.6900	2.50998	7.93725	**6.80**	46.2400	2.60768	8.24621
6.31	39.8161	2.51197	7.94355	6.81	46.3761	2.60960	8.25227
6.32	39.9424	2.51396	7.94984	6.82	46.5124	2.61151	8.25833
6.33	40.0689	2.51595	7.95613	6.83	46.6489	2.61343	8.26438
6.34	40.1956	2.51794	7.96241	6.84	46.7856	2.61534	8.27043
6.35	40.3225	2.51992	7.96869	6.85	46.9225	2.61725	8.27647
6.36	40.4496	2.52190	7.97496	6.86	47.0596	2.61916	8.28251
6.37	40.5769	2.52389	7.98123	6.87	47.1969	2.62107	8.28855
6.38	40.7044	2.52587	7.98749	6.88	47.3344	2.62298	8.29458
6.39	40.8321	2.52784	7.99375	6.89	47.4721	2.62488	8.30060
6.40	40.9600	2.52982	8.00000	**6.90**	47.6100	2.62679	8.30662
6.41	41.0881	2.53180	8.00625	6.91	47.7481	2.62869	8.31264
6.42	41.2164	2.53377	8.01249	6.92	47.8864	2.63059	8.31865
6.43	41.3449	2.53574	8.01873	6.93	48.0249	2.63249	8.32466
6.44	41.4736	2.53772	8.02496	6.94	48.1636	2.63439	8.33067
6.45	41.6025	2.53969	8.03119	6.95	48.3025	2.63629	8.33667
6.46	41.7316	2.54165	8.03741	6.96	48.4416	2.63818	8.34266
6.47	41.8609	2.54362	8.04363	6.97	48.5809	2.64008	8.34865
6.48	41.9904	2.54558	8.04984	6.98	48.7204	2.64197	8.35464
6.49	42.1201	2.54755	8.05605	6.99	48.8601	2.64386	8.36062
6.50	42.2500	2.54951	8.06226	**7.00**	49.0000	2.64575	8.36660
N	N²	√N	√10N	N	N²	√N	√10N

Squares and Square Roots (*continued*)

N	N²	√N	√10N	N	N²	√N	√10N
7.00	49.0000	2.64575	8.36660	**7.50**	56.2500	2.73861	8.66025
7.01	49.1401	2.64764	8.37257	7.51	56.4001	2.74044	8.66603
7.02	49.2804	2.64953	8.37854	7.52	56.5504	2.74226	8.67179
7.03	49.4209	2.65141	8.38451	7.53	56.7009	2.74408	8.67756
7.04	49.5616	2.65330	8.39047	7.54	56.8516	2.74591	8.68332
7.05	49.7025	2.65518	8.39643	7.55	57.0025	2.74773	8.68907
7.06	49.8436	2.65707	8.40238	7.56	57.1536	2.74955	8.69483
7.07	49.9849	2.65895	8.40833	7.57	57.3049	2.75136	8.70057
7.08	50.1264	2.66083	8.41427	7.58	57.4564	2.75318	8.70632
7.09	50.2681	2.66271	8.42021	7.59	57.6081	2.75500	8.71206
7.10	50.4100	2.66458	8.42615	**7.60**	57.7600	2.75681	8.71780
7.11	50.5521	2.66646	8.43208	7.61	57.9121	2.75862	8.72353
7.12	50.6944	2.66833	8.43801	7.62	58.0644	2.76043	8.72926
7.13	50.8369	2.67021	8.44393	7.63	58.2169	2.76225	8.73499
7.14	50.9796	2.67208	8.44985	7.64	58.3696	2.76405	8.74071
7.15	51.1225	2.67395	8.45577	7.65	58.5225	2.76586	8.74643
7.16	51.2656	2.67582	8.46168	7.66	58.6756	2.76767	8.75214
7.17	51.4089	2.67769	8.46759	7.67	58.8289	2.76948	8.75785
7.18	51.5524	2.67955	8.47349	7.68	58.9824	2.77128	8.76356
7.19	51.6961	2.68142	8.47939	7.69	59.1361	2.77308	8.76926
7.20	51.8400	2.68328	8.48528	**7.70**	59.2900	2.77489	8.77496
7.21	51.9841	2.68514	8.49117	7.71	59.4441	2.77669	8.78066
7.22	52.1284	2.68701	8.49706	7.72	59.5984	2.77849	8.78635
7.23	52.2729	2.68887	8.50294	7.73	59.7529	2.78029	8.79204
7.24	52.4176	2.69072	8.50882	7.74	59.9076	2.78209	8.79773
7.25	52.5625	2.69258	8.51469	7.75	60.0625	2.78388	8.80341
7.26	52.7076	2.69444	8.52056	7.76	60.2176	2.78568	8.80909
7.27	52.8529	2.69629	8.52643	7.77	60.3729	2.78747	8.81476
7.28	52.9984	2.69815	8.53229	7.78	60.5284	2.78927	8.82043
7.29	53.1441	2.70000	8.53815	7.79	60.6841	2.79106	8.82610
7.30	53.2900	2.70185	8.54400	**7.80**	60.8400	2.79285	8.83176
7.31	53.4361	2.70370	8.54985	7.81	60.9961	2.79464	8.83742
7.32	53.5824	2.70555	8.55570	7.82	61.1524	2.79643	8.84308
7.33	53.7289	2.70740	8.56154	7.83	61.3089	2.79821	8.84873
7.34	53.8756	2.70924	8.56738	7.84	61.4656	2.80000	8.85438
7.35	54.0225	2.71109	8.57321	7.85	61.6225	2.80179	8.86002
7.36	54.1696	2.71293	8.57904	7.86	61.7796	2.80357	8.86566
7.37	54.3169	2.71477	8.58487	7.87	61.9369	2.80535	8.87130
7.38	54.4644	2.71662	8.59069	7.88	62.0944	2.80713	8.87694
7.39	54.6121	2.71846	8.59651	7.89	62.2521	2.80891	8.88257
7.40	54.7600	2.72029	8.60233	**7.90**	62.4100	2.81069	8.88819
7.41	54.9081	2.72213	8.60814	7.91	62.5681	2.81247	8.89382
7.42	55.0564	2.72397	8.61394	7.92	62.7264	2.81425	8.89944
7.43	55.2049	2.72580	8.61974	7.93	62.8849	2.81603	8.90505
7.44	55.3536	2.72764	8.62554	7.94	63.0436	2.81780	8.91067
7.45	55.5025	2.72947	8.63134	7.95	63.2025	2.81957	8.91628
7.46	55.6516	2.73130	8.63713	7.96	63.3616	2.82135	8.92188
7.47	55.8009	2.73313	8.64292	7.97	63.5209	2.82312	8.92749
7.48	55.9504	2.73496	8.64870	7.98	63.6804	2.82489	8.93308
7.49	56.1001	2.73679	8.65448	7.99	63.8401	2.82666	8.93868
7.50	56.2500	2.73861	8.66025	**8.00**	64.0000	2.82843	8.94427
N	N²	√N	√10N	N	N²	√N	√10N

Squares and Square Roots (*continued*)

N	N²	√N	√10N	N	N²	√N	√10N
8.00	64.0000	2.82843	8.94427	**8.50**	72.2500	2.91548	9.21954
8.01	64.1601	2.83019	8.94986	8.51	72.4201	2.91719	9.22497
8.02	64.3204	2.83196	8.95545	8.52	72.5904	2.91890	9.23038
8.03	64.4809	2.83373	8.96103	8.53	72.7609	2.92062	9.23580
8.04	64.6416	2.83549	8.96660	8.54	72.9316	2.92233	9.24121
8.05	64.8025	2.83725	8.97218	8.55	73.1025	2.92404	9.24662
8.06	64.9636	2.83901	8.97775	8.56	73.2736	2.92575	9.25203
8.07	65.1249	2.84077	8.98332	8.57	73.4449	2.92746	9.25743
8.08	65.2864	2.84253	8.98888	8.58	73.6164	2.92916	9.26283
8.09	65.4481	2.84429	8.99444	8.59	73.7881	2.93087	9.26823
8.10	65.6100	2.84605	9.00000	**8.60**	73.9600	2.93258	9.27362
8.11	65.7721	2.84781	9.00555	8.61	74.1321	2.93428	9.27901
8.12	65.9344	2.84956	9.01110	8.62	74.3044	2.93598	9.28440
8.13	66.0969	2.85132	9.01665	8.63	74.4769	2.93769	9.28978
8.14	66.2596	2.85307	9.02219	8.64	74.6496	2.93939	9.29516
8.15	66.4225	2.85482	9.02774	8.65	74.8225	2.94109	9.30054
8.16	66.5856	2.85657	9.03327	8.66	74.9956	2.94279	9.30591
8.17	66.7489	2.85832	9.03881	8.67	75.1689	2.94449	9.31128
8.18	66.9124	2.86007	9.04434	8.68	75.3424	2.94618	9.31665
8.19	67.0761	2.86182	9.04986	8.69	75.5161	2.94788	9.32202
8.20	67.2400	2.86356	9.05539	**8.70**	75.6900	2.94958	9.32738
8.21	67.4041	2.86531	9.06091	8.71	75.8641	2.95127	9.33274
8.22	67.5684	2.86705	9.06642	8.72	76.0384	2.95296	9.33809
8.23	67.7329	2.86880	9.07193	8.73	76.2129	2.95466	9.34345
8.24	67.8976	2.87054	9.07744	8.74	76.3876	2.95635	9.34880
8.25	68.0625	2.87228	9.08295	8.75	76.5625	2.95804	9.35414
8.26	68.2276	2.87402	9.08845	8.76	76.7376	2.95973	9.35949
8.27	68.3929	2.87576	9.09395	8.77	76.9129	2.96142	9.36483
8.28	68.5584	2.87750	9.09945	8.78	77.0884	2.96311	9.37017
8.29	68.7241	2.87924	9.10494	8.79	77.2641	2.96479	9.37550
8.30	68.8900	2.88097	9.11043	**8.80**	77.4400	2.96648	9.38083
8.31	69.0561	2.88271	9.11592	8.81	77.6161	2.96816	9.38616
8.32	69.2224	2.88444	9.12140	8.82	77.7924	2.96985	9.39149
8.33	69.3889	2.88617	9.12688	8.83	77.9689	2.97153	9.39681
8.34	69.5556	2.88791	9.13236	8.84	78.1456	2.97321	9.40213
8.35	69.7225	2.88964	9.13783	8.85	78.3225	2.97489	9.40744
8.36	69.8896	2.89137	9.14330	8.86	78.4996	2.97658	9.41276
8.37	70.0569	2.89310	9.14877	8.87	78.6769	2.97825	9.41807
8.38	70.2244	2.89482	9.15423	8.88	78.8544	2.97993	9.42338
8.39	70.3921	2.89655	9.15969	8.89	79.0321	2.98161	9.42868
8.40	70.5600	2.89828	9.16515	**8.90**	79.2100	2.98329	9.43398
8.41	70.7281	2.90000	9.17061	8.91	79.3881	2.98496	9.43928
8.42	70.8964	2.90172	9.17606	8.92	79.5664	2.98664	9.44458
8.43	71.0649	2.90345	9.18150	8.93	79.7449	2.98831	9.44987
8.44	71.2336	2.90517	9.18695	8.94	79.9236	2.98998	9.45516
8.45	71.4025	2.90689	9.19239	8.95	80.1025	2.99166	9.46044
8.46	71.5716	2.90861	9.19783	8.96	80.2816	2.99333	9.46573
8.47	71.7409	2.91033	9.20326	8.97	80.4609	2.99500	9.47101
8.48	71.9104	2.91204	9.20869	8.98	80.6404	2.99666	9.47629
8.49	72.0801	2.91376	9.21412	8.99	80.8201	2.99833	9.48156
8.50	72.2500	2.91548	9.21954	**9.00**	81.0000	3.00000	9.48683
N	N²	√N	√10N	N	N²	√N	√10N

Squares and Square Roots (*continued*)

N	N²	√N	√10N	N	N²	√N	√10N
9.00	81.0000	3.00000	9.48683	**9.50**	90.2500	3.08221	9.74679
9.01	81.1801	3.00167	9.49210	9.51	90.4401	3.08383	9.75192
9.02	81.3604	3.00333	9.49737	9.52	90.6304	3.08545	9.75705
9.03	81.5409	3.00500	9.50263	9.53	90.8209	3.08707	9.76217
9.04	81.7216	3.00666	9.50789	9.54	91.0116	3.08869	9.76729
9.05	81.9025	3.00832	9.51315	9.55	91.2025	3.09031	9.77241
9.06	82.0836	3.00998	9.51840	9.56	91.3936	3.09192	9.77753
9.07	82.2649	3.01164	9.52365	9.57	91.5849	3.09354	9.78264
9.08	82.4464	3.01330	9.52890	9.58	91.7764	3.09516	9.78775
9.09	82.6281	3.01496	9.53415	9.59	91.9681	3.09677	9.79285
9.10	82.8100	3.01662	9.53939	**9.60**	92.1600	3.09839	9.79796
9.11	82.9921	3.01828	9.54463	9.61	92.3521	3.10000	9.80306
9.12	83.1744	3.01993	9.54987	9.62	92.5444	3.10161	9.80816
9.13	83.3569	3.02159	9.55510	9.63	92.7369	3.10322	9.81326
9.14	83.5396	3.02324	9.56033	9.64	92.9296	3.10483	9.81835
9.15	83.7225	3.02490	9.56556	9.65	93.1225	3.10644	9.82344
9.16	83.9056	3.02655	9.57079	9.66	93.3156	3.10805	9.82853
9.17	84.0889	3.02820	9.57601	9.67	93.5089	3.10966	9.83362
9.18	84.2724	3.02985	9.58123	9.68	93.7024	3.11127	9.83870
9.19	84.4561	3.03150	9.58645	9.69	93.8961	3.11288	9.84378
9.20	84.6400	3.03315	9.59166	**9.70**	94.0900	3.11448	9.84886
9.21	84.8241	3.03480	9.59687	9.71	94.2841	3.11609	9.85393
9.22	85.0084	3.03645	9.60208	9.72	94.4784	3.11769	9.85901
9.23	85.1929	3.03809	9.60729	9.73	94.6729	3.11929	9.86408
9.24	85.3776	3.03974	9.61249	9.74	94.8676	3.12090	9.86914
9.25	85.5625	3.04138	9.61769	9.75	95.0625	3.12250	9.87421
9.26	85.7476	3.04302	9.62289	9.76	95.2576	3.12410	9.87927
9.27	85.9329	3.04467	9.62808	9.77	95.4529	3.12570	9.88433
9.28	86.1184	3.04631	9.63328	9.78	95.6484	3.12730	9.88939
9.29	86.3041	3.04795	9.63846	9.79	95.8441	3.12890	9.89444
9.30	86.4900	3.04959	9.64365	**9.80**	96.0400	3.13050	9.89949
9.31	86.6761	3.05123	9.64883	9.81	96.2361	3.13209	9.90454
9.32	86.8624	3.05287	9.65401	9.82	96.4324	3.13369	9.90959
9.33	87.0489	3.05450	9.65919	9.83	96.6289	3.13528	9.91464
9.34	87.2356	3.05614	9.66437	9.84	96.8256	3.13688	9.91968
9.35	87.4225	3.05778	9.66954	9.85	97.0225	3.13847	9.92472
9.36	87.6096	3.05941	9.67471	9.86	97.2196	3.14006	9.92975
9.37	87.7969	3.06105	9.67988	9.87	97.4169	3.14166	9.93479
9.38	87.9844	3.06268	9.68504	9.88	97.6144	3.14325	9.93982
9.39	88.1721	3.06431	9.69020	9.89	97.8121	3.14484	9.94485
9.40	88.3600	3.06594	9.69536	**9.90**	98.0100	3.14643	9.94987
9.41	88.5481	3.06757	9.70052	9.91	98.2081	3.14802	9.95490
9.42	88.7364	3.06920	9.70567	9.92	98.4064	3.14960	9.95992
9.43	88.9249	3.07083	9.71082	9.93	98.6049	3.15119	9.96494
9.44	89.1136	3.07246	9.71597	9.94	98.8036	3.15278	9.96995
9.45	89.3025	3.07409	9.72111	9.95	99.0025	3.15436	9.97497
9.46	89.4916	3.07571	9.72625	9.96	99.2016	3.15595	9.97998
9.47	89.6809	3.07734	9.73139	9.97	99.4009	3.15753	9.98499
9.48	89.8704	3.07896	9.73653	9.98	99.6004	3.15911	9.98999
9.49	90.0601	3.08058	9.74166	9.99	99.8001	3.16070	9.99500
9.50	90.2500	3.08221	9.74679	**10.00**	100.000	3.16228	10.0000
N	**N²**	**√N**	**√10N**	**N**	**N²**	**√N**	**√10N**

Appendix 2. Areas Under the Normal Curve

z or $\frac{\chi}{\sigma}$	Area Between Mean and z	Area Beyond z	z or $\frac{\chi}{\sigma}$	Area Between Mean and z	Area Beyond z
1	2	3	1	2	3
0.00	.0000	.5000	0.35	.1368	.3632
0.01	.0040	.4960	0.36	.1406	.3594
0.02	.0080	.4920	0.37	.1443	.3557
0.03	.0120	.4880	0.38	.1480	.3520
0.04	.0160	.4840	0.39	.1517	.3483
0.05	.0199	.4801	0.40	.1554	.3446
0.06	.0239	.4761	0.41	.1591	.3409
0.07	.0279	.4721	0.42	.1628	.3372
0.08	.0319	.4681	0.43	.1664	.3336
0.09	.0359	.4641	0.44	.1700	.3300
0.10	.0398	.4602	0.45	.1736	.3264
0.11	.0438	.4562	0.46	.1772	.3228
0.12	.0478	.4522	0.47	.1808	.3192
0.13	.0517	.4483	0.48	.1844	.3156
0.14	.0557	.4443	0.49	.1879	.3121
0.15	.0596	.4404	0.50	.1915	.3085
0.16	.0636	.4364	0.51	.1950	.3050
0.17	.0675	.4325	0.52	.1985	.3015
0.18	.0714	.4286	0.53	.2019	.2981
0.19	.0753	.4247	0.54	.2054	.2946
0.20	.0793	.4207	0.55	.2088	.2912
0.21	.0832	.4168	0.56	.2123	.2877
0.22	.0871	.4129	0.57	.2157	.2843
0.23	.0910	.4090	0.58	.2190	.2810
0.24	.0948	.4052	0.59	.2224	.2776
0.25	.0987	.4013	0.60	.2257	.2743
0.26	.1026	.3974	0.61	.2291	.2709
0.27	.1064	.3936	0.62	.2324	.2676
0.28	.1103	.3897	0.63	.2357	.2643
0.29	.1141	.3859	0.64	.2389	.2611
0.30	.1179	.3821	0.65	.2422	.2578
0.31	.1217	.3783	0.66	.2454	.2546
0.32	.1255	.3745	0.67	.2486	.2514
0.33	.1293	.3707	0.68	.2517	.2483
0.34	.1331	.3669	0.69	.2549	.2451

Areas Under the Normal Curve (*continued*)

z or $\frac{X}{\sigma}$	Area Between Mean and z	Area Beyond z	z or $\frac{X}{\sigma}$	Area Between Mean and z	Area Beyond z
1	2	3	1	2	3
0.70	.2580	.2420	1.05	.3531	.1469
0.71	.2611	.2389	1.06	.3554	.1446
0.72	.2642	.2358	1.07	.3577	.1423
0.73	.2673	.2327	1.08	.3599	.1401
0.74	.2704	.2296	1.09	.3621	.1379
0.75	.2734	.2266	1.10	.3643	.1357
0.76	.2764	.2236	1.11	.3665	.1335
0.77	.2794	.2206	1.12	.3686	.1314
0.78	.2823	.2177	1.13	.3708	.1292
0.79	.2852	.2148	1.14	.3729	.1271
0.80	.2881	.2119	1.15	.3749	.1251
0.81	.2910	.2090	1.16	.3770	.1230
0.82	.2939	.2061	1.17	.3790	.1210
0.83	.2967	.2033	1.18	.3810	.1190
0.84	.2995	.2005	1.19	.3830	.1170
0.85	.3023	.1977	1.20	.3849	.1151
0.86	.3051	.1949	1.21	.3869	.1131
0.87	.3078	.1922	1.22	.3888	.1112
0.88	.3106	.1894	1.23	.3907	.1093
0.89	.3133	.1867	1.24	.3925	.1075
0.90	.3159	.1841	1.25	.3944	.1056
0.91	.3186	.1814	1.26	.3962	.1038
0.92	.3212	.1788	1.27	.3980	.1020
0.93	.3238	.1762	1.28	.3997	.1003
0.94	.3264	.1736	1.29	.4015	.0985
0.95	.3289	.1711	1.30	.4032	.0968
0.96	.3315	.1685	1.31	.4049	.0951
0.97	.3340	.1660	1.32	.4066	.0934
0.98	.3365	.1635	1.33	.4082	.0918
0.99	.3389	.1611	1.34	.4099	.0901
1.00	.3413	.1587	1.35	.4115	.0885
1.01	.3438	.1562	1.36	.4131	.0869
1.02	.3461	.1539	1.37	.4147	.0853
1.03	.3485	.1515	1.38	.4162	.0838
1.04	.3508	.1492	1.39	.4177	.0823

Areas Under the Normal Curve (*continued*)

z or $\frac{\chi}{\sigma}$	Area Between Mean and z	Area Beyond z	z or $\frac{\chi}{\sigma}$	Area Between Mean and z	Area Beyond z
1	2	3	1	2	3
1.40	.4192	.0808	1.75	.4599	.0401
1.41	.4207	.0793	1.76	.4608	.0392
1.42	.4222	.0778	1.77	.4616	.0384
1.43	.4236	.0764	1.78	.4625	.0375
1.44	.4251	.0749	1.79	.4633	.0367
1.45	.4265	.0735	1.80	.4641	.0359
1.46	.4279	.0721	1.81	.4649	.0351
1.47	.4292	.0708	1.82	.4656	.0344
1.48	.4306	.0694	1.83	.4664	.0336
1.49	.4319	.0681	1.84	.4671	.0329
1.50	.4332	.0668	1.85	.4678	.0322
1.51	.4345	.0655	1.86	.4686	.0314
1.52	.4357	.0643	1.87	.4693	.0307
1.53	.4370	.0630	1.88	.4699	.0301
1.54	.4382	.0618	1.89	.4706	.0294
1.55	.4394	.0606	1.90	.4713	.0287
1.56	.4406	.0594	1.91	.4719	.0281
1.57	.4418	.0582	1.92	.4726	.0274
1.58	.4429	.0571	1.93	.4732	.0268
1.59	.4441	.0559	1.94	.4738	.0262
1.60	.4452	.0548	1.95	.4744	.0256
1.61	.4463	.0537	1.96	.4750	.0250
1.62	.4474	.0526	1.97	.4756	.0244
1.63	.4484	.0516	1.98	.4761	.0239
1.64	.4495	.0505	1.99	.4767	.0233
1.65	.4505	.0495	2.00	.4772	.0228
1.66	.4515	.0485	2.01	.4778	.0222
1.67	.4525	.0475	2.02	.4783	.0217
1.68	.4535	.0465	2.03	.4788	.0212
1.69	.4545	.0455	2.04	.4793	.0207
1.70	.4554	.0446	2.05	.4798	.0202
1.71	.4564	.0436	2.06	.4803	.0197
1.72	.4573	.0427	2.07	.4808	.0192
1.73	.4582	.0418	2.08	.4812	.0188
1.74	.4591	.0409	2.09	.4817	.0183

Areas Under the Normal Curve (*continued*)

z or $\frac{\chi}{\sigma}$	Area Between Mean and z	Area Beyond z	z or $\frac{\chi}{\sigma}$	Area Between Mean and z	Area Beyond z
1	2	3	1	2	3
2.10	.4821	.0179	2.45	.4929	.0071
2.11	.4826	.0174	2.46	.4931	.0069
2.12	.4830	.0170	2.47	.4932	.0068
2.13	.4834	.0166	2.48	.4934	.0066
2.14	.4838	.0162	2.49	.4936	.0064
2.15	.4842	.0158	2.50	.4938	.0062
2.16	.4846	.0154	2.51	.4940	.0060
2.17	.4850	.0150	2.52	.4941	.0059
2.18	.4854	.0146	2.53	.4943	.0057
2.19	.4857	.0143	2.54	.4945	.0055
2.20	.4861	.0139	2.55	.4946	.0054
2.21	.4864	.0136	2.56	.4948	.0052
2.22	.4868	.0132	2.57	.4949	.0051
2.23	.4871	.0129	2.58	.4951	.0049
2.24	.4875	.0125	2.59	.4952	.0048
2.25	.4878	.0122	2.60	.4953	.0047
2.26	.4881	.0119	2.61	.4955	.0045
2.27	.4884	.0116	2.62	.4956	.0044
2.28	.4887	.0113	2.63	.4957	.0043
2.29	.4890	.0110	2.64	.4959	.0041
2.30	.4893	.0107	2.65	.4960	.0040
2.31	.4896	.0104	2.66	.4961	.0039
2.32	.4898	.0102	2.67	.4962	.0038
2.33	.4901	.0099	2.68	.4963	.0037
2.34	.4904	.0096	2.69	.4964	.0036
2.35	.4906	.0094	2.70	.4965	.0035
2.36	.4909	.0091	2.71	.4966	.0034
2.37	.4911	.0089	2.72	.4967	.0033
2.38	.4913	.0087	2.73	.4968	.0032
2.39	.4916	.0084	2.74	.4969	.0031
2.40	.4918	.0082	2.75	.4970	.0030
2.41	.4920	.0080	2.76	.4971	.0029
2.42	.4922	.0078	2.77	.4972	.0028
2.43	.4925	.0075	2.78	.4973	.0027
2.44	.4927	.0073	2.79	.4974	.0026

Areas Under the Normal Curve (*continued*)

z or $\dfrac{\chi}{\sigma}$	Area Between Mean and z	Area Beyond z	z or $\dfrac{\chi}{\sigma}$	Area Between Mean and z	Area Beyond z
1	2	3	1	2	3
2.80	.4974	.0026	3.15	.4992	.0008
2.81	.4975	.0025	3.16	.4992	.0008
2.82	.4976	.0024	3.17	.4992	.0008
2.83	.4977	.0023	3.18	.4993	.0007
2.84	.4977	.0023	3.19	.4993	.0007
2.85	.4978	.0022	3.20	.4993	.0007
2.86	.4979	.0021	3.21	.4993	.0007
2.87	.4979	.0021	3.22	.4994	.0006
2.88	.4980	.0020	3.23	.4994	.0006
2.89	.4981	.0019	3.24	.4994	.0006
2.90	.4981	.0019	3.30	.4995	.0005
2.91	.4982	.0018	3.40	.4997	.0003
2.92	.4982	.0018	3.50	.4998	.0002
2.93	.4983	.0017	3.60	.4998	.0002
2.94	.4984	.0016	3.70	.4999	.0001
2.95	.4984	.0016			
2.96	.4985	.0015			
2.97	.4985	.0015			
2.98	.4986	.0014			
2.99	.4986	.0014			
3.00	.4987	.0013			
3.01	.4987	.0013			
3.02	.4987	.0013			
3.03	.4988	.0012			
3.04	.4988	.0012			
3.05	.4989	.0011			
3.06	.4989	.0011			
3.07	.4989	.0011			
3.08	.4990	.0010			
3.09	.4990	.0010			
3.10	.4990	.0010			
3.11	.4991	.0009			
3.12	.4991	.0009			
3.13	.4991	.0009			
3.14	.4992	.0008			

Appendices

Appendix 3. Student's t Distribution*

Area in One-Tail

n	$P = .1$	.05	.02	.01	.001
1	6.314	12.706	31.821	63.657	636.619
2	2.920	4.303	6.965	9.925	31.598
3	2.353	3.182	4.541	5.841	12.941
4	2.132	2.776	3.747	4.604	8.610
5	2.015	2.571	3.365	4.032	6.859
6	1.943	2.447	3.143	3.707	5.959
7	1.895	2.365	2.998	3.499	5.405
8	1.860	2.306	2.896	3.355	5.041
9	1.833	2.262	2.821	3.250	4.781
10	1.812	2.228	2.764	3.169	4.587
11	1.796	2.201	2.718	3.106	4.437
12	1.782	2.179	2.681	3.055	4.318
13	1.771	2.160	2.650	3.012	4.221
14	1.761	2.145	2.624	2.977	4.140
15	1.753	2.131	2.602	2.947	4.073
16	1.746	2.120	2.583	2.921	4.015
17	1.740	2.110	2.567	2.898	3.965
18	1.734	2.101	2.552	2.878	3.922
19	1.729	2.093	2.539	2.861	3.883
20	1.725	2.086	2.528	2.845	3.850
21	1.721	2.080	2.518	2.831	3.819
22	1.717	2.074	2.508	2.819	3.792
23	1.714	2.069	2.500	2.807	3.767
24	1.711	2.064	2.492	2.797	3.745
25	1.708	2.060	2.485	2.787	3.725
26	1.706	2.056	2.479	2.779	3.707
27	1.703	2.052	2.473	2.771	3.690
28	1.701	2.048	2.467	2.763	3.674
29	1.699	2.045	2.462	2.756	3.659
30	1.697	2.042	2.457	2.750	3.646
40	1.684	2.021	2.423	2.704	3.551
60	1.671	2.000	2.390	2.660	3.460
120	1.658	1.980	2.358	2.617	3.373
∞	1.645	1.960	2.326	2.576	3.291

* Abridged from Table 111 of Fisher and Yates: *Statistical Tables for Biological, Agricultural, and Medical Research*, published by Oliver & Boyd, Ltd., Edinburgh, by permission of the authors and publishers.

Appendix 4. Transformation of r to z*

r	z	r	z	r	z
.01	.010	.34	.354	.67	.811
.02	.020	.35	.366	.68	.829
.03	.030	.36	.377	.69	.848
.04	.040	.37	.389	.70	.867
.05	.050	.38	.400	.71	.887
.06	.060	.39	.412	.72	.908
.07	.070	.40	.424	.73	.929
.08	.080	.41	.436	.74	.950
.09	.090	.42	.448	.75	.973
.10	.100	.43	.460	.76	.996
.11	.110	.44	.472	.77	1.020
.12	.121	.45	.485	.78	1.045
.13	.131	.46	.497	.79	1.071
.14	.141	.47	.510	.80	1.099
.15	.151	.48	.523	.81	1.127
.16	.161	.49	.536	.82	1.157
.17	.172	.50	.549	.83	1.188
.18	.181	.51	.563	.84	1.221
.19	.192	.52	.577	.85	1.256
.20	.203	.53	.590	.86	1.293
.21	.214	.54	.604	.87	1.333
.22	.224	.55	.618	.88	1.376
.23	.234	.56	.633	.89	1.422
.24	.245	.57	.648	.90	1.472
.25	.256	.58	.663	.91	1.528
.26	.266	.59	.678	.92	1.589
.27	.277	.60	.693	.93	1.658
.28	.288	.61	.709	.94	1.738
.29	.299	.62	.725	.95	1.832
.30	.309	.63	.741	.96	1.946
.31	.321	.64	.758	.97	2.092
.32	.332	.65	.775	.98	2.298
.33	.343	.66	.793	.99	2.647

* From Table B of McNemar: *Psychological Statistics*, John Wiley and Sons Inc., New York, 1962, by permission of the author and publishers.

Appendix 5. The X^2 Distribution*

Areas in the Upper Tail

df	.30	.20	.10	.05	.02	.01	.001
1	1.07	1.64	2.71	3.84	5.41	6.64	10.83
2	2.41	3.22	4.60	5.99	7.82	9.21	13.82
3	3.66	4.64	6.25	7.82	9.84	11.34	16.27
4	4.88	5.99	7.78	9.49	11.67	13.28	18.46
5	6.06	7.29	9.24	11.07	13.39	15.09	20.52
6	7.23	8.56	10.64	12.59	15.03	16.81	22.46
7	8.38	9.80	12.02	14.07	16.62	18.48	24.32
8	9.52	11.03	13.36	15.51	18.17	20.09	26.12
9	10.66	12.24	14.68	16.92	19.68	21.67	27.88
10	11.78	13.44	15.99	18.31	21.16	23.21	29.59
11	12.90	14.63	17.28	19.68	22.62	24.72	31.26
12	14.01	15.81	18.55	21.03	24.05	26.22	32.91
13	15.12	16.98	19.81	22.36	25.47	27.69	34.53
14	16.22	18.15	21.06	23.68	26.87	29.14	36.12
15	17.32	19.31	22.31	25.00	28.26	30.58	37.70
16	18.42	20.46	23.54	26.30	29.63	32.00	39.25
17	19.51	21.62	24.77	27.59	31.00	33.41	40.79
18	20.60	22.76	25.99	28.87	32.35	34.80	42.31
19	21.69	23.90	27.20	30.14	33.69	36.19	43.82
20	22.78	25.04	28.41	31.41	35.02	37.57	45.32
21	23.86	26.17	29.62	32.67	36.34	38.93	46.80
22	24.94	27.30	30.81	33.92	37.66	40.29	48.27
23	26.02	28.43	32.01	35.17	38.97	41.64	49.73
24	27.10	29.55	33.20	36.42	40.27	42.98	51.18
25	28.17	30.68	34.38	37.65	41.57	44.31	52.62
26	29.25	31.80	35.56	38.88	42.86	45.64	54.05
27	30.32	32.91	36.74	40.11	44.14	46.96	55.48
28	31.39	34.03	37.92	41.34	45.42	48.28	56.89
29	32.46	35.14	39.09	42.56	46.69	49.59	58.30
30	33.53	36.25	40.26	43.77	47.96	50.89	59.70

* Abridged from Table IV of Fisher and Yates: *Statistical Tables for Biological, Agricultural, and Medical Research*, published by Oliver & Boyd, Ltd., Edinburgh, by permission of the authors and publishers.

INDEX